MANUFACTURING
PROCESSES

MANUFACTURING
PROCESSES

Third
Edition

MYRON L. BEGEMAN

Professor of Mechanical Engineering
The University of Texas

JOHN WILEY & SONS, INC., NEW YORK
CHAPMAN & HALL, LIMITED, LONDON

PREFACE
To the Third Edition

Industry, spurred on by necessity and aided by intensive research, is constantly perfecting new materials, machine tools, and processes. A knowledge of the possibilities and limitations of these new developments is essential if low factory costs are to be obtained. This revision includes many of these recent changes and new techniques.

By combining into one volume the subjects usually taken up in metal processing or shop laboratory courses, the need for several texts is eliminated. Approximately fifty per cent of the book is devoted to the subjects of foundry practice, pattern work, plastic molding, powder metallurgy, hot and cold working of metals, heat treatment, and welding. The latter half of the book is given over to measuring instruments, cutting tools, machines and their accessories. In all cases the information is fundamental in character, describing the machine or process as well as discussing its range of application and limitations. In preparing this material, an attempt has been made to present it in a logical sequence so as to give the reader a comprehensive picture of present-day manufacturing processes. The subject matter is condensed as much as possible, omitting those details that can easily be covered by lecture. The purpose of the text continues to be the training of engineers in technical fundamentals of important manufacturing processes, engineering materials, and in the modern machine tools necessary for processing these materials. It should also be found useful as reference reading for graduate engineers, especially those engaged in production work, designing, and tool engineering.

New chapters in this edition are Introduction, Cold Forming of Metals—Miscellaneous Processes, and Cold Forming of Metals—Press Work. In addition, the chapters, Special Casting Methods, Plastic Molding, and Welding and Allied Processes, have been rewritten with much new material added. All other chapters have been carefully revised with particular emphasis on recent developments of the various machines and processes and the tools they use. Special attention has been given to the illustrations, most of which are new.

The co-operation of many industrial firms in furnishing illustrative material and information pertaining to their equipment is acknowledged, as well as the helpful suggestions received from colleagues and others who have been using the text. I wish also to acknowledge the assistance of Professor J. R. Holmes in preparing various line diagrams; Mr. H. C. Barber in preparing micrographs; Professor W. K. Griffis in revising the chapters pertaining to metal casting; Mr. C. R. Maxon in preparing the material on die-casting alloys; and Mr. C. G. Herbruck in revising the material on welding.

MYRON LOUIS BEGEMAN

Austin, Texas
October 1951

CONTENTS

LIST OF TABLES

INTRODUCTION

Present-day manufacturing requires tools and machines that can produce both economically and accurately. Economy in manufacturing depends to a large extent on the proper selection of the machine and process for the job that will give the desired quality of finished product. This selection is influenced in turn by the quantity of items to be produced, as often there is one machine best suited for a certain desired output. For example, in small-lot or jobbing-type manufacture, general-purpose machines such as the lathe, drill press, and planer may prove to be the best type. They are adaptable to numerous types of jobs, have lower initial cost, require less maintenance, and possess the flexibility to meet changing conditions in the shop. However, a special-purpose machine should be considered where large quantities of a standardized product are to be produced. Such a machine built for one type of work or operation as grinding a piston or surfacing a cylinder head will usually do the job well, quickly, and at low cost, requiring only the service of a semiskilled operator. A knowledge of the advantages and limitations of both types is essential for the proper selection of equipment.

Many of the special-purpose machines or tools differ from the usual standard type in that they have built into them some of the skill of the operator. A simple bolt may be produced on either a lathe or an automatic screw machine. The lathe operator must not only know how to make the bolt but also be sufficiently skilled to operate the machine so that the desired accuracy is accomplished. On the automatic machine the sequence of operations and movements of tools are all controlled by cams and stops, and each item produced is identical with the previous one. This "transfer of skill" into the machine makes possible the use of operators of less skill. Usually it is not economical to make a machine completely automatic, as the cost of such machines becomes prohibitive.

Close dimensional control must be maintained in manufacturing operations to turn out parts that are interchangeable and that give

1

the best operating service.   The ability to select any one of a quantity of parts to fit in a given assembly is a necessity for mass production. A product made of interchangeable parts is quickly assembled, low in cost, and easily serviced.

The selection of the best machine or process to use for a given product requires a knowledge of all possible production methods. Factors that must be considered are volume of production, quality of finished product, and the advantages and limitations of the various types of equipment capable of doing the work.   Too much emphasis cannot be given to the fact that most items can be produced by several methods, but usually there is one way that is most economical.

Manufacturing processes used in the working of metals may be classified as follows:

1. Processes used primarily to change the shape of materials

   (a) Casting.
   (b) Forging.
   (c) Extruding.
   (d) Rolling.
   (e) Drawing.
   (f) Pressing.
   (g) Piercing.
   (h) Swaging.
   (i) Metal spinning.
   (j) Stretch forming.
   (k) Roll forming.
   (l) Bending.

2. Processes used to finish parts to desired dimension

   (a) Turning.
   (b) Planing.
   (c) Shaping.
   (d) Drilling.
   (e) Boring.
   (f) Reaming.
   (g) Sawing.
   (h) Broaching.
   (i) Milling.
   (j) Grinding.
   (k) Hobbing.
   (l) Torch cutting.

3. Processes used primarily to obtain surface finish

   (a) Polishing.
   (b) Abrasive belt grinding.
   (c) Barrel tumbling.
   (d) Electroplating.
   (e) Honing.
   (f) Lapping.
   (g) Superfinishing.
   (h) Metal spraying.
   (i) Painting.
   (j) Parkerizing.
   (k) Enameling.
   (l) Sheradizing.

In the first group material is changed into its primary form for some selected part.   In some cases the parts are suitably finished for commercial use, as in metal spinning, cold rolling of shafting, die casting, stretch forming of sheet metal, and drawing of wire.   However, in other cases, neither the dimensions nor surface finish are satisfactory for the final product, and further work on the part is necessary.

The processes listed in the second group are for the most part machining operations; that is, metal is removed from the parts in small chips.   Such operations are performed on machines commonly called machine tools. This term includes all the various power-driven machines found in the machine shop which are used in the cutting of metal. All of these machines operate on either a reciprocating or rotary-type principle; that is, either the tool or the work reciprocates or rotates. The planer is an excellent example of a reciprocating machine, since the work reciprocates past the tool which is held in a stationary position. In other machines, such as the shaper, the work is stationary and the tool reciprocating. Rotary machines are exemplified by the lathe, which has the work rotating and the tool stationary. However, in the drill press it is the tool that is rotating. All machine tools operate on one of these two principles.

In the third group are those processes that cause little change in dimension and primarily result in giving the surface a certain desired finish. However, there is an overlapping between this group and the second group, as some of the processes, such as grinding, remove some metal and bring the part to a desired dimension in addition to giving it a good finish. In the processes such as honing, lapping, and polishing it is a matter of fitting and removing small scratches with little changes in dimension. Plating processes, used for obtaining rust-resisting surfaces or just for an improved appearance, do not change dimensions materially.

Welding and heat treating might well be included in the above classification under separate headings. Welding is a process of uniting metal parts together and is distinguished from other methods of fastening in that the parts are actually fused together. Heat treating includes a number of processes which primarily result in changing the properties and structure of metals.

Engineers engaged in manufacturing work should be familiar with the processes listed above, since it is their responsibility to see that all products are made at minimum costs commensurate with the desired quality. The following chapters discuss the various manufacturing processes with emphasis on their advantages and limitations.

CHAPTER
2

FOUNDRY PRACTICE

From early historic time, castings have been fundamental to man's progress. With the gradual advancement of civilization to the present industrial age, castings have constituted a basic foundation for the development of mechanical processes. The field for cast parts is increasing constantly, because scientific research has brought about applications and adaptations which hitherto were not considered within the scope of the castings industry.

Casting is the process of pouring molten metal into a mold and allowing it to solidify. By this process, intricate parts can be given strength and rigidity frequently not obtainable by any other method. While all metals can thus be formed to shape, iron is especially adapted to this method, because of its fluidity, its small shrinkage, and the ease with which its properties can be controlled.

The *mold,* into which the metal is poured, is made of some heat-resisting material. Sand is most often used, as it is easily packed to shape, is somewhat porous, and resists high temperatures. However, permanent molds of metal can be used for small castings, particularly those of nonferrous composition. In die casting metal molds are used exclusively.

Sand molds are filled by pouring the molten metal into an opening at the top of the mold. Properly constructed passages allow the metal to flow to all parts of the mold by gravity. Permanent molds can be filled the same way; but in die casting, the practice is to force the metal into the mold under pressure, either by compressed air or by an operating plunger. In centrifugal casting, the metal is introduced into the mold by gravity, additional pressure being obtained by centrifugal force.

Tools and Equipment for Molding

Small or medium-sized castings are made in a *flask*—a box-shaped container without top or bottom. It is made in two parts, held in alignment by dowel pins. The top part is called the *cope* and the lower part the *drag*. If the flask is made in three parts, the center is called a *cheek*. These flasks can be made of either wood or metals. Wood is the cheapest material, and wooden flasks can be quickly made, but they have the disadvantage of wearing out rapidly and of being destroyed by contact with hot metal. Metal flasks of steel, cast iron, magnesium, or aluminum alloys are widely used in production work because of their rigidity and permanence.

One type of flask often used in the production of small castings and in machine molding is the *snap flask*. This flask can be removed from the mold by releasing the latches at one corner and immediately used again for making additional molds. A steel slip jacket is placed over the mold to hold it together and to prevent breaking from pressure of the molten metal as it enters the mold. These jackets assist in holding the halves of the mold in proper alignment and eliminate difficulties caused by shifting of the cope. Being of steel, they are not seriously damaged by occasional contact with hot metal.

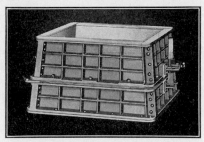

Courtesy American Foundry Equipment Company.

FIG. 1. Side View of Standard-Weight Dowmetal or Aluminum Tapered Flask.

The flask shown in Figure 1 is an all-metal taper strip flask. The inside surfaces of these flasks are accurately ground to a smooth finish and have an inside taper of 5 degrees. The entire flask lifts off the mold without the necessity of unlatching the corner hinges. Metal jackets for the molds, made on the same dimensional form as used for assembling the flasks, preserve the mold in the same shape as it was in the flask. These flasks are made either of aluminum or of Dowmetal.

A *molding board* and a *bottom board* complete the flask. The molding board is a smooth board on which the flask and patterns are placed when the mold is started. It should be perfectly flat and well reinforced with cleats on the bottom. When the mold is turned over, the function of this board is ended; the mold is placed on a similar board, called a bottom board, which acts as a support for the mold until it is poured.

Before any metal is poured into a mold, it is necessary that the flask be clamped in some way to prevent the buoyant effect of the molten metal from lifting up the cope. Small molds are usually held down by flat cast-iron weights placed on the top of the molds. Larger flasks are held together by clamps placed on the sides or ends—either

U-shaped clamps held tight by driving wooden wedges under the end or clamps that can be quickly adjusted to fit the height of the flask.

A *gagger* is a small L-shaped metal accessory used in floor molds to help support hanging bodies of sand in the cope. It is used only in large molds having crossbars. The gagger is first coated with a clay wash and then placed next to one of the crossbars. The lower end should be close to the pattern, and the upper end should extend to the top of the mold.

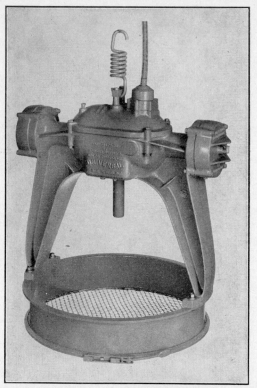

Courtesy Foundry Supplies Manufacturing Company.

Fig. 2. Universal Free-Wheeling Power Riddle.

The hand tools of a molder are few and need little explanation. A brief description of the most important tools is given here:

Riddle. A riddle of a standard mesh screen is used to remove lumps or foreign particles from the sand. Both hand and power riddles are available, the latter being used where large volumes of sand are involved. A power riddle which gives the sand a rapid vibrating movement is shown in Figure 2.

Rammer. Hand rammers are used to pack the sand in the mold. One edge of the rammer, called the peen end, is wedge-shaped; the other, called the butt end, is flat. Floor rammers are similar in construction but have long handles. Pneumatic rammers are used in large molds, saving considerable labor and time.

Bellows. Standard hand-operated bellows are used for blowing loose sand from the cavities and surface of the mold.

Trowel. Small trowels of various shapes are used for finishing and repairing mold cavities as well as for smoothing over the parting surface of the mold. The usual trowel is rectangular in shape and has either a round or a square end.

Slick. The principal hand tool for repairing molds is called a slick. It is a small double-ended tool having a flat on one end and a spoon on the other. This tool is also made in a variety of other shapes.

Lifter. Lifters are used for smoothing and cleaning out depressions in the mold. They are made of thin sections of steel of various widths and lengths with one end bent at right angles. A combination slick and lifter is known as a Yankee lifter.

Swab. This tool is used for moistening the sand around the edge before the pattern is removed. A simple swab is a small brush having long hemp fibers; a bulb swab has a rubber bulb to hold the water and a soft hair brush at the open end. Pressure on the bulb forces the water out through the brush.

Draw spike or screw. The draw spike is a pointed steel rod, with a loop at one end. It is driven into a wood pattern to hold the pattern when it is withdrawn from the sand. The draw screw is similar in shape but threaded on the end to engage metal patterns.

Vent wire. This wire has a sharp point and is used to punch holes through the sand after it has been rammed. In this manner the mold is provided with vents which carry off the steam and gases generated by the hot metal in contact with the sand.

Gate cutter. This tool is a U-shaped piece of thin metal used for cutting a shallow trough in the mold to act as a passage for the hot metal.

Molding Processes

Molding practice in the ordinary commercial foundry may be classified according to (1) the *processes* used in making the mold or (2) the *type of material* of which the mold is made. Under the first heading we have the following divisions:

1. Bench molding. This type of molding is for small work, done on a bench of a height convenient to the molder.

2. Floor molding. As the size of castings (with resultant difficulty in handling) increases, the work is done on the foundry floor. This type of molding is used for practically all medium- and large-sized castings.

3. Pit molding. Extremely large castings are frequently molded in a pit instead of a flask. The pit acts as the drag part of the flask, and a separate cope is used above it. The sides of the pit are brick-lined, and

Courtesy Steel Founders' Society of America.

Fig. 3. Large Pit Mold Partially Completed.

on the bottom there is a thick layer of cinders with connecting vent pipes to the floor level. Since pit molds can resist pressures developed by the hot gases, this practice saves greatly on pattern expenses. Figure 3 shows a large pit mold partially completed.

4. Machine molding. Machines have been developed to do a number of the operations that the molder ordinarily does by hand. Such operations as ramming the sand, rolling the mold over, forming the gate, and drawing the pattern can be done by these machines much better and more efficiently than by hand. So far, no machine has been developed that is completely automatic. A discussion of these machines appears later in this chapter.

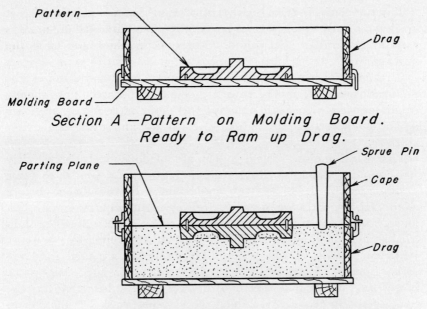

Section A —Pattern on Molding Board.
Ready to Ram up Drag.

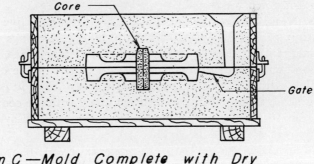

Section B —Drag Rolled over and Pattern
Assembled Ready to Ram Cope.

Section C —Mold Complete with Dry
Sand Core in Place.

Fig. 4. Procedure for Making Mold.

Molds classified as to the materials commonly used in making are:

1. **Green-sand molds.** This most common method, consisting of forming the mold from damp molding sand, is used in most of the processes previously described. Figure 4 illustrates the procedure for making this type of mold.

2. **Skin-dried molds.** Two general methods are used in preparing the skin-dried molds. In one, the sand around the pattern to a depth

of about ½ inch, is mixed with a binder so that when it is dried it will leave a hard surface on the mold. The remainder of the mold is made up of ordinary green sand. The other method is to make the entire mold of green sand and then coat its surface with a spray or wash which hardens when heat is applied. Sprays used for this purpose include linseed oil, molasses water, gelatinized starch, and similar liquid solutions. In both methods the mold must be dried either by air or by a torch to harden the surface and drive out excess moisture.

3. Dry-sand molds. These molds are made entirely from fairly coarse molding sand mixed with a binding material similar to these already mentioned. Since such molds must be oven-baked before being used, the flasks are of metal. Such a mold holds its shape when poured and is free from gas troubles due to moisture. Both the skin-dried and dry-sand molds are widely used in steel foundries.

4. Loam molds. Loam molds, like pit molds, are used for large work. The mold is first built up with bricks or large iron parts. These parts are then plastered over with a thick loam mortar, the shape of the mold being obtained with sweeps or skeleton patterns. The mold is then allowed to dry thoroughly so that it can resist the heavy rush of molten metal. Such molds take a long time to make and are not extensively used.

5. Metal molds. Metal molds have their principal use in the die casting of low-melting-temperature alloys. Castings are accurately shaped with a smooth finish, thus eliminating much machine work. The disadvantages of metal molds are their expense of manufacture, their gradual deterioration by oxidation of surface in contact with the hot metal, their inability to contract along with the cooling metal, and the severe chilling effect they have upon some alloys. Some metal molds are also hard to vent.

6. Special molds. Plastics, cement, plaster, paper, wood, and rubber are all mold materials used to fit particular applications. These are discussed in more detail in Chapter 5, Special Casting Processes.

Molding Sand

Silica sand, found in many natural deposits, is well suited for molding purposes because of its ability to withstand a high temperature without decomposition. Sharp, irregular-shaped grains are usually preferred because of their ability to interlock and add strength to the mold. If associated with quantities of other elements such as lime-stone, soda, and magnesia, the melting temperature of the sand is reduced, and there may be some tendency for the sand to fuse with the molten metal.   The proportion of these ingredients should not exceed 2 to 3%.

Pure silica sand is not suitable in itself for molding, since it lacks binding qualities.   The latter can be obtained by adding 8 to 15% of clay.   Some natural molding sands are adequately bonded with clay when quarried and need little alteration to make them suitable for use.   Clay, when added to the sand and dampened by water, forms a mixture which becomes very cohesive and is easily shaped into molds. Synthetic molding sands are made up of washed sharp-grained silica to which bentonite clay is added in desired amounts.

The size of the sand grains will depend on the type of work to be molded.   For small and intricate castings the use of a fine sand is desirable so that all the details of the mold will be brought out sharply.   As the size of the casting increases, the sand particles like-wise should be coarser to permit the ready escape of gases that are generated in the mold.

Good molding sand should be:

1. Refractory—to resist the high temperatures of the molten iron without fusing.

2. Cohesive, when moistened—to provide sufficient bond to hold together.

3. Porous or permeable—to permit the escape of gases and steam formed in the mold.

When a mold is made in two or more parts, it is necessary to provide some means of keeping the sand from sticking together at the parting surface.   This is accomplished by dusting or spreading the surface with pure silica sand that is very fine and free from clay. This is called *parting sand*.

Molding Procedure

In order to understand fully the use of patterns, we must first become somewhat familiar with foundry practice. Assume, for example, that we wish to make a cast-iron gear blank.   The pro-cedure for molding this part is illustrated in Figure 4.   The mold for this blank is made in the usual flask, which consists of two parts. The two parts are held in a definite relation to one another by means of pins on either side of the drag which fit into openings in angle clips fastened to the sides of the cope.

The first step in making a mold is to place the pattern on a molding board, which fits the flask being used.   Next, the drag is placed on the board with the pins down, as shown in section *A* of Figure 4.

Molding sand, which has previously been tempered, is then riddled in to cover the pattern. This sand should be pressed around the pattern with the fingers; then the drag should be completely filled. The sand is then firmly packed in the drag by means of a hand rammer. In ramming the sand around the sides of the flask, the peen end should be used first, additional sand being placed into the drag as the sand is packed down. The inside area of the drag is then packed down with the butt end of the rammer. The amount of ramming necessary can be determined only by experience. Obviously, if the mold is not sufficiently rammed, it will not hold together when handled or when the molten iron strikes it. On the other hand, if it is rammed too hard, it will not permit the steam and gas to escape when the molten iron comes into the mold.

After the ramming has been finished, the excess sand is leveled off with a straight bar known as a *strike rod*. In order to insure the escape of the gases when the casting is poured, small vent holes are made through the sand to within a fraction of an inch of the pattern.

The completed lower half of the mold is now ready to be turned over so that the cope may be placed in position and the mold finished. A little sand is sprinkled over the mold, and a bottom board placed on top. This board should be moved back and forth several times to insure an even bearing over the mold. The drag is then rolled over and the molding board removed, exposing the pattern. The surface of the sand is first smoothed over with a trowel and is then covered with a fine coating of dry parting sand. This is done to prevent the sand in the cope from sticking to the sand in the drag when the mold is separated to remove the pattern.

The cope is next placed on the drag, as shown in section *B* of Figure 4, the pins on either side holding it in proper position. In order to provide a place for the iron to enter the mold, a tapered pin known as a *sprue pin* is placed approximately an inch to one side of the pattern. The operations of filling, ramming, and venting of the cope proceed in the same manner as in the drag.

The mold is now complete except for the removal of the pattern and the sprue pin. The latter is first withdrawn and a funnel-shaped opening is scooped out at the top so there will be a reasonably large opening into which to pour the iron. Next, the cope half of the flask is carefully lifted off and set to one side. Before the pattern is withdrawn, the sand around the edge of the pattern should be moistened with a swab so that the edges of the mold will hold firmly together when the pattern is withdrawn. To loosen the pattern, a draw spike is driven into it and rapped lightly in all directions. The pattern can then be withdrawn by lifting up on the draw spike.

Finally, before the mold is closed again, a small passage known as a *gate* must be cut from the mold at the bottom of the sprue opening. The completed mold is shown in section *C*, Figure 4. This passage is shallowest at the mold, so that, after the iron has been poured, the metal in the gate may be broken off close to the casting. In order to insure a better surface on the casting, the mold is usually faced

Courtesy American Foundryman.

FIG. 5.   Forming Drag Part of Mold for Bell Casting.

with powdered graphite or plumbago. When the iron comes in contact with this material, it causes it to burn and form a thin film on the surface of the mold which assists in keeping the iron from penetrating the sand. In some cases, where snap flasks are used, the flask may be removed and a metal jacket placed around the mold. This permits using the same flask for other molds and eliminates the danger of having the hot iron burn the flask. Before the iron is poured into the mold, a weight should be put on top to keep it in place and to eliminate any tendency of the liquid iron to separate the cope and drag.

Molding procedure varies slightly from the above description, depending on the type of pattern used. For example, in Figure 5 is shown the drag part of a mold for a bell casting which is brought to shape by means of a sweep instead of a conventional-type pattern. Such patterns are cheap and well suited for molding symmetrical forms. Molding with match-plate patterns, as is done in most production work, differs in that the operator is relieved of much of the manual work and usually some of the operations are combined with others.

Gates and Risers

The usual-type gate to bring the metal from the bottom of the sprue hole is shown in Figures 4C and 6. If possible, these gates

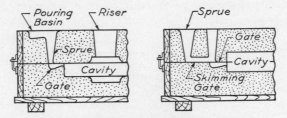

FIG. 6. Methods Used in Introducing Metal to Mold Cavity.

should be so located that the metal can enter near the bottom of the mold and rise quietly with a minimum of turbulence. Multiple gating is recommended for large mold cavities, as this permits more

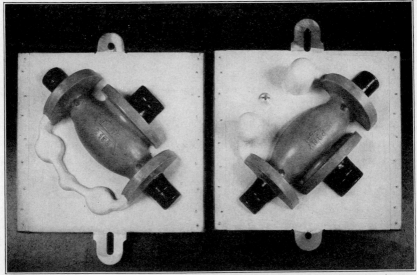

Courtesy American Foundryman.

FIG. 7. Pattern with Blind Risers for Supplying Hot Metal to Casting during Solidification.

uniform cooling and the metal may be poured at a lower temperature. A *pouring basin,* next to the top of the sprue hole, is often provided on large molds to simplify the pouring and to keep slag from entering the mold. Metal should be poured rapidly so that the pouring basin and sprue hole are filled all the time. *Skimming gates,* such as the one shown in Figure 6, may also be used to trap slag or other light particles into the second sprue hole. The gate to the mold cavity is restricted somewhat to allow time for the floating particles to rise into the skimmer.

Risers are often provided in molds to feed molten metal into the main casting cavity to compensate for the shrinkage taking place. They should be large in section, so as to remain molten as long as possible and should be located near heavy sections that will be subject to heavy shrinkage. If they are placed at the top of the section, as shown in the figure, gravity will assist in feeding the metal into the casting proper. Risers also serve as a large vent for generated steam and gases, as well as affording a place for collecting loose sand or slag that may be in the mold.

Blind risers, as shown on the match plate in Figure 7, are also employed for feeding hot metal to the main casting during its solidification. The domelike risers are in the cope half of the flask directly on the gate where the metal feeds into the mold cavity and, hence, will have the hottest metal when the pouring is complete.

Sand-Conditioning Equipment

Properly conditioned sand is an important factor in obtaining good castings. Conditioning is difficult to do by hand, since the moisture content must be controlled, and the binder material should be uniformly distributed around the sand grains. The most desirable sand for molding has a minimum of binder and moisture. A typical mixer for preparing the sand is shown in Figure 8. This mixer consists of a circular pan, in which is mounted a combination of plows and mullers driven by a vertical shaft. This arrangement gives a shoveling action to the sand, turning it over on itself and lining it up in front of the mullers, which give an intensive kneading and rubbing action. The result is a thorough distribution of the sand grains with the bonding material. After the sand is mixed, it is discharged through a door in the bottom of the pan. Both green sand and core sand may be prepared in this manner.

A representative sand-reclamation and conditioning installation is shown in Figure 9. As the molds are shaken out at the ends of the roller conveyor line, the sand falls through a grate onto a belt conveyor which is shown in the figure in phantom view. This conveyor carries the used sand to a smaller belt conveyor equipped with a magnetic separator. The sand is then discharged onto a bucket

elevator from which it goes through an enclosed revolving screen into
the storage bin.   It is delivered from this bin to one or more mullers,
similar to the one shown in the previous figure, and conditioned for
re-use.   From here it is discharged to an overhead belt conveyor
through an aerator which separates the sand grains and improves its
flowability for molding.   The cycle is complete when the sand is
discharged into the several hoppers serving the molding stations.

FIG. 8.   Section View of Simpson Intensive Mixer for Conditioning Foundry Sand.

The advantages of such sand conditioning for all classes of foundries
have been demonstrated many times.   Some of these advantages are
economy of new sand and binder, close control, uniformity of sand
condition, and low cost in preparing the sand; likewise, all the sand,
or a considerable portion of it, is taken off the floor, releasing this
space for molding and other facilities.   Such a system greatly improves
the general operating conditions of the foundry.   The units with
overhead sand storage have high production of uniform high-quality
castings, hold closely to tolerances and weights with a minimum of
defects, and reduce cleaning labor to a minimum.   The fact that all
the sand in the system is mulled each time it is used, so that some is

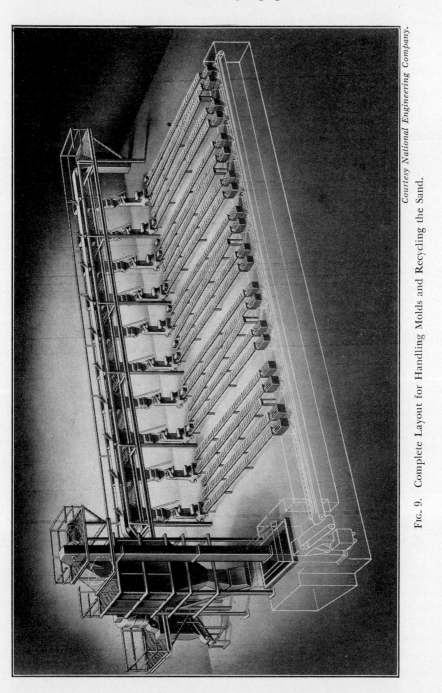

Courtesy National Engineering Company.

Fig. 9. Complete Layout for Handling Molds and Recycling the Sand.

maintained virtually at facing grade, eliminates the preparation of special facing sands as such. It also is possible to reduce the number of grades of sand used for different types of work, one grade of sand ordinarily being adequate when properly reconditioned.

Sand Testing

Periodic tests are necessary to determine the essential qualities of foundry sand. The properties change by contamination of foreign materials, by washing action in tempering, by the gradual change and distribution of grain size, and by continual subjection to high temperatures. Tests may be either chemical or mechanical; but aside from determining undesirable elements in the sand, the chemical tests are little used. Most mechanical tests are simple and do not require elaborate equipment.

Test for moisture content. Moisture content of foundry sands varies according to the type of molds being made and the kind of metal being poured. For a given condition there is a close range within which the moisture percentage should be held in order to produce satisfactory results. Any system of sand control should include a periodic check on moisture content, and complete records should be kept for future reference.

The most accurate method of moisture determination in molding sand is that of drying out the sand and noting weights before and after. The moisture teller shown in Figure 10 contains electric-heating units and a blower for forcing warm air through the filter pan containing the sand sample. Fifty grams of tempered sand, accurately weighed, is placed in the pan. The timer for the blower is set for the required time to dry the sand (approximately 5 minutes), and air at 235 F is blown over and through the sand. By weighing the sand after it is dried and noting the difference in the initial and final readings the percentage of moisture can be determined. The moisture content will vary from 2 to 8%, depending on the type of molding being done.

Another method employing a sand rammer is based on the fact that the more moisture there is in sand the closer it will be packed together. A gage on the indicator measures the compression and may also be calibrated to record moisture content direct if desired. Still another method measures the flow of current between the electrodes imbedded in the sand, and the moisture can be determined by comparing the reading with known impedance value for certain conditions.

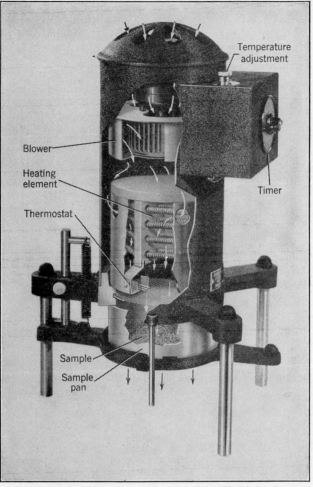

Courtesy Harry W. Dietert Company.

FIG. 10. Moisture Teller for Quick Moisture Tests of Foundry Sands.

Permeability test. One of the essential qualities of molding sand is sufficient porosity to permit the escape of gases generated by the hot metal. This depends on several factors, including shape of sand grains, fineness, degree of packing, moisture content, and amount of binder present. Permeability is measured by the quantity of air that will pass through a given sample of sand in a prescribed time and under standard conditions. A permeability meter, meeting AFA Standard Testing Specifications, is shown in Figure 11. Additional pieces of equipment necessary for conducting the test are a sand rammer, balance, and weights.

The permeability meter consists of an aluminum casting in the form of a water tank and a base. Inside the tank floats a balanced air drum which is sealed at the bottom by the water. The air tube

Courtesy Harry W. Dietert Company.

Fig. 11.   Direct-Reading Permeability Meter for Measuring Green and Dry AFA Permeability of Molding and Sand Cores.

extending down to the specimen opens into the air space of the drum. The sand specimen is placed in the small cup at the base and is sealed with mercury. In taking a permeability reading, the observer may calculate the permeability by obtaining the time in seconds required for 2000 cc of air to pass through the specimen and dividing it into 3007.2. However, if the unit is furnished with an electric timer unit and equipped with a direct-reading dial, permeability values may be obtained by direct reading.

Green-sand permeability is determined by packing sand in a standard tube; dry sand or core permeability by clamping the specimen in a special tube on a rubber gasket and pouring mercury around it to seal the sides. Permeability values obtained are actual volumes of air that the sands will pass. The manufacturer of this equipment lists the following permeability figures as being satisfactory for various types of castings:

Aluminum castings	7–13
Brass and bronze castings	13–20
Light iron castings	18–25
Medium iron castings	40–60
Heavy iron castings	80–120
Steel castings—green sand	130–300
Steel castings—dry sand	100–200

Courtesy Harry W. Dietert Company.

FIG. 12. Mold-Hardness Tester for Measuring the Surface Hardness of Green-Sand Molds.

Mold and core hardness test. The mold hardness tester shown in Figure 12 operates on the same principle as a Brinell hardness tester.* A steel ball 0.2 inch in diameter is pressed into the surface of the mold, and the depth of penetration is indicated on the dial in thousandths of an inch. The reading will not change, even with excessive pressure on the tester. Medium-rammed molds give a value around 50. Such a quick method of checking mold hardness is particularly useful in investigating mold uniformity and different machine settings. Mold hardness readings to be expected for the molding conditions listed are:

Soft-rammed molds	40
Medium-rammed molds	50
Hard-rammed molds	70

Clay-content test. The purpose of this test is to determine the percentage of clay in molding sands. The equipment necessary consists of a drying oven, balance and weights, and a sand washer. A small quantity of sand is thoroughly dried out, and a sample of 50 grams is selected and placed in a wash bottle. To this sand is added 475 cc of distilled water and 25 cc of a 3% caustic soda solution. This mixture is then stirred 5 minutes in a rapid sand stirrer or 1 hour if a rotating sand washer is used. Sufficient water is then added to fill the bottle up to a level line marked on the bottle, and, after settling for about 10 minutes, the liquid is siphoned off. The bottle

* The Brinell test consists of indenting the surface of a metal specimen with a 10-mm hardened-steel ball by means of a predetermined load.

is then refilled twice more and the siphoning operation repeated, time being allowed for the sand to settle. The bottle is finally placed in the oven, and, after the sand is dried out, a sample is weighed. The percentage of clay is determined by the difference in the initial and final weights of the sample.

Fineness test. This test, to determine the percentage distribution of grain sizes in the sand, is performed on a dried-sand sample from which all clay substance has been removed. A set of standard testing sieves is used having U. S. Bureau of Standard meshes 6, 12, 20, 30 40, 50, 70, 100, 140, 200, and 270. These sieves are stacked and placed in one of the several types of motor-driven shakers. The sand is placed on the coarsest sieve at the top, and, after 15 minutes of vibration, the weight of the sand retained on each sieve is obtained and converted to a percentage basis.

To obtain the AFA fineness number, each percentage is multiplied by a factor as given in the following example. The fineness number is obtained by adding all the resulting products and dividing the total by the percentage of sand grain.

EXAMPLE OF AFA FINENESS CALCULATION

Mesh	Percentage Fineness	Multiplier	Product
6	0	3	0
12	0	5	0
20	0	10	0
30	2.0	20	40.0
40	2.5	30	75.0
50	3.0	40	120.0
70	6.0	50	300.0
100	20.0	70	1400.0
140	32.0	100	3200.0
200	12.0	140	1680.0
270	9.0	200	1800.0
Pan	4.0	300	1200.0
Totals	90.5		9615.0

$$\text{Grain fineness number} = \frac{9615}{90.5} = 106$$

This number is a useful means of comparing different sands for uses in the foundry. A check of sands in use should be made every month.

Sand-strength test. Several strength tests have been devised to test the holding power of various bonding materials in green and dry sand. Compression tests are the most common, although tension, shear, and transverse tests are sometimes used in strength investigations.

Procedure varies according to the type of equipment used, but, in general, the tests are similar to those used for other materials. The fragile nature of sand requires special consideration in the handling and loading of test specimens.

A universal sand-strength machine is shown in Figure 13. This machine consists of a frame, on which is mounted a pendulum weight and a pusher arm. It is motor-driven, although hand operation may

Courtesy Harry W. Dietert Company.

FIG. 13.   Universal Sand-Strength Machine.

be used if desired. In testing green strength under compression, a cylindrical specimen of sand is placed between the pusher arm and the compression head of the pendulum weight. The compression load is applied by the motor at the rate of 7.5 pounds per 15 seconds. Pressure is continued until the specimen fails, at which time the compression value (indicated by a small magnetic bar) is read directly on the curved scale.

The tests just described are the ones most commonly used in sand control. In addition to these, there are several others used to check various properties. New sand may be given a sintering test to determine whether or not it has a tendency to burn on to the metal at high temperatures. Chemical analysis is frequently necessary in order to check the composition of sand grains, since some elements greatly reduce the refractory qualities of the sand. Strength at high temperatures and expansion coefficients of different sands can be determined to check the action of the sand in contact with hot metal. The object of all these tests is to improve foundry operations and the quality of castings produced.

Molding Machines

Machines can eliminate much of the hard work of molding and at the same time produce better molds. Molding machines, varying

Courtesy The Tabor Manufacturing Company.

FIG. 14. Plain Jolt Flask Lift Molding Machine.

considerably in design and method of operation, are named according to the manner in which the ramming operation is performed by squeezing, jolting, or some similar means.

Jolt machine. The plain jolt molding machine, shown in Figure 14, is equipped with adjustable flask-lifting pins to permit the use of flasks of various sizes within the capacity of the machine. In the operation of this machine the flask is raised a short distance by the machine table and then dropped. This sudden action causes the sand to be packed evenly about the pattern. The density of the sand is greatest around the pattern and at the parting line, and varies according to the height of the drop or the depth of the sand in the flask. The uniform ramming about the pattern gives added strength to the mold and reduces the possibility of swells, scabs, or runouts. Furthermore castings produced under such conditions will not vary in size or weight. The lifting pins on the machine engage the flask and raise it from the match plate after the mold is complete. Jolt machines quite obviously can take care of only one part of a flask at a time and are especially adapted to large work.

Squeezer machine. Squeezer machines press the sand in the flask between the machine table and an overhead platen. Greatest mold density is obtained at the side of the mold from which the pressure is applied. Because it is impossible to obtain uniform mold density by this method, squeezing machines are limited to molds only a few inches in thickness.

Jolt-squeeze machine. Many machines, such as the ones shown in Figures 15 and 17, have incorporated both the jolt and squeeze principle.

To produce a mold on this machine, the flask is assembled with the match plate between the cope and drag, and the assembly is placed upside down on the machine table. Sand is shoveled into the drag and leveled off, and a bottom board is placed on top. The jolting action then rams the sand in the drag. The assembly is turned over and the cope filled with sand and leveled off. A pressure board is placed on top of the flask, and the top platen of the machine is brought into position. By the application of pressure the flask is squeezed between the platen and table, which packs the sand in the cope to the proper density. After the pressure is released, the platen is swung out of the way. The cope is then lifted from the match plate while the plate is vibrated, after which the plate is removed from the drag. This machine eliminates six separate hand operations: ramming, smoothing the parting surface, applying parting sand, swabbing around the patterns, rapping the pattern, and cutting the gate.

Actually the machine shown in Figure 15 is called a jolt-squeeze pin stripping machine and differs slightly from a plain jolt-squeeze machine in that it is provided with pins to assist in lifting the cope from the match plate. When a mold is complete, the match plate is vibrated, and the pins raise the cope, thus drawing it from the patterns without damage to the mold.

Stripper-plate machine. Some patterns are difficult to withdraw without cracking or otherwise damaging the mold. To eliminate this trouble stripper-plate machines may be used. One type of this machine is identical with the pin-type stripping machine except that a stripper plate, having the same outline as the pattern, supports the

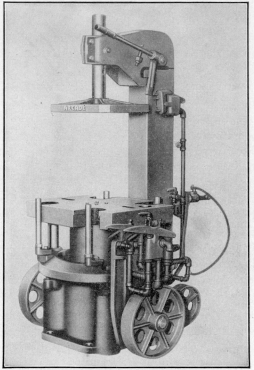

Courtesy Arcade Manufacturing Company.

Fig. 15. Jolt-Squeeze Pin Stripping Machine.

sand in the flask during the drawing operation. When the pins raise, they contact the stripper plate which is lifted with the mold. In some machines the mold remains stationary, and the patterns are lowered through the stripper plate.

Jolt rollover power-draw machine. For large molds that are heavy and difficult to handle, machines as shown in Figure 16 have been developed which roll the mold over and draw the pattern. In the operation of this machine, the flask is first packed with sand by jolting and is rolled over, and the pattern is then withdrawn. Some machines are provided with a small car or section of roller conveyor to receive the mold and provide means of transferring it to the place where it is assembled for pouring.

Jolt-squeeze rollover machine. In operating the machine shown in Figure 17, the drag is rammed by jolting as in the conventional jolt-squeeze machine. Two rollover arms then engage the trunnions of the flask and lift it a sufficient height so that it may be rolled over. The cope is then filled with sand and rammed by squeezing action, after

Courtesy International Molding Machine Company.

FIG. 16. Jolt Rollover Power-Draw Machine.

which it is clamped by the two air clamps on the upper platen and drawn from the match plate. This lifting device handles the cope while the match plate is manually removed from the drag. When the mold is ready to be closed, the cope is swung back into position and the drag raised until the mold halves are together. This machine is designed to handle larger flasks than can be conveniently handled on the usual jolt-squeeze machine.

Sandslinger. Uniform packing of the sand in molds is an important operation in the production of castings. To accomplish this operation in a satisfactory manner, particularly for large molds, a mechanical device known as the sandslinger has been developed. Figure 18 shows a motive-type sandslinger, which is a self-propelled unit operating on a narrow-gage track. The supply of sand is carried in a large tank of about 300 cubic feet capacity, which may be refilled at intervals by overhead handling equipment. A delivery belt feeding out of a hopper on the frame at the fixed end conveys the sand to the rotating

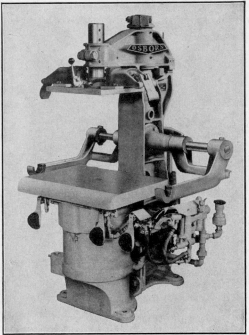

Courtesy Osborn Manufacturing Company.

Fig. 17. Rota-Lift Jolt-Squeeze Molding Machine.

impeller head. The impeller head, which is enclosed, contains a single rotating cup-shaped part which slings the sand into the mold. This part, rotating at high speed, slings over a thousand small buckets of sand a minute. The ramming capacity of this machine is 7 to 10 cubic feet, or 1000 pounds of sand per minute. The density of the packing can be controlled by the speed of the impeller head. For high production, machines of this type are available having a capacity of 4000 pounds of sand per minute.

Similar machines can also be obtained either with a tractor mounting or as a stationary unit. Tractor-type sandslingers travel along the sand piled on the floor and are used in foundries having no auxiliary sand-handling equipment. In addition to the ramming operation, these machines cut, riddle, and magnetically separate the sand from

Courtesy The Beardsley & Piper Company.

FIG. 18. Motive-Type Sandslinger in Operation.

the scrap. The stationary machine is adapted to production work and must be served by sand preparation and conditioning equipment, as well as conveyors for removing the molds. Sandslinger machines greatly increase foundry production and insure the uniform ramming of molds so necessary for good castings.

Cores

When a casting is to have a cavity or recess in it, such as a hole for a bolt, some form of *core* must be introduced into the mold. A core is sometimes defined as "any projection of the sand into the mold." This projection may be formed by the pattern itself or made elsewhere and introduced into the mold after the pattern is withdrawn. Either internal or external surfaces of a casting can be formed by a core.

Types of cores. Cores may be classified under two headings: *green-sand cores* and *dry-sand cores*. Figure 19 shows various types of cores commonly used. Green-sand cores, as shown in Figure 19*A*, are those formed by the pattern itself and made from the same sand as the rest

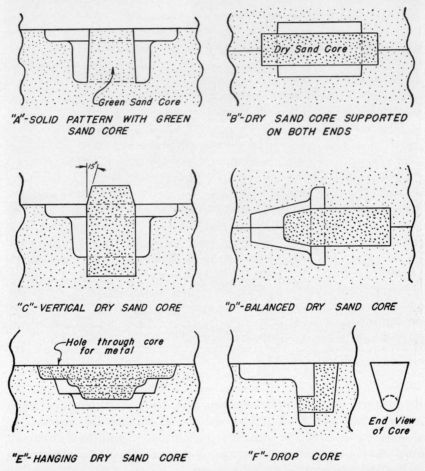

"*A*"-SOLID PATTERN WITH GREEN   "*B*"-DRY SAND CORE SUPPORTED
          SAND CORE   ON BOTH ENDS

"*C*"- VERTICAL DRY SAND CORE   "*D*"-BALANCED DRY SAND CORE

"*E*"- HANGING DRY SAND CORE   "*F*"- DROP CORE

FIG. 19. Various Types of Cores Used in Connection with Patterns.

of the mold. This drawing shows how a flanged casting can be molded with the hole through the center "cored out" with green sand.

Dry-sand cores are those formed separately to be inserted after the pattern is withdrawn but before the mold is closed. They are usually made of sharp river sand, which is mixed with a binder and then baked to give the desired strength. The box in which they are formed to proper shape is called a *core box*.

Several types of dry-sand cores are illustrated in Figure 19. At *B* is the usual arrangement for supporting a core when molding a cylindrical bushing. The projections on each end of the cylindrical pattern are known as *core prints* and form the seats which support and hold the core in place. A vertical core is shown at *C*, the upper end of which requires considerable taper so as not to tear the sand in the cope when the flask is assembled. Cores which have to be supported only at one end must have the core print of sufficient length to prevent the core from falling into the mold. Such a core, shown at *D*, is known as a *balanced core*. A core supported above and hanging into the mold is shown at *E*. This type usually requires a hole through the upper part to permit the metal to reach the mold. A *drop core*, shown at *F*, is required when the hole is not in line with the parting surface and must be formed at a lower level.

In general, green-sand cores should be used where possible to keep the pattern and casting cost to a minimum. Separate cores naturally increase the production cost. Core boxes must be made, and the cores must be formed separately, baked, and properly placed in the molds, all of which adds to the molding cost. However, more accurate holes can be made with dry-sand cores, for they give a better surface and are less likely to be washed away by the molten metal.

The designer of cores must remember that long, thin cores are very difficult to remove from the casting. If a core is surrounded by a heavy section of metal, the pressure of the liquid metal may be sufficient to force some of the metal into the core. This adds greatly to the cleaning costs.

In setting dry-sand cores into molds, adequate supports must be provided. Ordinarily, these supports are formed into the mold by the pattern; but, for large or intricate cores, additional supports in the form of *chaplets* (small metal shapes made of low-melting alloy) are placed in the mold to give additional support to the core until the molten metal enters the mold and fuses the chaplets into the casting. The use of chaplets should be limited as much as possible because of the difficulty in securing proper fusion of the chaplet with the metal.

Essential qualities for dry-sand cores. A core must have sufficient *strength* to support itself. Naturally this strength depends on the kind of sand and binding material used. Sharper grains of sand will bond together better and form a stronger core. It is also advisable to have sand of a uniform grain size to provide plenty of voids through which the escaping gases may pass. The size of the sand depends largely on the finish desired, but is also dependent on the size of work being cast.

Porosity or permeability is also an important consideration in the making of cores. As the hot metal pours over the cores, gases are generated by the heat's being in contact with the binding material, and provision must be made to carry away these gases. The size of the sand grain and its freedom from fines in between the grains largely determine its permeability. In addition to the natural porosity of the sand, it is usually advisable to vent the core as well. This may be done with an ordinary vent wire or, where two pieces go together to make up a core, the vent may be scraped out with the sharp corner of a trowel. Sometimes strings of wax are used, being placed in the core when it is first made up. During the process of baking, the wax is melted out, leaving a passage for the escaping gases.

To insure a smooth casting, the core must have a *smooth surface*. This smoothness depends largely on the grain size of the sand, although the surface may be improved by coating the core with a thin mixture of water and graphite. In the attempt to produce a smooth surface care must be exercised not to go too far, since permeability is lost as the fineness of the sand increases.

All cores must have sufficient *refractory* property to resist the action of the heat until the hot metal has found its place in the mold. Sand naturally is very refractory; so a binder must be selected that will stand the temperature required of the core. A thin coating of graphite or similar material adds considerably to its ability to withstand the intense heat momentarily. It must be kept in mind that it is not desirable to have the core remain hard after the metal has cooled: the binding material used should disintegrate or be burned out by the prolonged contact with the hot metal so that the core may be removed easily from the finished casting. This is also important from the standpoint of preventing shrinkage cracks during cooling.

Core making. The first consideration in making dry-sand cores is to mix and prepare the sand properly. If the binder is dry, it should be thoroughly mixed with the sand before any moisture is added. In any event, the mixture must be homogeneous so that the core will be of uniform strength throughout. All ingredients should be measured out exactly, and care should be taken not to get the mixture too wet. Wet material sticks to the tools and core box, causes the cores to sag before they are baked, and tends to produce a hard core. Large foundries generally use some sort of mechanical mixer.

The core is formed by being rammed into a core box or by the use of sweeps. Fragile and medium-sized cores should be reinforced with wires to give added strength to withstand deflection and the floating action of the metal. In large cores perforated pipes or arbors are used. In addition to giving the core strength, they also serve as a large vent.

When the cores are properly formed, they are placed on small metal plates which support them during the baking period. These plates are placed in the core oven and heated to a temperature ranging from 350 to 450 F. The actual process of baking consists of first driving off the volatile matter and moisture that is in the core and then allowing sufficient time for the binder to become oxidized and hard. The color of the cores on emerging from the oven is a good index of their condition. The usual color for oil binders is a nut brown, whereas flour or similar binding materials produce a light brown. A burnt core is very dark and crumbles when handled.

One of the most critical stages in core making is the fitting of the cores after baking, since many mistakes can be corrected at this point. The fitting consists of procuring two halves of a core, scraping or filing the contact surfaces so that a perfect fit is obtained, venting by cutting a trough in each half, and finally gluing them together. A graphite or silica wash can be applied to the surface of the core to improve surface smoothness and add to its refractory property. After the drying process, cores should again be inspected to insure a proper fit into the mold.

Binders and core mixtures. Among several types of binders used in making cores are those classified as oil binders. One of these, linseed oil, is the principal binder used in the making of small cores. The oil forms a film around the sand grain which hardens when oxidized by the action of the heat. Such cores should be baked at between 350 and 425 F. A common mixture uses 40 parts of river sand and 1 part of linseed oil. An advantage of this core is that it does not absorb water readily and retains its strength in the mold for some time. A similar core oil having the following analysis has proved very successful: raw linseed oil, 42.5–45%, gum rosin, 27.5–30%, with the remainder kerosene which is water-white and acid-free. The gum rosin, although having some binding properties, is also used to prevent the thinned oil from draining to the bottom of the core on standing. About a pint of this oil is required for 100 pounds of core sand.

In another group of binders, soluble in water, we find wheat flour, dextrin, molasses, gelatinized starch, and many commercial preparations. The ratio of binder to sand in these mixtures is rather high, being 1 to 8 or more parts of sand. Frequently a small percentage of old sand is used in place of new sand. Such mixtures are all moistened with water to the proper dampness for working, a temperature of about 350 F being sufficient to harden the cores. One mixture using wheat flour contains 1 part of flour, 6 parts of sharp river sand, and 2 parts of molding sand. This should be mixed thoroughly and wet with a thin clay wash. Another cereal binder, obtained from the corn-products industry, contains about 90% starch and 6% glucose. It is available in powdered form and, when used in the same proportions as an oil binder, produces a weaker and softer core.

In addition, pulverized pitch or rosin may be used. During the baking, these products melt and flow between the sand grains and, when cooled, form a very hard core. Both these binders melt at below 350 F. Such cores are not very refractory, on account of the rapid melting and consequent softening of the core when it comes in contact with the hot metal.

Several types of thermosetting plastics, including urea and phenol formaldehyde, are being successfully used as core binders. Binders* of this type are made in both the liquid and powder form and, when used, are mixed with such other ingredients as silica flour, cereal binder, water, kerosene, and a parting liquid. Urea resin binders are baked at 325 to 375 F and the phenolic binders at 400 to 450 F. Both respond to dialectric heating and are completely combustible under the heat of the metal. Their success as core binders is based on their high adhesive strength, moisture resistance, low burnout characteristic, and ability to provide a smooth surface to the core.

There are many other commercial binder preparations, the analyses of which are difficult to obtain, but most of them contain one or more of the afore-mentioned materials. Considerable experimental work is advisable in large foundries in order to work out mixtures and proportions that give best results in practice. No single binder can answer all the requirements in a diversified foundry.

Core-making machines. Pneumatic core-blowing machines offer a rapid means of producing cores in quantity production work. In this method, sand is blown into a core box at high velocity and under pressure. The resulting core is of uniform structure with a high degree of permeability.

A machine of this type, together with a unit for rolling over core box and drawing core, is shown in Figure 20. When set up for use, the blowing machine has a sand hopper above it, not shown in figure, which feeds sand to the reservoir and blow plate beneath.

* H. K. Salzberg, "Plastic Binders for Foundry Sand Practice," *American Foundryman.*

In operation, the core box is placed on the table and clamped in position. The table and box are then raised, sealing the space between the blow plate and top of the core box. Compressed air, at

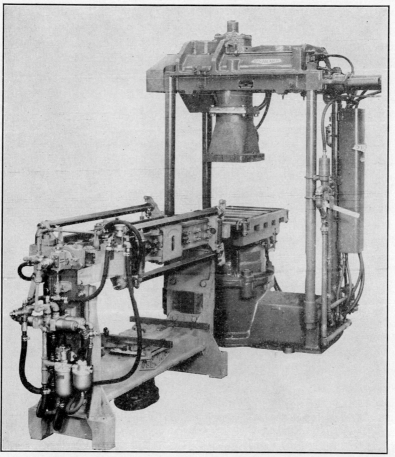

Courtesy Osborn Manufacturing Company.

Fig. 20. Core-Blowing Machine with Core Rollover and Draw Machine.

pressures ranging from 100 to 120 pounds per square inch, is introduced into the reservoir, forcing the sand through the small holes in the blow plate to the mold cavity. Suitable vents are built into the core box or blow plate to permit the air to escape. These vents must be small enough to resist any flow of sand through them, as their sole purpose is to relieve the air from the box. Their location plays an important part in successful core making, since they are used to direct the flow of sand to the desired parts of the core. A core box, filled in a few seconds, is then rolled from the machine onto the rollover draw machine. Here a drier plate is positioned and clamped over the core box. This assembly is then rolled over and the box automatically drawn from the core. During this operation, and while the operator places the drier plate with core on a rack, a second core can be made if a duplicate core box is available.

The holes in the blow plate are countersunk and vary in size from $\frac{3}{16}$ inch to $\frac{1}{2}$ inch in diameter. The larger holes are placed opposite the larger portions of the core and the smaller ones opposite small or restricted pockets that would not tend to fill from the main openings; thus, their size and position offer a means of controlling the flow of sand into the core-box cavities. No definite rule can be given concerning the number and size of holes, each installation being worked out in accordance with past experiences and best judgment.

Core boxes for this process should be made of metal. Cast iron, aluminum, and magnesium are the metals most commonly used. For medium- and large-sized boxes it is economical to use the lighter alloys. All boxes must fit properly to avoid excess air leakage at parting lines. In addition, the outer surfaces should be machined to fit squarely in the clamping fixture.

Sand used in this process need not differ from that of regular core-making practice. It should, however, have good flowability and a minimum of moisture content. Sharp silica sand which has been thoroughly cleaned is recommended.

This type of equipment is especially adapted to production work and is limited to applications where the expense of metal core boxes is justified. It is rapid in its operation, and cores produced are true to form with excellent permeability.

Stock cores of uniform cross section may be produced continuously by an extrusion process. The machine consists of a hopper in which the sand is mixed, and horizontally below it is a spiral screw conveyor which forces the prepared sand through a die tube at uniform speed and pressure. These machines require little skill in their operation and have an output of around 10 feet of core per minute.

Core ovens. Core baking is the process of hardening the core by drying out the binder in a controlled-temperature oven. A variety of core ovens is available, the choice depending on the nature and size of the cores as well as the quantity involved. These ovens may be classified according to their general design as shelf type, drawer type, rack type, car type, and continuous. The last type may be further subdivided into vertical and horizontal arrangements.

The shelf-type oven is the simplest design. Cores are placed on core plates which in turn are placed on the oven shelves. Temperature control in these ovens is difficult, as much heat is lost each time the door is opened. The drawer type, as shown in Figure 21, is a better arrangement for conserving heat, as only one drawer is opened at a

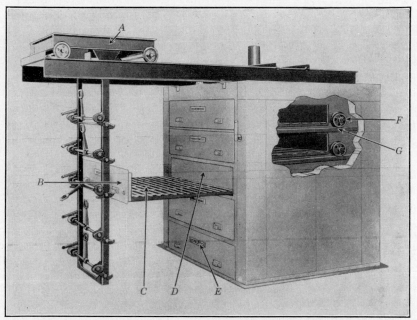

Courtesy The Foundry Equipment Company.

A. Trolley or drawer-puller. *B*. Insulated drawer front with lifting lugs. *C*. Place for cores. *D*. Rear plate to close opening. *E*. Time indicator. *F*. Drawer rollers. *G*. Rails to carry drawer.

FIG. 21. Coleman Drawer-Type Core Oven.

time during loading and unloading periods. Both these types are used for small and medium-sized cores. The rack-type oven is similar to those just mentioned except that the rack on which the cores are placed is portable. It may be conveniently loaded adjacent to the core maker's bench and moved about with hand-lift trucks. This arrangement permits easy loading of the racks and saves much walking between the work station and oven. For very large cores and molds the car-type oven is best. Work of this type is placed on the cars by hoists and cranes, and the car is rolled into the oven.

Continuous ovens are those in which the cores are placed on some sort of a conveyor that moves them slowly through the ovens. They are especially adapted to drying out cores of approximately the same size, as the time through the oven is constant for a given run. Loading and unloading is a continuous operation, and high production can be obtained from these furnaces. Vertical ovens of this type are widely used since they conserve floor space. A suspended tray-type elevator which holds the tray in a horizontal position at all times is

Courtesy The Foundry Equipment Company.

Fig. 22. Continuous Single-Strand Horizontal Core Oven.

the usual means of conveying the cores. A single-strand horizontal oven is illustrated in Figure 22. Designs of this type are very flexible in that the overhead chain carrying the racks can be installed to pass by coremakers' benches and it is not restricted to movements in either the horizontal or the vertical direction. Flight-, apron-, or roller-type conveyors also find some application in horizontal ovens.

In all core ovens the time and temperature must be carefully controlled so as not to over- or underbake. Gas is an ideal fuel as it is clean, easily controlled, and low in cost. Other fuels, as oil, coal, coke, and electricity, are all used and prove satisfactory under certain conditions. Dielectric heating, the placing of cores between electrodes charged with high-frequency current, has a limited use in the baking of cores with plastic binders.

Review Questions

1. What materials may be used for molds?
2. Describe a flask, and list its essential parts.
3. Under what conditions are snap flasks used?
4. List the hand tools of a molder, and give a brief description of each.
5. What are the various processes used in making molds?
6. How are skin-dried molds made, and for what type of work are they used?
7. What are the essential qualities of a good molding sand?
8. Briefly describe how a simple gear blank would be molded.
9. Show by sketch how a skimming gate is constructed.
10. Why are risers used on some molds?
11. Explain how pressure feeding of metal to the casting is obtained by the use of blind risers.
12. What is the usual procedure followed in a representative sand-reclamation and conditioning installation?
13. Describe the procedure for determining moisture and clay contents of molding sand.
14. How is the permeability of molding sand measured?
15. Describe a mold-hardness tester.
16. What are the various types of machines used for packing sand into molds?
17. Describe the operation of a jolt-squeeze molding machine.
18. What is a stripper-plate machine, and why is it used?
19. What is a sandslinger, and how does it operate?
20. What is a core?
21. Name and sketch five kinds of cores.
22. What are the qualities that a dry-sand core should possess?
23. What type of plastics are used for core binders?
24. List and briefly describe the different types of core ovens used.

References

BARNETT, C. A., "Modern Foundry Core and Mold Ovens," *American Foundryman*, May 1949.

CAMPBELL, H. L., *Metal Castings*, John Wiley & Sons, 1936.

Cast Metals Handbook, 3d edition, American Foundrymen's Association, 1944.

LAING, J., and R. T. ROLFE, *A Manual of Foundry Practice*, Sherwood Press, 1934.

LINCOLN, R. F., "Fundamentals of Core Blowing," *Foundry*, February–March 1940.

MAREK, C. T., *Fundamentals in the Production and Design of Castings*, John Wiley & Sons, 1950.

Steel Castings Handbook, Steel Founders' Society of America, 1950.

WENDT, R. E., *Foundry Work*, 4th edition, McGraw-Hill Book Company, 1942.

CHAPTER
3

PATTERN WORK

The first step in making a casting is to prepare a model, known as a pattern, which differs in a number of respects from the resulting casting. These differences, known as pattern allowances, compensate for metal shrinkage, provide sufficient metal for machined surfaces, and facilitate molding. A thorough understanding of these allowances is necessary for successful pattern design and construction.

Most patterns are made of wood because of its cheapness and ability to be worked easily. Also, only a small percentage of patterns go into quantity production work, and therefore the majority do not need to be made of material that will stand hard usage in the foundry. Where durability and strength are required, patterns are made from metal, usually aluminum alloy, brass, or magnesium alloy. In large work, steel or cast-iron patterns may be preferred. For metal patterns, a wooden master pattern must first be made from which the metal pattern is cast.

Before a pattern is made, the pattern maker must visualize from the blueprint what the casting will look like when completed and how it can best be molded. This preliminary estimate is important, as the molding expense in the foundry depends to a great extent on proper pattern construction. After the molding procedure and the general form the pattern will take have been decided upon, a layout of the pattern as it will be built is made. Such layouts are, in general, reproductions of the detail on the drawings submitted, laid out to full-size scale.

A flat smooth board of suitable size is selected for the layout and dressed so that at least two of the edges are smooth and square. The layout is made on this board with the square, shrink rule, marking gage, dividers, and a pocket knife. The usual practice is to make all lines in the layout with a sharp-pointed tool, as such practice tends toward narrow lines and insures greater accuracy than is obtained by using a soft lead pencil. All necessary pattern allowances are taken into account in the making of this layout, and, when complete, it serves as a full-sized detail from which the pattern maker may easily check his work.

Types of Patterns

In Figure 1 are shown seven types of pattern construction. The simplest form is the solid or single-piece pattern shown at *A*. Many patterns cannot be made in a single piece because of the difficulties encountered in molding them. To eliminate this difficulty, some patterns are made in two parts, as shown in the figure at *B*, so that half of the pattern will rest in the lower part of the mold and half in the upper part. The split in the pattern occurs at the parting line of the mold. At *C* is shown a pattern with two loose pieces which are necessary to facilitate withdrawing it from the mold. The method of constructing this pattern is discussed later in connection with Figure 2. In production work where many castings are required, *gated patterns,* as shown in *D,* may be used. Such patterns are made of metal to give them strength and to eliminate any warping tendency. The gates or runners for the molten metal are formed by the connecting parts between the individual patterns. *Match plates* provide a substantial mounting for patterns and are widely used in connection with machine molding. At *E* is shown such a plate, upon which are mounted the patterns for two small dumbbells. It consists of a flat metal or wooden plate, to which the patterns and gate are permanently fastened. On either end of such plates are holes to fit onto a standard flask. The *follow board,* which is shown at *F,* may be used with either single- or multiple-gated patterns. Patterns requiring follow boards are usually somewhat complicated and difficult to make as a split pattern. The board is routed out so that the pattern rests in it up to the desired parting line, and this board then acts as a molding board for the first molding operation. Many molds of regular shape may be constructed using *sweep* patterns. Two examples of sweeps are illustrated at *G* in the figure. The curved sweep might be used to form part of the mold for a large cast-iron kettle; the straight sweep for any type of groove or ridge. The principal advantage of this type of pattern is that it eliminates expensive pattern construction.

The type of pattern to be made for a given part depends largely on the judgment and experience of the pattern maker. Pattern cost and number of castings to be made also help govern this decision. When only a few castings are to be made, it is quite obvious that the pattern should be constructed in the cheapest manner possible. In such a case a single pattern of wood construction would best serve

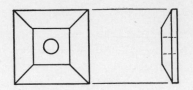

"A"-SOLID   PATTERN

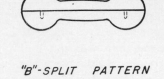

"B"-SPLIT   PATTERN

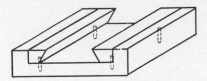

"C"-LOOSE PIECE   PATTERN

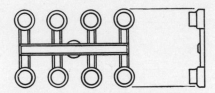

"D"-GATED   PATTERN

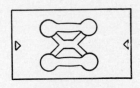

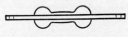

"E"-MATCH PLATE

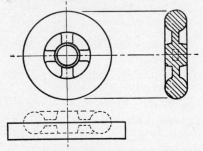

"F"-FOLLOW BOARD FOR WHEEL
PATTERN

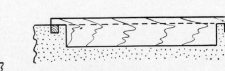

Curved Sweep for Shaping Large
Green Sand Core

Straight Sweep

"G" - SWEEP   PATTERNS

Fig. 1. Types of Patterns.

the purpose. Single wood patterns may also be used with economy
in the production of large castings for two reasons: (1) Wood is a
light material, and the pattern is easy to handle.   (2) Large castings
are usually cast singly in a mold, and a multiple or gated pattern

would only increase molding and casting difficulties. In large castings there is a distinct saving in pattern cost if the sweep or skeleton type of pattern can be used. This type can well be used for large patterns having a uniform symmetrical section. Practically all high-production work on molding machines use the match-plate type of pattern. Aside from the fact that several castings may be molded simultaneously with the pattern of this type, there are also numerous savings affected by the machine molding. Although expensive to make, such patterns will last a long time under severe use.

Pattern Allowances

In pattern work the question may arise why a finished gear blank or any other object could not be used for making molds without the trouble and expense of making a pattern. In some cases this can be done, but, in general, this procedure is not practical for several reasons.

Shrinkage. When any metal cools, it naturally shrinks in size. Hence, if the object or model itself were used for the pattern, the resulting casting would be slightly smaller than desired. To compensate for this possibility, a *shrink rule* must be used in laying out the measurements for the pattern. A shrink rule for cast iron is $\frac{1}{8}$ inch longer per foot than a standard rule, which is the average shrinkage for cast iron. If the gear blank was planned to have an outside diameter of 6 inches when finished, the shrink rule in measuring it 6 inches would actually make it $6\frac{1}{16}$ inches in diameter, thus compensating for the shrinkage. Such a rule naturally saves a great deal of time which would otherwise be used in computing the proper shrinkage of the various dimensions. The shrinkage for brass varies with its composition but is usually close to $\frac{3}{16}$ inch per foot. For steel the shrinkage is $\frac{1}{4}$ inch per foot and for aluminum and magnesium $\frac{5}{32}$ inch per foot. These shrinkage allowance figures are only approximate and vary slightly, depending on the casting design, section thickness, and metal analysis.

When metal patterns are to be cast from original patterns, double shrinkage must be allowed. For example, if the metal pattern is to be made of aluminum and the resulting castings of cast iron, the shrinkage on the original wood pattern would have to be $\frac{5}{32}$ inch plus $\frac{1}{8}$, or $\frac{9}{32}$ inch per foot.

Draft. When a pattern is drawn from a mold, there is always some danger of tearing away the edges of the mold in contact with the pattern. This tendency is greatly decreased if the surfaces of the pattern, parallel to the direction it is being withdrawn, are given a slight taper. This tapering of the sides of the pattern, known as *draft,* is done to provide a slight clearance for the pattern as it is lifted up.

The amount of draft on exterior surfaces is about ⅛ to ¼ inch per foot. On interior holes which are fairly small the draft should be larger; for such conditions it is usually around ¾ inch per foot. These figures are influenced considerably by the size of the pattern and the method to be used in molding it. In allowing for draft, the usual practice is to add it to the pattern; that is, the top dimensions would be slightly larger than they would be if no draft were allowed. Draft should be kept to a minimum and an effort made to maintain uniform metal thickness.

Finish. When a draftsman draws up the details of a part to be made, each surface to be machined is indicated by a finish mark. This mark indicates to the pattern maker that additional metal must be provided at this point so that there will be some metal to machine. In other words, surfaces of parts that have to be machined must be made thicker. The amount that is to be added to the pattern depends on the size and shape of the casting, but, in general, the allowance for small and average-size castings is ⅛ inch. When patterns are several feet long, this allowance must be increased because of the tendency of castings to warp in cooling. A pattern maker soon learns from experience the proper allowances that he must make for various conditions. It must be kept in mind that the term "finish" does not in any way apply to the sanding or finishing of the pattern itself.

Distortion. This allowance applies only to those castings of irregular shape which are distorted in the process of cooling. The distortion is a result of metal shrinkage and is influenced by the mold design and material. A casting in the form of a letter U will contract at the closed end on cooling, while the open end will be held by the sand in fixed position. Hence, the legs of the U pattern should converge slightly so that, when the casting is made, the sides will be parallel. Such an allowance depends on the judgment and experience of the pattern maker as well as on a knowledge of the shrinkage characteristics of the metal.

Shake. When a pattern is rapped in the mold before it is withdrawn, the cavity in the mold is slightly increased. In an average-size casting, this increase in the size can be ignored, but, in large castings or ones that must fit together without machining, shake allowance should be considered. This is accomplished by making the pattern slightly smaller to compensate for the rapping of the mold. No figures can be given for this allowance, as it depends on a number of conditions and must be left to the judgment of the pattern maker.

Method of Constructing a Solid Pattern

The details of a cast-iron V block are shown in Figure 2*A*. The first step in constructing this pattern is to make a layout of the part,

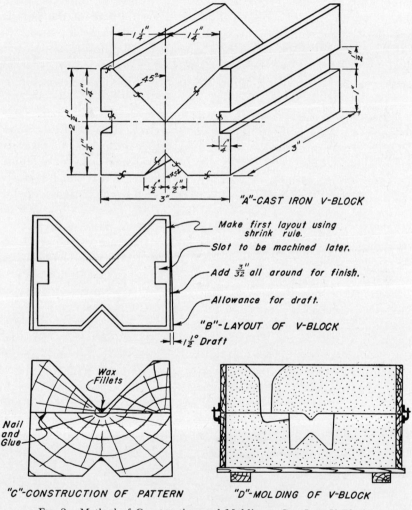

Fig. 2. Method of Constructing and Molding a Cast-Iron V Block.

taking into account the various allowances. Such a layout is shown in part *B* of the figure. In making this layout, the end view is drawn first, using a shrink rule. As the detail calls for "finish" all over, an additional amount of metal must be provided which is shown by the second outline of the V block on the layout. In providing for the draft, consideration must be given to the method of molding the pattern. This is shown at *D* in the figure. A slight taper is provided on all vertical surfaces of the pattern to facilitate its removal from the sand. The final outline on the layout board represents the actual size and shape of the pattern and is the outline that is used for constructing the pattern.

The method of constructing the V-block pattern is shown at *C*. The three parts are nailed and glued together, and sharp interior corners are filleted to eliminate the tendency for metal shrinkage cracks to develop at such points. This same procedure should be followed in making any pattern that requires some degree of accuracy.

Pattern Construction Details

Fillets. A fillet is a concave connecting surface or the rounding out of a corner at two intersecting planes. In all castings sharp corners should be avoided for several reasons. Rounded corners and fillets assist materially in molding, as there is less tendency for the sand to break out when the pattern is drawn. The metal flows into the mold more easily, and there is less danger of its washing sand into the mold. The appearance of the casting is improved, and it is generally stronger, having fewer internal or shrinkage strains.

A casting in a mold cools on the outside first. As the cooling progresses to the center, the grains of the metal arrange themselves normal to the surface in a dendritic structure. In patterns that have sharp corners there is a tendency for the metal at the corners to open up because of shrinkage. In patterns with rounded corners this tendency is eliminated, and a sound casting is the result.

Fillets are made of wood, leather, metal, or wax. In lathe work the fillets can usually be taken care of very well in the turning. Wood fillets may also be used in other shapes, but, if they are made with a feather edge, they are quite fragile. For irregular shapes and patterns which are to be subject to considerable use in the foundry, leather fillets have been found to be very satisfactory. They are cut to the desired length, laid face down on a flat surface, and brushed over with glue. They are then put on the pattern and rubbed into place, a fillet tool of the proper curvature being used. Wax fillets are used a great deal on small work, because they are cheap and easy to apply. The most convenient way to have this wax is in strips which have been extruded to proper shape. A strip is laid in a corner and formed into place by means of a fillet tool, the end of which has previously been heated. This melts the wax and forms it to the curve of the tool being used.

Section thickness. So far as service and design factors permit, all sections should be as uniform as possible. When light sections must be adjacent to heavy sections, the transition should be as gradual as possible. Abrupt changes in thickness always result in strains which are apt to cause cracks in the casting. Solidification should normally progress from the points farthest from where the metal enters the gate and risers and should be as uniform as possible.

Sanding and shellacking patterns. Since the best possible finish is desired on a casting, it is important that the pattern itself be carefully finished so as to produce a smooth mold. No special allowance is made for the sanding that is required prior to shellacking or varnishing. All that is necessary is to remove the tool marks and other slight irregularities on the wood surface. The sanding operation should always be the last. No tool work should be done later, because the cutting edge would be spoiled by the small particles of sand imbedded in the wood.

Shellac seems to be the best material for finishing patterns. It fills the pores of the wood, gives a smooth finish, and leaves a surface that is impervious to moisture. Shellac for pattern work is obtained by dissolving shellac gum with alcohol, the proportion being about 3 pounds of gum to 1 gallon of alcohol. In preparing it, an earthenware, glass, or aluminum container should be used, because most metal containers cause some oxidation, which discolors the shellac. The container should be as nearly air-tight as possible, to prevent evaporation of the alcohol.

Shellac can be applied either by spraying or by using a brush, although in most cases the latter method is used. It dries very quickly, and in a few hours the pattern can be handled. After one coat, the surface will appear quite rough owing to the raised grain of the wood. The pattern should then be sanded once more with a fine grade of sandpaper and a second coat given. Three coats are usually required to give a good surface.

Pattern colors. Many foundries have a color scheme of their own for indicating the kind of metal to be cast, core prints, and the like. The following color scheme for all foundry patterns and core boxes of wood construction is recommended by the American Standards Association and is in general use:

1. Surfaces to be left unfinished are to be painted black.

2. Surfaces to be machined are to be painted red.

3. Seats of and for loose pieces are to be marked by red stripes on a yellow background.

4. Core prints and seats for loose core prints are to be painted yellow.

5. Stop-offs are to be indicated by diagonal black stripes on a yellow base.

Materials Used for Patterns

Wood. Although patterns are made from a variety of woods, white pine is employed chiefly for them. This wood is straight grained, light, and easy to work, and has little tendency to warp or check. When a more durable wood is necessary for fragile patterns or hard use, mahogany is preferred. Other woods suitable for this work are cherry, beech, poplar, basswood, and maple. Maple is especially desirable for work on the lathe. Lumber from mature trees is best for pattern work, as the structure of such wood is more compact and less susceptible to shrinkage.

Before lumber can be used commercially, it must be dried or seasoned; that is, the moisture must be taken out of the pores or cells of the wood. This may be done by either natural or artificial means. Frequently both methods are used, the lumber being first air-seasoned for a period of time and then kiln-dried.

Air drying consists of piling the lumber in such a manner that air can circulate around all the boards. This process requires considerable time and is said to be complete when the wood ceases to lose weight. However, it may still contain 10 to 15% moisture, and, if this amount is considered excessive, kiln drying must be resorted to. In this process the lumber is dried by the application of heat in a kiln. The process, which requires only a short time, reduces the moisture to a minimum, drives off volatile matter in the wood, hardens the resin, and, to some extent, makes the wood less susceptible to future absorption of moisture. A minimum moisture content in wood is an advantage in pattern work, because the wood is in better condition for taking glue and shellac and is less likely to change in shape.

Metal. Many of the patterns used in production work are made of metal because of its ability to withstand hard use. Furthermore metal patterns do not change their shape when subjected to moist conditions and require a minimum of maintenance work to keep them in operating condition. Single metal patterns are usually limited to cases where the pattern is fragile or has thin sections. In cases where limited production is desired, metal patterns are sometimes assembled on gates. The most important application of metal for pattern use is the making of production match plates.   Small metal patterns may be either mounted on plates or cast integrally with the plate.

Metals used for patterns include brass, white metal, cast iron, and aluminum.   Aluminum is probably the best all-around metal because it is easy to work, light in weight, and resistant to corrosion.   Pattern shops making principally metal patterns must of necessity use standard metal-working machines, as described in later chapters of this text.

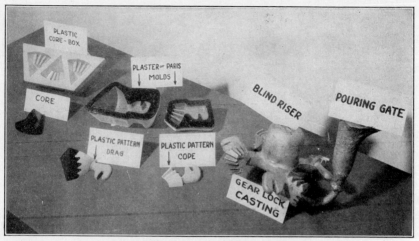

Courtesy American Foundryman.

FIG. 3.   Plaster of Paris Molds Used for Casting Plastic Patterns; also Plastic Core Box for Making Cores.

Plastics.   Plastics are especially well adapted for pattern materials because they do not absorb moisture, are strong and dimensionally stable, and have a very smooth surface.   They can be produced economically by casting in a fashion similar to metal casting.   Duplicate patterns can be quickly made, and the process of finishing them is rapid.   Wood-working tools are used, and no protective coating is necessary on the pattern.

In the process of making a plastic pattern it is necessary first to make a master pattern which forms the mold into which the plastic resin is poured.   These molds may be made of a variety of materials including wood, rubber, plastics, metal, or plaster of Paris, the last two being the ones most commonly used.   Plaster, although somewhat fragile, is simple to prepare, and a mold capable of producing a number of castings can be quickly made.   To facilitate parting, the mold should be coated with acid-resisting paint followed by a light coating of wax.   Upon completion, a phenol formaldehyde type casting resin is poured into the mold.* It is then necessary to bake the mold at a temperature of about 140 F in order to cure and harden the resin.

Figure 3 shows some plaster of Paris molds used for casting plastic patterns of a gear lock casting and also a plastic core box used for making cores. The patterns in this case were mounted on a wood plate not shown in the figure. On the right is shown a completed casting with gates and risers attached.

Courtesy E. J. McAfee, Puget Sound Naval Shipyard.

Fɪɢ. 4. Plastic Match Plate.

The process† employed in making the plastic match plate shown in Figure 4 is somewhat different in that a bismuth–lead alloy (melting point 158 F) is sprayed onto the master pattern so as to form a rigid shell mold about 1/8 inch thick. After both shell halves are complete, they are assembled in the flask and held in place by either ramming sand behind them or using plaster of Paris. The mold should then be coated with a parting agent and necessary gates and risers provided; the mold is then ready for casting the phenolic resins. If a match plate is desired, it is placed between the cope and drag with holes provided so the resins can flow through the plate as well as anchor the patterns to the plate.

    * C. R. Simmons, "Liquid Phenolic Resins for Casting," *American Foundryman,* May 1947.

     † E. J. McAfee, "Making Plastic Patterns," *American Foundryman,* July 1947.

Plaster. Gypsum cements* are now available having characteristics that make possible their use for patterns and core boxes. They have a high compressive strength and can be readily worked with wood tools. The cement is a high-expansion setting type and can be readily controlled to have setting expansions up to 0.02 inch per inch; thus the shrinkage allowance of the metal can be provided for by this expansion. When the cement is mixed with water, it forms a plastic mass capable of being cast into a mold or formed to shape by sweeps or template.

Wax and mercury. Both these materials are presently being used for patterns for precision castings. Their use is described in Chapter 4, Special Casting Methods.

Hand Tools Used in Pattern Work

The tools used in pattern work are essentially the same as those of the carpenter and cabinet maker. However, certain requirements of accuracy and special pattern allowances make the work of the pattern maker more detailed. It is assumed that those starting out in shop work have had some manual-training experience and have already a fundamental knowledge in the use of bench tools. Although much of the work in making patterns is done with machine tools, skill in the use of hand tools is an essential accomplishment for a pattern maker. Most patterns of medium and large size are built up from small pieces of wood, necessitating considerable fitting and assembly work. In general, it can be stated that pattern work requires more skill and accuracy in the use of hand tools than other types of wood work.

Wood-Working Machines for Pattern Work

In addition to the many hand tools required, there are a number of machine tools that are indispensable to the pattern maker. These tools are great time savers and are especially valuable in preparing stock and working large patterns. Care must be exercised in the operation of all such equipment because of the high speed involved and the rapidity with which the machine will cut. Chief among these machines are the band saw, circular saw, sander, jointer, planer, wood milling machine, combination tool grinder, and wood lathe.

Band saw. The band saw is adapted to a large variety of work and may be used either for straight or curved cutting. Since many patterns are made up of irregular shapes, this machine is indispensable.

* E. H. Schleede, "Gypsum Cement—Practical Pattern Making Applications," *American Foundryman*, January 1947.

The adjustable work table makes it possible to cut on an angle and bevel the work.

Circular saw. The circular saw is provided permanently with two arbors carrying a rip saw and a cross-cut saw, respectively. They are adjusted into cutting position by means of a hand wheel. The table is

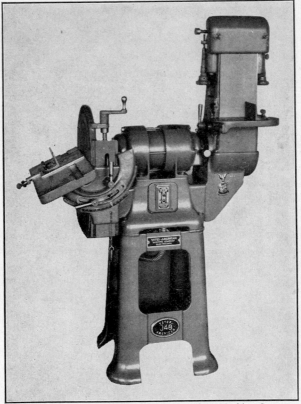

Courtesy Yates American Machine Company.

Fig. 5.   Disk and Belt Sander.

adjustable to any position up to 45 degrees and is provided with adjustable gages for controlling the width and angle of the cut. This machine is a great help in preparing stock for patterns and may also be used for grooving and making special joints.

Sander. The four main types of sanders used are the disk sander, the vertical spindle sander, the drum sander, and the belt sander. The first one mentioned (shown in Figure 5) is most commonly used and is usually made in combination with one of the other types.

In front of the disk is a table for holding the work, capable of being adjusted to various angles although it normally rests at 90 degrees with the disk. The sand or garnet paper is easily replaced, and it cuts rapidly, leaving a very smooth finish. This machine is used to true up pieces and to give a smooth finish to the work. On small patterns the necessary draft may be put on the work by tilting the table slightly.

Jointer and planer. The work of the jointer and planer is quite similar, although each has a well-defined use which justifies its difference in design. Illustrations of these two machines are shown in

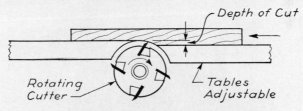

FIG. 6. Illustrating Operation of a Jointer.

Figures 6 and 7. The rotating cutter on a jointer operates underneath the work and is supported between two parallel iron tables, one of which is capable of vertical adjustment on wedge parallels to control the thickness of the cut. As a board is pushed over the cutters, it is planed to a smooth surface on the bottom side. Likewise, if the board is turned over, the other side can be dressed smooth; but the

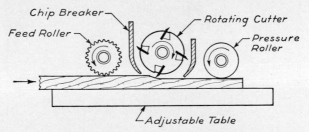

FIG. 7. Planer or Single Surfacer.

board will not necessarily be of uniform thickness. In order to have both sides of the board parallel and of a definite thickness, the last operation must be performed on a single-surface planer. This machine has a horizontal table on which the board rests, and the rotating cutter is above the board. The previously smoothed surface of the board is placed on the table and the board fed to the cutter

by means of a feed roller. A pressure roller is also placed just ahead
of the cutter to keep the board in place. As the board passes through
the planer, the rotating cutter finishes off the top side of the board
parallel to the lower surface.

Wood milling machine. The most highly developed machine for
pattern making, one that has a wide variety of uses, is the wood

Courtesy Oliver Machinery Company.

Fig. 8. Wood Milling Machine.

milling machine. Such a machine is shown in Figure 8. It consists
of a vertical rotating spindle, to which cutters may be attached,
with an adjustable table beneath. The work is attached to the table
and can be fed against the rotating cutter in any direction desired.
It is especially adapted to the working of large patterns and core
boxes, but may also be used for gear cutting, making fillets, grooving,
forming irregular shapes, and for many other intricate and special
jobs. Special machines of this same type have been developed to

take care of core-box work. The versatiliy of this machine is illustrated in Figure 9.

Wood lathe. The wood-turning lathe shown in Figure 10 is a high-speed lathe, much simpler in construction than the metal-turning type. In the best lathes the headstock is connected directly to a motor having a variable-speed controller which gives a speed regulation of 600 to 3000 rpm. The tailstock is adjustable on the lathe

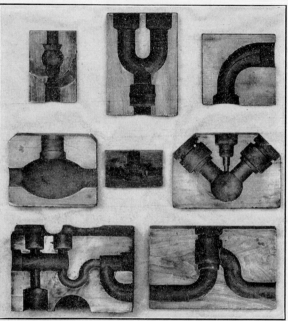

Courtesy Oliver Machinery Company.

Fɪɢ. 9. Specimens of Work Done on "Oliver" Pattern Millers.

bed according to the length of the stock to be turned. Inasmuch as the tools used in turning work are all held by hand, a plain adjustable tool rest is provided.

Two types of work can be done on a lathe: namely, turning between centers and face-plate turning. In turning between centers, the centers of the stock at the ends must first be located. The stock is then driven onto the live center with a wood mallet, and the dead center, which does not turn, is forced into the wood by a forward movement of the tailstock spindle. Both centers should be forced into the wood a sufficient distance to make a deep impression. A little wax or oil on the dead center will prevent squeaking or overheating through friction.

For turning short pieces that cannot be mounted between centers, it is necessary to use a face plate which screws onto the headstock spindle. A variety of sizes of these face plates is usually provided with each lathe, and the work to be turned is held to the face plate

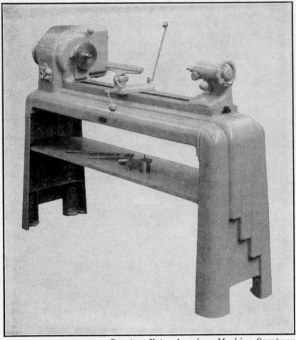

Courtesy Yates American Machine Company.

Fig. 10. Speed Lathe for Wood Turning.

by means of wood screws. When the work is so large in diameter that it interferes with the bed of the lathe, the face plate is mounted on the outer end of the spindle. A floor stand for supporting the tools is provided for such work.

Construction of Typical Patterns

Solid gear pattern. Assume that a pattern for the gear blank shown in Figure 11 is to be turned. A face plate, as shown at *B*, is used for a pattern of this size. The pattern stock should be prepared by cutting it out on a band saw slightly larger than the finished diameter and by smoothing off one side on the sander. The work should then be screwed to the wood face plate by one or more screws. With this mounting most of the outside diameter and one side can be finished.

A template should be provided to check the size of the recess in the pattern.

After this much of the pattern is made, it should be removed from the face plate. The face plate should then be recessed, as shown at *C*, so that the finished diameter of the gear blank fits in closely.

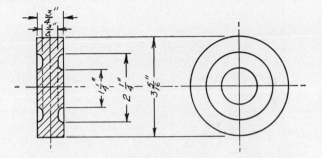

"A"— CAST   IRON   GEAR   BLANK   Solid Pattern

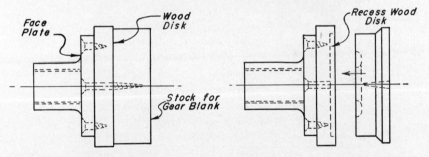

"B"—METHOD OF HOLDING   "C"—MOUNTING BLANK ON FACE
STOCK ON FACE PLATE   PLATE FOR LAST OPERATION

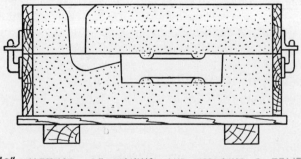
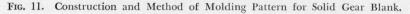

"D"— METHOD OF MAKING AND MOLDING A SOLID
PATTERN GEAR BLANK

FIG. 11. Construction and Method of Molding Pattern for Solid Gear Blank.

This insures that the pattern will be fastened perfectly true and concentric with the previous turning. The gear blank may now be completed in the same manner as the first half. The method of molding the gear blank in the foundry is shown at *D*.

Patterns with loose pieces. In some cases patterns have to be made with projections or overhanging parts so that it is impossible to remove them from the sand, even though they are parted. In such patterns the projections have to be fastened loosely to the main pattern by means of wooden or wire dowel pins. When the mold is being made, such loose pieces remain in the mold until after the pattern is withdrawn and are then drawn out separately through the cavity formed by the main pattern.

The use of loose pieces is illustrated in the pattern for a gib casting which fits over a dovetailed slide. See Figure 12*A* for a detail of this casting.

In beginning this pattern it is necessary first to make a layout, with all allowances for draft, finish, and shrinkage. Next it should be decided how the pattern is to be molded. Two methods are possible, as illustrated at *D* and *E* of the figure. The first method requires two loose pieces to facilitate withdrawing the pattern from the sand. The main pattern is first withdrawn, leaving the two loose pieces in the sand. These pieces may then be withdrawn from the sand, owing to the additional space occupied by the main part of the pattern. The pattern constructed in this manner is made up of five pieces, as shown in the figure at *B*.

The loose pieces may be eliminated by using a dry-sand core. If such construction is desired, the pattern would then be made as shown at *C*. In addition, a core box would be necessary. This latter method is less economical because of the expense involved in making the core box and core.

Patterns for pipe fittings. The pipe elbow shown in Figure 13 is typical of many cast fittings. In production work, the patterns would be mounted on a match plate, but, for only a few castings, a split pattern would be used.

The round part of the elbow is turned on a face plate, as shown in *B*. Four pieces of wood are prepared and screwed to the wood face plate and are then turned to shape, a template being used to check the curvature. The work is then sanded and removed from the face plate.

The enlarged parts at each end of the elbow are turned separately with the core prints as illustrated at *C*. If only a single pattern is made, it will be necessary to have balanced core prints, but, in the best construction, a double pattern is made.   A section of such a pattern after it is assembled is shown at *D*.

Pattern and core box for jackscrew base.   The detail for this part is shown in Figure 14*A*.   Such a pattern requires a rather long core

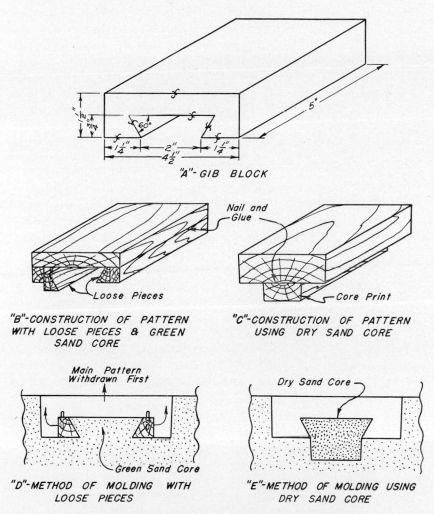

"A"- GIB BLOCK

"B"-CONSTRUCTION OF PATTERN WITH LOOSE PIECES & GREEN SAND CORE

"C"-CONSTRUCTION OF PATTERN USING DRY SAND CORE

"D"-METHOD OF MOLDING WITH LOOSE PIECES

"E"-METHOD OF MOLDING USING DRY SAND CORE

Fig. 12.   Alternate Methods of Making Gib-Block Patterns.

print in order to balance and hold the dry-sand core in place.   A layout is first made to take care of the various allowances and to provide a working detail for the pattern and core box.   The completed pattern is illustrated at *B*.   The body of the pattern is made up of two pieces of stock assembled as shown at *C*.   Dowel pins are located and drilled before the turning starts.   At the completion of the turning, the two ends held by corrugated fasteners are sawed off and the necessary draft sanded on the ends of the pattern.

The core box and its construction are shown at *D* and *E*.   It is designed to mold half of the core at a time.   After being baked, the halves are assembled and glued together.   They are then ready for use in a mold.   The two blocks which make up the main part of the

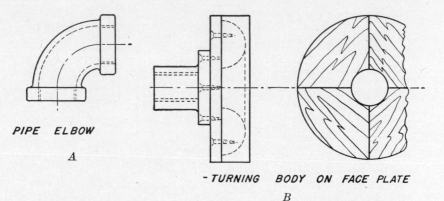

PIPE   ELBOW

A

-TURNING   BODY   ON   FACE   PLATE

B

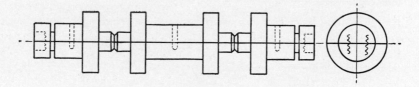

-METHOD   OF   TURNING   CORE   PRINTS

C

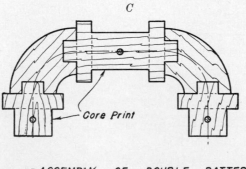

Core Print

-ASSEMBLY   OF   DOUBLE   PATTERN

D

FIG. 13.   Construction of Pattern for Pipe Elbow.

box must have their sides square and be carefully laid out as shown in the figure. The layout lines on each block represent the outline of the wood that is to be cut out. When this is done, the two blocks are assembled on a bottom board, and draft is provided at each end of the box by sanding. The box is completed when both end pieces

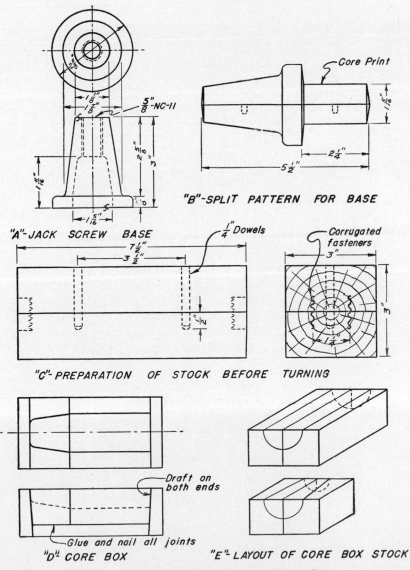

FIG. 14. Construction of Pattern for Jackscrew Base.

are put on.   Any corner that becomes an inside corner in the casting should be filleted.

Review Questions

1. What is a pattern?
2. Why are some patterns made in two parts?
3. What is a match plate, and for what type of work is it used?
4. What is the purpose of a follow board?
5. List and define the various allowances that must be considered in making a pattern.
6. How does a shrink rule differ from a standard rule?
7. What is meant by draft as applied to pattern work? Must all surfaces on a pattern have draft?
8. Why should fillets be used at connecting surfaces of a pattern?
9. What is shellac? Why is it used, and how is it applied?
10. What is the accepted color scheme for use on wood patterns?
11. Why is wood seasoned, and how is it done?
12. How are plastic patterns made?
13. List the various materials used for making patterns.
14. What is the difference between a jointer and a planer?
15. List the essential wood-working machines for a pattern shop.
16. What type of work may be done on a wood milling machine?
17. Briefly describe how a solid gear blank pattern would be made.
18. Why are some patterns made with loose pieces?
19. Distinguish among a core, a core print, and a core box.
20. Describe the procedure for turning a split pattern on a lathe.

References

BENEDICT, O. JR., *Manual of Foundry and Pattern Shop Practice*, McGraw-Hill Book Company, 1947.

"Cost of Castings Reduced by Skeleton Patterns," *Iron Age*, August 20, 1936.

HANLEY, E. C., *Wood Pattern Making*, Bruce Publishing Company, 1924.

HARBISON, C. B., "Designers Should Cooperate with Foundrymen," *Steel*, June 22, 1936, pp. 54, 56.

HOLLAND, KILEY, *Pattern Design*, 1st edition, International Text Book Company, 1939.

McCASLIN, H. J., *Wood Pattern Making*, 4th edition, McGraw-Hill Book Company, 1946.

RICHARDS, W. H., *Principles of Pattern and Foundry Practice*, McGraw-Hill Book Company, 1930.

RITCHEY, MONROE, HALL, BEESE, *Pattern Making*, American Technical Society, 1946.

CHAPTER

4

METAL CASTING

Cast Iron

Cast iron is a general term applied to a wide range of iron–carbon–silicon alloys in combination with smaller percentages of several other elements. It is an iron alloy containing so much carbon, or its equivalent, that it is not malleable. The principal difference among cast iron, steel, and wrought iron is the carbon content. The approximate carbon limits are:

Cast iron	$C > 2.0\%$
Steel	$C < 2.0\%$, but $> 0.1\%$
Wrought iron	$C < 0.1\%$

Quite obviously, cast iron may have a wide range of properties, since small percentage variations of its elements may cause considerable change in the physical properties. Cast iron should not be thought of as a metal containing a single element, but rather as one having in its composition at least six elements. All cast irons contain iron, carbon, silicon, manganese, phosphorus, and sulfur. If the iron is in the category of alloy cast iron, still other elements will be present. These elements which go to make up cast iron should not be thought of as impurities, for they all have important effects on the physical properties. Pure iron, known as ferrite, is very soft and has few uses in industrial work. All the desirable properties, such as strength, hardness, and machinability, are controlled by regulating the elements other than ferrite in the cast iron.

The principal raw material for iron castings is *pig iron,* the product of the *blast furnace.* Pig iron is obtained by smelting iron ore with coke and limestone, the final analysis depending primarily on the kind of ore used. Table 1 lists the principal iron ores used in the production of pig iron.

Figure 1 is a diagrammatic view of a blast furnace for producing pig iron. The average blast furnace is about 20 feet in diameter and around 100 feet in height. Daily capacities of such furnaces range

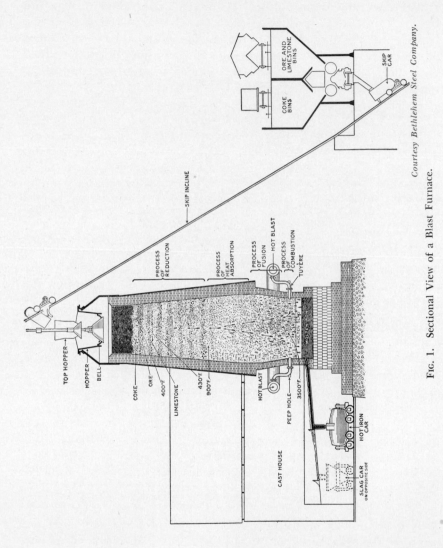

Courtesy Bethlehem Steel Company.

FIG. 1.　Sectional View of a Blast Furnace.

from 600 to 1000 tons of pig iron per 24 hours. The raw materials—ore, coke, and limestone—are brought to the top of the furnace with a skip hoist and dumped into the double-valve hopper. The hot blast of air enters the furnace through *tuyères* placed around the furnace just above the hearth. As the coke burns, the ore is reduced by contact with the hot carbon monoxide gas. The limestone added with the charge combines with the gangue materials of the ore to render it into a fluid slag. Slag floats over the molten iron and is

TABLE 1. IRON ORES

Name	Symbol	Color	% Metallic Iron	Location
Hematite	Fe_2O_3	Red	70	Lake Superior District
Magnetite	Fe_3O_4	Black	72.4	N. Y., Ala.; Sweden
Siderite	$FeCO_3$	Brown	48.3	N. Y., Ohio; Germany, England
Limonite	$Fe_2O_3 \cdot X(H_2O)$	Brown	60–65	Eastern U. S., Tex., Mo., Colo., France

withdrawn at frequent periods; the iron is tapped at intervals of 4 to 6 hours. In addition to the equipment shown in the figure, there are three or four *stoves*—large cylindrical towers for preheating the air blown into the furnace. These stoves are heated by blast-furnace gas taken from the top of the blast furnace and passed through suitable cleaners to remove ashes. The remainder of the gas is washed and used for generating power and as fuel in other furnaces about the plant.

TABLE 2. CLASSIFICATION OF PIG IRON

Grade of Iron	Silicon	Sulfur	Phosphorus	Manganese
No. 1 Foundry	2.5 –3.0	Under 0.035	0.05–1.0	Under 1.0
No. 2 Foundry	2.0 –2.5	Under 0.045	0.05–1.0	Under 1.0
No. 3 Foundry	1.5 –2.0	Under 0.055	0.05–1.0	Under 1.0
Malleable	0.75–1.5	Under 0.050	Under 0.2	Under 1.0
Bessemer	1.0 –2.0	Under 0.050	Under 0.1	Under 1.0
Basic	Under 1.0	Under 0.050	Under 1.0	Under 1.0

By regulation of operating conditions and proper selection of ore mixtures, the composition of the pig iron can be controlled. Common grades of pig iron produced in the United States are shown in Table 2.

Kinds of Cast Iron

1. Direct-iron castings. This iron is a product of the blast furnace and is usually known as pig iron. It is not suitable for most commercial castings until it has been remelted in a cupola or furnace of other type. Furthermore, the output of a blast furnace is so large that it would be difficult to provide sufficient commercial molds to take care of the output.

2. Gray iron. Gray iron is the name given to the ordinary commercial iron, which is so called because of the grayish color of the fracture. This color is due to the carbon's being principally in the

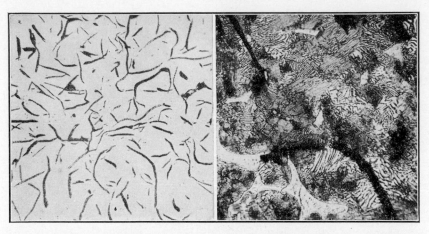

FIG. 2. Structure of Gray Cast Iron (ASTM Class 40). Graphite Flakes in Unetched Matrix. Magnification ×125.

FIG. 3. Structure of Gray Cast Iron (ASTM Class 40). Etched in 5% Nital Showing Graphite, Pearlite, and Steadite. Magnification ×562.

form of flake graphite. This iron is easily machined and has a high compression strength, a low tensile strength, and no ductility. The percentages of the several elements may vary considerably, but are usually within the following limits:

Carbon	3.00–3.50
Silicon	1.00–2.75
Manganese	0.40–1.00
Phosphorus	0.15–1.00
Sulfur	0.02–0.15
Iron	Remainder

Figures 2 and 3 are micrographs showing the structure of gray cast iron. If a specimen is polished and examined under the microscope, the appearance is as shown in Figure 2. The dark lines are small flakes of graphite which greatly impair the strength of the iron. The strength of cast iron is increased if these flakes are small and uniformly distributed throughout the metal. Etching a specimen with a dilute solution of nitric acid results in the structure shown in Figure 3. The light-colored constituent appears to be steadite, a structural component in cast iron that contains phosphorus; the other new constituent is known as pearlite. *Steadite* can be identified by its white dendritic formation and is a eutectic structure of alpha iron and iron phosphide. Ferrite or pure iron also appears as a constituent of gray irons having a high silicon content or irons that have been slowly cooled. *Pearlite* (composed of alternate lamellae of ferrite and iron carbide) is found in most irons and is similar to the pearlite found in carbon steels. This constituent adds to the strength and wear resistance of the iron. The dark graphite flakes may also be seen in this microphotograph.

3. White iron. This iron shows a white fracture, which is due to the fact that the carbon is in the form of a carbide, Fe_3C. The carbide, known as *cementite,* is the hardest constituent of iron and

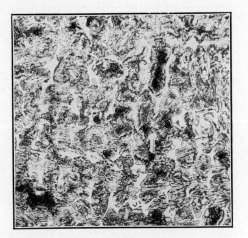

Fig. 4. Structure of White Cast Iron as Cast. Etched in 5% Nital Showing Pearlite and Cementite. Magnification ×125.

makes it hard and brittle. White iron with a large percentage of carbide cannot be machined. The principal constituents shown in the micrograph (Figure 4) are cementite and pearlite. The dark area is the pearlite and the light area the cementite.

White cast iron may be produced by casting against metal chills or by regulating the analysis. Chills are used when a hard wear-resisting surface is wanted for such products as car wheels, rolls for crushing grain, and jaw-crusher plates. The first step in the production of malleable iron is to produce a white-iron casting by controlling the analysis of the metal.   One specification* for the production of these castings is as follows:

Carbon	1.75–2.30
Silicon	0.85–1.20
Manganese	Less than 0.40
Phosphorus	Less than 0.20
Sulfur	Less than 0.12
Iron	Remainder

4. Mottled cast iron.   This is a product intermediary between gray and white cast iron, the name being again derived from the appearance of the fracture.   It is obtained in castings where certain wearing surfaces have been chilled.

5. Malleable cast iron.   As in the production of white iron, malleable iron castings, when first cast, have all the carbon in the

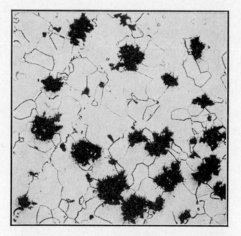

Fig. 5.   Structure of Malleable Iron.   Etched in 5% Nital Showing Temper Carbon in Ferrite Matrix.   Magnification ×125.

carbide form.   Several types of furnaces, including the cupola, air furnace, and electric furnace, are utilized for producing this type of iron.   In some cases, two furnaces are used combined to gain the advantages of each.   This arrangement, known as duplexing, is frequent with the cupola and air furnace.   It permits continuous pouring as well as more accurate control of the pouring temperatures and analysis of the metal.   The castings obtained are packed in pots and placed in an annealing oven so arranged as to allow free circula-

* ASTM Specification A47–33, Grade 35018.

tion of heat around each unit. The annealing time lasts 3 to 4 days at temperatures varying from 1500 to 1850 F. In this process, the hard iron carbides are changed into nodules of *temper* or *graphitic carbon* in a matrix of comparatively pure iron, as shown in the micrograph in Figure 5. Malleable iron has a tensile strength of around 55,000 pounds per square inch and an elongation of 18%. Castings have considerable shock resistance and good machinability. Malleable castings are used principally by the railroad, automotive, pipe-fitting, and agricultural-implement industries.

6. Nodular iron. A high-strength high-ductility iron, having the carbon in the form of graphite nodules, is now being produced as shown in the micrograph of Figure 6. This is accomplished by adding a small amount of a magnesium-containing agent such as magnesium-nickel or magnesium-copper-ferrosilicon alloy. Magnesium required to produce graphite depends on the amount of sulfur present. Sulfur is first eliminated by being converted to magnesium

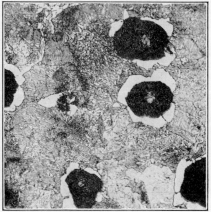

Courtesy The International Nickel Company, Inc.

Fig. 6. Structure of Nodular or Ductile Cast Iron. Magnification ×250.

sulfide, additional magnesium present changing the graphite to the nodular form. This type of iron is usually obtained in the as-cast condition; however, casting followed by a short annealing period is often employed to obtain certain desired properties. In this process, the time for annealing is much shorter than that used in the manufacture of malleable iron. With the improved physical properties exhibited by this iron, its potential applications are many. It is being used a great deal in the casting of crankshafts as well as for miscellaneous parts in a wide variety of machines.

Effect of Chemical Elements on Cast Iron

Carbon. Although any iron containing over 2.0% carbon is in the cast-iron range, gray cast iron has a carbon content of 3 to 4%. The amount depends on the carbon content in the pig iron and scrap used and that absorbed from the coke during the melting process. The final properties of the iron depend not only on the amount of carbon but also on the form in which it exists. The formation of graphitic carbon depends on slow cooling and on the silicon content. High silicon promotes the formation of graphitic carbon. Carbon in this state acts as a softener for the iron, reduces the shrinkage, and gives the iron machinability. The strength of the iron increases with the percentage of carbon in the combined form.

Silicon. Silicon up to 3.25% is a softener in iron and is the predominating element in determining the amounts of combined and graphitic carbon. It combines with iron that otherwise would combine with carbon, thus allowing the carbon to change to the graphitic state. After an equilibrium is reached, additional silicon unites with the ferrite to form a hard compound. Hence, silicon above 3.25% acts as a hardener. In melting, the average loss of silicon is about 10% of the total silicon charged into the cupola. High silicon content is recommended for small castings and low for large castings. When it is used in percentages from 13 to 17, an alloy having acid and corrosion resistance is formed.

Manganese. Manganese in small amounts does not have an appreciable effect, but in amounts over 0.5% it combines with sulfur to form a manganese sulfide. The mixture has a low specific gravity and is eliminated from the metal with the slag. In addition to its acting as a purifier for eliminating sulfur, it also has some action as a deoxidizer. Other effects are to increase fluidity, strength, and hardness of the iron. If the percentage is increased appreciably over the usual amounts, it will promote the formation of combined carbon and rapidly increase the hardness of the iron. Of the manganese originally charged, 10 to 20% is lost in the melting process.

Sulfur. There is nothing good to be said for sulfur in cast iron. It promotes the formation of combined carbon, with accompanying hardness, and causes the iron to lose fluidity, with resultant blow holes. Sulfur gets into the iron from the ore and also from the coke during the melting process. Each time the iron is remelted there is a slight pickup in sulfur, frequently as much as 0.03%. To counteract this increase, manganese should be added to the charge in the form of ferromanganese briquettes and spiegeleisen.

Phosphorus. The principal effects of phosphorus are to increase the fluidity of the molten metal and to lower the melting temperature. For this reason phosphorus up to 1% is used both in small castings and in those having thin sections. Large castings should have low phosphorus content, as additional fluidity in the iron is not required. There is a slight increase in strength and shock resistance as the percentage increases. There is little change in the phosphorus content during the melting process, although in some calculations it is assumed that there is a pickup of about 0.02%. The action of any remelting process upon phosphorus is principally one of concentration, as this element does not oxidize readily except under special conditions. In order to control this element, care should be exercised in selecting the grade of scrap that is used.

Phosphorus also forms a constituent known as *steadite,* a mixture of iron and phosphide, which is hard, brittle, and of rather low melting point. It contains about 10% phosphorus, so that an iron with 0.50% phosphorus would have 5% steadite by volume. Steadite appears as a light structureless area under the microscope but may appear as a network if sufficient phosphorus is present.

Cupola

Description. The production of iron castings is accomplished by remelting scrap along with pig iron in a furnace called a cupola. The construction of this furnace is simple, consisting of a vertical stack lined with a refractory material with provisions for introducing an air blast near the bottom. A cross section of a cupola is shown in Figure 7, with the principal parts labeled.

The entire cupola rests on a circular plate, which is supported above the floor by four columns suitably spaced so that the hinged bottom doors can swing freely without hitting them. In operation, these doors are swung into horizontal position and held in place by a vertical prop. The charging door is located about halfway up the vertical shell, and the top of the cupola is open except for a metal shield or spark arrester.

The openings for introducing the air to the coke bed are known as *tuyères.* Usual practice is to have a single row around the circumference of the wall, although some large cupolas have two rows. The tuyères, flaring in shape with the large end on the inside to cause the air to spread evenly, are placed fairly close together to obtain as nearly uniform air distribution as possible. The number of tuyères varies with the cupola diameter, ranging from four on small cupolas to eight or more on large installations; and the combined area of the inlets is roughly one fourth of the cross-sectional area of the cupola. Normally, the bottom plate of the iron tuyère casting is about 20 inches above the bed of the cupola, although this height will vary according to whether the type of operation is intermittent or continuous. A shallow hearth is satisfactory for long heats, as less coke is required.

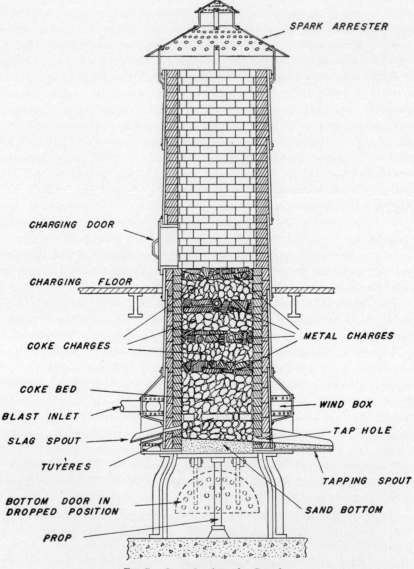

FIG. 7.   Cross Section of a Cupola.

Surrounding the cupola at the tuyères is a wind box or jacket for the air supply. Small windows covered with mica are located opposite each tuyère so that conditions in the cupola can be inspected. The air blast, furnished by a positive displacement or centrifugal type of blower, enters the side of the wind jacket.

The opening through which the metal flows to the spout is called the tap hole. Opposite the pouring spout at the rear of the cupola is located another spout for slag disposal. This opening is a few inches below the tuyères to prevent slag running into them and also to prevent possible chilling of the slag by the air blast.

Preparing and charging. The first operation in preparing a cupola is to clean out the slag and refuse on the lining and around the tuyères from the previous run. Care must be exercised in doing this so as not to damage the refractory lining. Any bad spots or broken bricks are repaired with a daubing mixture of fire clay and silica sand or ganister. Brick and clay in the breast are removed preparatory to rebuilding it with new materials. After the lining is repaired, the bottom doors are swung into position and the prop placed under them. All cracks are closed with fire clay, and a layer of black molding sand is placed on the bottom. This sand is rammed down and given a slope towards the spout, the depth being not less than 4 inches at the lowest point. The breast opening at the spout is made up of a mixture of fire clay and sand, or a separate breast brick can be used. A small tap hole about ¾ to 1 inch in diameter is provided.

The firing of a cupola is started 2½ to 3 hours before the first metal is to be tapped. Kindling wood is thrown in the charging door after a few flat pieces are placed on the bottom to protect the packed sand. A sufficient amount of wood should be used to ignite a bed of coke. All the tuyères are open when the fire is started, and only a natural draft is used. Coke is added from time to time until the bed is built up to its proper height above the tuyères. The height of the bed coke is important, as it determines the height of the melting zone and affects both the temperature and oxidation of the metal. Another controlling factor is the pressure of the air blast, as with increased pressure a higher bed is necessary. Depending on the afore-mentioned conditions, the bed height may range from 20 to 50 inches above the top of the tuyères. The height of the bed should be gaged by dropping a gage bar from the charging door to coke level.

As soon as the coke bed is thoroughly ignited, the pig iron and scrap may be charged. The alternate charges of coke and iron are made in a ratio of 1 part of coke to 8 or 10 parts of iron, measured by weight. The ratio depends on the heating value of the coke, the size of the iron pieces making up the charge, and the metal temperature desired. A ratio of 1 to 8 probably represents average practice. The size of the charge depends on the diameter of the cupola and also on the amount of coke that is necessary to provide sufficient fuel for the charge. In general, a uniform layer thickness of 6 to 8 inches is used between each charge. By calculating the weight of the coke necessary for this layer and knowing the coke–iron ratio, the weight of the iron charge may be obtained. If the coke layer in a small cupola weighs 60 pounds, the iron charge will be 480 pounds.

In addition to charging iron and coke, a fluxing material should also be used if the runs are to be long. The object of adding a flux is to remove impurities in the iron, protect the iron from oxidation, and render the slag more fluid for easy removal from the cupola. Limestone ($CaCO_3$) is the principal fluxing material, although fluorspar (CaF_2) and soda ash (Na_2CO_3) are also used. This material is applied over the coke charges in small lumps not exceeding 2 inches in diameter. Although limestone is the cheapest, fluorspar gives the slag more fluidity. Experience has proved that about 75 pounds of limestone should be used per ton of iron. Frequently fluorspar is added in a ratio of 1 to 2 or 3, replacing part of the limestone. The amount of fluxing materials is subject to considerable variation, depending on the amount of coke ash formed and the cleanness of the metal. Slag that is formed floats on the metal accumulated on the hearth and flows continuously from the slag hole at the rear of the cupola during the heat.

After the cupola is fully charged up to the charging door, it is desirable for the iron to soak in the heat about three fourths of an hour or longer. No forced draft is used during this period, the only draft coming from the tuyère peep holes and the spout opening. Before turning on the blast, the tuyère openings should be closed. After the blast has been on a few minutes, molten metal starts accumulating in the hearth. The tap hole is then stopped up until a sufficient amount of molten metal is accumulated in the cupola to warrant pouring operations. During operation the cupola should be kept filled to the charging door by addition of successive charges as rapidly as room is provided by the settling of the material. This is important, for the settling of the charges permits a rapid escape of the gases, and the iron that is charged loses the advantage of this heat. The length of a heat may be as much as 16 hours, although most runs are only a few hours in length.

Intermittently the tap hole of the cupola is opened, allowing the metal to flow into a large ladle. It is then closed again with a conical clay plug called a *bot*. This procedure is repeated until all the metal is melted and poured. At the end of the run, the blast is shut off and the prop under the bottom doors knocked down, allowing the remains in the cupola to drop to the floor. The bed of hot iron, slag, and coke is quenched with water as quickly as possible and removed from beneath the cupola. Any coke or iron in the remains is salvaged and taken into account in the cupola calculations for the heat.

Cupola air supply. The amount of air required to melt a ton of iron depends on the quality of coke and the coke–iron ratio. Theoretically, 113 cubic feet of air at 14.7 pounds per square inch and at 60 F is required for one pound of carbon. For other operating conditions some correction should be made to get the correct volume of air. For coke the previous figure should be reduced slightly to compensate for the ash content. Assuming a 1 to 8 ratio, we find that 250 pounds of coke is required to melt one ton of iron. Multiplying 250 by 105 gives 26,250 cubic feet of air required to melt one ton. Actually, in practice perfect combustion is not obtained, and a larger volume of air is required. A value of 30,000 cubic feet of air per ton of iron is frequently used in estimating the capacity of a blower.

The pressure of the blast to be maintained will depend on the size of the cupola, compactness of the charge, kind of iron being melted, and the temperature. Small cupolas may require a pressure of only 5 to 8 ounces; large cupolas may operate as high as 28 ounces. No definite rule for pressure can be laid down; the proper value can be obtained only by actual operating experience.

The best type of blower for cupola operation is the positive-displacement type, because it delivers a constant volume of air to the cupola, irrespective of changing furnace conditions. In making calculations a small air-slippage loss should be taken into account. This loss is a known value for a given blower. Variations in capacity are obtained by speed regulation. With centrifugal blowers the volume to the cupola varies according to the pressure in the wind jacket, which in turn is affected by the height of charge and other conditions in the cupola. Volume may be controlled by a gate in the blast line connected with suitable electric controls. The regulation is obtained by changing the power input of the motor driving the blower.

Hot-blast type. Combustion in the cupola may be appreciably improved by preheating the air as is done in regenerative-type melting furnaces. One method used removes the stack gases from the cupola just below the charging door and completes their combustion in a furnace adjacent to the cupola. Incoming air goes through a preheater in this furnace and then into the wind box of the cupola, the temperature being around 600 F. The other method preheats the air in a separate external furnace and does not attempt to reclaim any heat from the cupola operation. One advantage of this method is that the hot blast is ready as soon as the cupola is started. Both methods improve the melting rate and save appreciably on the amount of fuel required.

Calculation of cupola charge. Careful consideration must be given to the materials charged into a cupola if a uniform product is desired from day to day. Raw materials vary in composition, and there are also changes that take place during the melting operation. For some elements (silicon and manganese) there is a definite percentage loss due to oxidation. Carbon also has a loss due to oxidation, but this is compensated by absorption from the coke. Sulfur does not suffer any loss from oxidation and actually picks up additional amounts from the coke. There is little change in the phosphorus content. Most cupolas operate on a fairly large percentage of return scrap, which is close to the desired analysis. In computing a charge, however, both return and new scrap must be included as well as the various grades of pig iron. The following problem illustrates the procedure involved in calculating a charge.

Problem. Given the following materials to work with, what would the final iron analysis be, using cupola melting? Assume a 3000-pound charge made up of metals of the following composition:

Iron	Carbon	Silicon	Manganese	Phosphorus	Sulfur
No. 1 pig iron	3.5	2.50	0.72	0.180	0.016
No. 2 pig iron	3.5	3.00	0.63	0.120	0.018
New cast-iron scrap	3.4	2.30	0.50	0.200	0.030
Returns from foundry	3.3	2.50	0.65	0.170	0.035

The material is to be used in the following proportions: no. 1 pig—10%; no. 2 pig—20%; returns—40%; new scrap—30%.

(a) Carbon content; oxidation loss = gain from coke

No. 1 pig	$3000 \times 0.10 \times 0.035 =$	10.5 lb
No. 2 pig	$3000 \times 0.20 \times 0.035 =$	21.0 lb
New scrap	$3000 \times 0.30 \times 0.034 =$	30.6 lb
Returns	$3000 \times 0.40 \times 0.033 =$	39.6 lb
		101.7 lb

$$\text{Per cent carbon} = \frac{101.7}{3000} \times 100 = 3.39$$

(b) Silicon content; oxidation loss = 10%

No. 1 pig	$3000 \times 0.10 \times 0.025 =$	7.5 lb
No. 2 pig	$3000 \times 0.20 \times 0.030 =$	18.0 lb
New scrap	$3000 \times 0.30 \times 0.023 =$	20.7 lb
Returns	$3000 \times 0.40 \times 0.025 =$	30.0 lb
		76.2 lb

$$\text{Per cent silicon} = \frac{76.2 - (76.2 \times 0.10)}{3000} \times 100 = 2.28$$

(c) Manganese content; oxidation loss = 20%

No. 1 pig	$3000 \times 0.10 \times 0.0072 =$	2.16 lb
No. 2 pig	$3000 \times 0.20 \times 0.0063 =$	3.78 lb
New scrap	$3000 \times 0.30 \times 0.0050 =$	4.50 lb
Returns	$3000 \times 0.40 \times 0.0065 =$	7.80 lb
		18.24 lb

$$\text{Per cent manganese} = \frac{18.24 - (18.24 \times 0.2)}{3000} \times 100 = 0.49$$

(d) Phosphorus; oxidation loss = 0

No. 1 pig	$3000 \times 0.10 \times 0.0018 =$	0.54 lb
No. 2 pig	$3000 \times 0.20 \times 0.0012 =$	0.72 lb
New scrap	$3000 \times 0.30 \times 0.0020 =$	1.80 lb
Returns	$3000 \times 0.40 \times 0.0017 =$	2.04 lb
		5.10 lb

$$\text{Per cent phosphorus} = \frac{5.10}{3000} \times 100 = 0.17$$

(e) Sulfur; oxidation loss = 0. Gain from coke is approximately 4% of sulfur in coke.

No. 1 pig	$3000 \times 0.10 \times 0.00016 =$	0.048 lb
No. 2 pig	$3000 \times 0.20 \times 0.00018 =$	0.108 lb
New scrap	$3000 \times 0.30 \times 0.00030 =$	0.270 lb
Returns	$3000 \times 0.40 \times 0.00035 =$	0.420 lb
		0.846 lb

Assuming a coke to iron melting ratio of 1 to 8 and a coke with a sulfur content of 0.50%, we have

$$375 \times 0.005 = 1.875 \text{ lb of sulfur}$$
$$\text{Pickup } 4\% = 0.075 \text{ lb}$$

$$\text{Then per cent sulfur} = \frac{0.846 + 0.075}{3000} \times 100 = 0.0307$$

Advantages and limitations. The cupola has been used extensively for many years because of its simplicity of construction and economy in operation. It melts iron continuously at a high production rate requiring a minimum of maintenance.

However, when metal is melted in contact with the fuel, some elements are picked up while others are lost. This affects the final analysis of the metal and necessitates close regulation of the cupola. Also, close temperature control is difficult to maintain.

Air Furnace

The air or reverberatory furnace shown in Figure 8 has been widely used for many years for the production of malleable-iron and high-test gray-iron castings. Early furnaces were hand-fired with bituminous coal, but most furnaces of today use pulverized coal or oil as fuel. Charging is done through the roof of the furnace by removing sections of the arch called *bungs*. This furnace lends itself to close control, since the metal can be tested at intervals. Furthermore, the metal is not in contact with the fuel as it is in the cupola furnace; and the

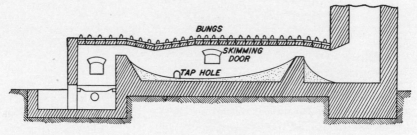

FIG. 8. Air Furnace.

analysis, particularly the carbon content, may be held to close limits. Since the initial and operating costs of this furnace are higher than those of a cupola, the air furnace does not have wide application except for malleable-iron castings. Capacities of these furnaces range from 5 to 50 tons per heat.

Steel Castings

Steel is a crystalline alloy of iron, carbon, and several other elements, which hardens when quenched above its critical temperature. It contains no slag and may be cast, rolled, or forged. Carbon is an important constituent because of its ability to increase the hardness and strength of the steel. Steel castings may be classified as follows:*

STEEL CASTINGS

1. Carbon steel
   (a) Low carbon (less than 0.20%).
   (b) Medium carbon (0.20 to 0.40%).
   (c) High carbon (over 0.40%).

2. Alloy steel
   (a) Low alloys (special alloying elements totaling less than 8.0%).
   (b) High alloys (special alloying elements totaling over 8.0%).

* *Cast Metals Handbook*, American Foundrymen's Association.

Medium-carbon–steel castings are the most frequently used in the carbon–steel range. They have ductility and good tensile strength in a normalized condition, ranging from 60,000 to 80,000 pounds per square inch. The range of chemical composition is given here.

MEDIUM-CARBON–STEEL CASTINGS

Carbon	0.20–0.40
Manganese	0.50–1.00
Silicon	0.20–0.75
Phosphorus	0.05–maximum
Sulfur	0.06–maximum
Ferrite	Remainder

Alloy castings may contain special elements in addition to those already listed, or they may have more than the usual percentage of some normal element. Special elements frequently added to foundry

FIG. 9. Structure of Medium-Carbon Cast Steel. Magnification ×200.

steel are aluminum, nickel, chromium, cobalt, molybdenum, vanadium, and copper. Steels alloyed with silicon and manganese, both normal constituents, are also frequently used. A great variety of steels is possible in this range, differing widely in strength, resistance to corrosion, high temperatures, and abrasion.

A typical microstructure of a medium-carbon cast steel is shown in Figure 9. The light areas are ferrite and the dark areas pearlite. The grain structure of most cast steels is large because of the high casting temperature of the metal combined with relatively slow cooling.

This defect can be remedied by subsequent heat treatment. For the
production of steel castings, four types of furnaces are used:

1. Open hearth (both acid and basic).
2. Electric (arc and induction).
3. Crucible.
4. Converter (acid).

The largest tonnage is produced in basic open-hearth furnaces. A
furnace of this type is shown in Figure 10. Because of the large
capacities of these furnaces, ranging from 25 to 100 tons, this process

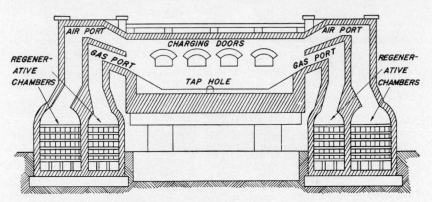

FIG. 10.   Open-Hearth Furnace.

is used principally for large castings. The basic process is preferred
to the acid process, because phosphorus can be controlled and sulfur
can be partly eliminated.

Although electric-arc furnaces are used principally for the production
of steel and alloy-steel castings, they are also used to a limited extent
for high-test iron castings. Furnaces of both the *direct-arc* and *indirect-arc* types are used.   In the direct-arc furnace, shown in Figure 11,
the current passes from the electrodes to the metal, through the metal,
and back to the electrodes or the hearth.   Indirect-arc furnaces have
horizontal electrodes above the metal which heat by radiation.   Heating costs for electric furnaces are higher than for furnaces of other
types, but this increase may be counteracted to some extent by using
low-priced materials in the furnace charges.   Furthermore, electric
furnaces lend themselves to close temperature control, and the analysis
of the metal may be held to accurate limits.

For steel castings the usual type of electric furnace is the direct-arc
type, as shown in Figure 11.   This is primarily a remelting furnace

using steel scrap as the raw material. The acid type of furnace is used when the raw material does not contain high phosphorus or sulfur. Foundry furnaces of this type range from ½ to 10 tons per heat. This furnace is the principal one used for small- and medium-steel castings. Electric induction furnaces are used primarily in the

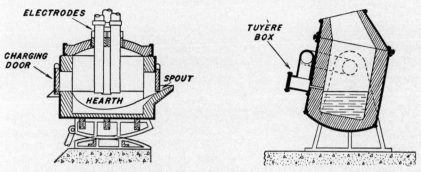

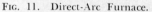

FIG. 11.   Direct-Arc Furnace.   FIG. 12.   Side-Blower Converter.

production of alloy-steel castings because of the accurate control of melting conditions and composition. These furnaces range in capacity from a few pounds to 4 tons.

The crucible process is the oldest process for making steel, but is little used today for steel castings. Wrought iron, washed metal, steel scrap, charcoal, and ferroalloys constitute the raw materials for this process. These materials are placed in crucibles having a capacity of around 100 pounds and melted in a regenerative furnace.

In making steel castings from a converter, liquid metal or cupola iron is poured into the converter, and the heat for the refining operation is produced by blowing air through the molten metal. The result is the oxidation of the silicon, manganese, and carbon. Side-blower converters, as shown in Figure 12, are used in foundry work and have a capacity of around 2 tons. Both the converter and crucible process have largely been replaced by electric-arc and induction furnaces.

Since the pouring temperature for steel castings is 2900 to 3200 F, it is necessary to use a highly refractory and permeable sand. Most molds for large and medium castings are either baked or skin-dried to eliminate gas troubles in the mold, but green sand may be used for light and intricate castings. Green sand has the advantage of offering less resistance to the normal contraction of the castings. Large risers must always be used on steel castings to compensate for the large amount of shrinkage.

Nonferrous Casting

The foundry practice for making nonferrous castings differs little from that used for iron castings. Molds are made in the same way and, in general, by the same tools and equipment, except for the kind of

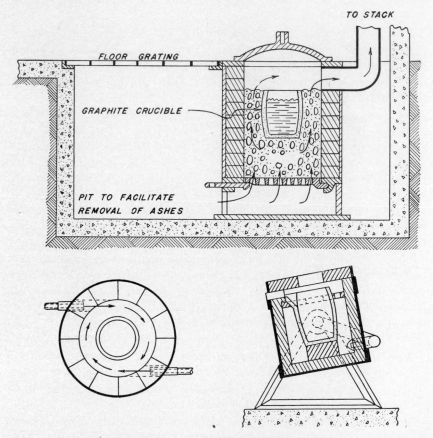

FIG. 13.   Crucible Furnace for Nonferrous Metals.

sand and the type of melting furnace used. The molding sand is usually of finer grain size, since most castings are fairly small and a smooth surface is desired. The sand need not be so refractory as sand for iron and steel castings, because the melting temperature for nonferrous alloys is lower.

The crucible furnace shown in Figure 13 is frequently used for this work. The furnace may be either the stationary or the tilting type. Coke is commonly used as the fuel for the stationary-pit furnaces, although oil or gas may be used equally well if available. The latter fuels have the advantage of melting more quickly than coke. Electrical-resistance, indirect-arc, and induction furnaces may be used under certain conditions. Such furnaces possess the advantages of accurate temperature control and low melting losses. Electric furnaces are widely used for laboratory and research work as well as for installations requiring large production.

Crucibles used in nonferrous melting are made of a mixture of graphite and clay. Although these crucibles are quite fragile when cold and must be handled with care, they possess considerable strength when heated. New crucibles contain a small percentage of moisture and should be dried out slowly and uniformly before use. When heated, a crucible becomes somewhat plastic, and serious strains are imposed upon it if the tongs do not fit properly.

In preparing a heat in a coke-fired furnace, as shown in Figure 13, a wood fire is first built in the furnace. From this fire a bed of coke is started and built up to a depth of about 12 inches. The crucible charged with metal is placed on this bed, and small pieces of coke are packed around the crucible up to the level of the top. The cover is then placed on the furnace, and the metal is heated with a natural draft through the bed of coke. As the metal in the crucible is melted, additional metal must be added from time to time. To remove the crucible from the furnace, special tongs are required which conform to the outside of the crucible. Before pouring, any coke, oxides, or other foreign materials should be skimmed from the surface.

Nonferrous Metals and Alloys

The common elements used in nonferrous castings are copper, aluminum, zinc, tin, and lead. Many alloys, however, have small amounts of other elements, such as antimony, phosphorus, manganese, nickel, and silicon.

Two of the most common alloys using copper are brass and bronze. *Brass* is essentially an alloy of copper and zinc. The percentages of each element may vary considerably, but in most cases the zinc percentage ranges from 10 to 40. The strength and hardness of the alloy are increased as the percentage of zinc is raised up to 40. Large percentages of zinc are not desirable, owing to a rapid decrease in strength and the tendency for the zinc to volatilize in melting. An addition of a small percentage of lead increases machinability. Brass has a wide application in industry because of its strength, appearance, resistance to corrosion, and ability to be rolled, cast, or extruded. Typical brass compositions are shown in Table 3.

Bronze is an alloy having copper and tin as the principal alloying elements. Many alloys classified as bronzes contain large percentages of other elements. Bronze is widely used for bearings because of the hardness imparted to the alloy by the tin. The percentage of tin seldom exceeds 10, since, above this amount, brittleness increases rapidly with a corresponding decrease in ductility. Table 3 gives several analyses of bronze alloys.

TABLE 3.   COPPER–ZINC–TIN ALLOYS *

Name	Cu	Sn	Zn	Pb	Ni	Si	Mn	Al	Fe	Use
Red brass	90		10							Hardware
Yellow brass	70		30							Cartridges, tubes
Leaded red brass	85	5	5	5						Castings, machinery
Leaded yellow brass	72	1	24	3						Plumbing fixtures
Tin bronze	88	10	2							Bearings, ship hardware
Bell metal	80	20								Bells
Bearing bronze	85	10		5						Machine bearings
Silicon bronze	95					4	1			Castings
Manganese bronze	60	1.5	23	1			1.5	1.5	1.5	High-strength parts
Aluminum bronze	78				5		3	10	4	Corrosion-resisting parts
Nickel silver	65	4	6	5	20					Dairy and laundry equipment

* *Cast Metals Handbook*, American Foundrymen's Association.

Because of their light weight and ability to resist many forms of corrosion, aluminum alloys have a wide application in industry today. Many of them respond to heat treatment and are suitable where high strength is needed. The usual casting aluminum of 92% aluminum and of 8% copper is widely used for miscellaneous castings. The copper adds to the hardness and strength of the alloy. An aluminum–silicon alloy containing 91–95% aluminum, 6–9% silicon, 0.4% iron is used for gears, propeller blades, and parts requiring resistance to salt water. An important alloy used in airplane work is Duralumin. It contains 95% aluminum, 4% copper, 0.5% manganese, and 0.5% magnesium. This alloy responds to heat treatment and may have a tensile strength as high as 55,000 pounds per square inch.

Several alloys utilizing magnesium have been developed by the Dow Chemical Company for sand-casting work. The casting of Dowmetal requires some special equipment, and slightly different molding and pouring methods are used. Dowmetal H is used for most commercial and aircraft sand castings, as it offers excellent resistance to salt water and alkalies. Its composition is approximately 6% aluminum, 0.2%

manganese, 3% zinc, 0.5% silicon, and 90% magnesium. Alloy P, also used for sand casting, is similar in composition except that the aluminum content is 10% and the zinc content is reduced to 1%. This alloy has increased hardness and tensile strength but is not recommended for shock conditions. Magnesium alloys are receiving much attention where light weight is essential. These alloys weigh about two thirds as much as ordinary aluminum alloys.

Many other nonferrous alloys of copper, aluminum, and magnesium are available where a combination of lightness, good strength, and machinability is desired. It is not within the scope of this book to list and discuss these various alloys, but complete information on analysis and physical properties may be found in the *Cast Metals Handbook,* published by the American Foundrymen's Association.

Pouring and Cleaning Castings

In jobbing and small production foundries, the molds are lined up on the floor as they are made, and the metal is brought to them in small

Courtesy Aluminum Company of America.

Fig. 14. Pouring Aluminum Sand Castings with Hand Ladle.

ladles. Figure 14 illustrates the use of a hand ladle in the pouring of aluminum into the molds. When more metal is required or if heavier metal is poured, ladle tongs designed for two men are used.

In large foundries, engaged in the mass production of castings, the problem of handling molds and molten metal is solved by placing the molds on conveyors, as shown in Figure 15, and passing them slowly by a pouring station. The pouring station may be located permanently next to the furnace, or metal may be brought to certain

Courtesy American Foundryman.

Fig. 15. Pouring Molds in a Production Foundry.

points by overhead handling equipment, as shown in the figure. The job illustrated is especially adapted to conveyor handling, as all flasks are of the same size. The conveyor serves as a storage place for the molds while they are being transported to the cleaning room.

After a casting has solidified and cooled to a suitable temperature for handling, it is shaken from the mold. Very often this is done at a ventilated mold shakeout, the dust being collected by a cyclone dust collector while the sand is collected underneath and transported to the conditioning station. All castings are retained on grate bars of the shakeout.

Nonferrous castings do not offer much of a cleaning problem, as they are poured at lower temperatures than iron or steel, and the sand has little tendency to adhere to the surface. Gates and sprues are cut

Courtesy Fox Grinders, Inc.

FIG. 16. High-Speed Cut-off Machine Removing Risers from Casting.

off either in a sprue press or with a metal band saw. Hand or rotary machine brushing is usually sufficient to prepare the casting for machining operations.

Iron and steel castings, however, offer a great problem, for they are covered with a layer of sand and scale which is somewhat difficult to remove. The gates and risers on iron castings may be broken off, but to remove them from steel castings a cutting torch or a high-speed cutting-off wheel is necessary. Figure 16 shows a high-speed cut-off machine built for removing gates and risers. The casting is held securely in a quick-acting clamping device, and the abrasive wheel used is 20 inches in diameter and $\frac{3}{4}$ inch thick—capable of removing risers 6 inches in diameter. Gates 3 inches in diameter may be removed in 20 to 30 seconds, depending on the hardness of the material.

To clean castings, several methods may be used, depending on the size, kind, and shape of the castings. The most common piece of

equipment used is the rotating cylindrical tumbling mill. The
cleaning is accomplished by the tumbling action of the castings upon
one another as the mill rotates. A similar piece of equipment, known
as Wheelabrator Tumblast, is shown in Figure 17. This is one of the
smaller-sized machines and is recommended for small shops. It will
clean 65 to 100 pounds of gray iron or malleable castings in 5 to 8

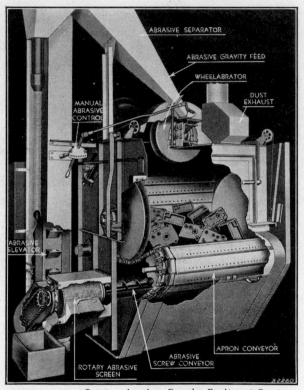

Courtesy American Foundry Equipment Company.

FIG. 17. Phantom View of Wheelabrator Tumblast.

minutes. Larger machines of this type have capacities of over a ton
per charge. The machine consists of a cleaning barrel formed by an
endless apron conveyor. The work is tumbled beneath a blasting
unit located just above the load, and metallic shot is blasted onto the
castings. After striking the load, the shot falls through holes in the
conveyor and is carried overhead to a separator and storage hopper.
From there it is fed by gravity to the blasting unit. The unit is

unloaded by reversing the apron conveyor. A dust collector is installed with the machine to eliminate dust hazards.

Sand-blasting units may be used separately for cleaning castings. Sharp sand is blown against castings inside a blasting cabinet. This removes all foreign matter completely and gives the casting a clean surface appearance. Castings that are to be plated or galvanized

Courtesy Fox Grinders, Inc.

FIG. 18. Swing-Frame Grinder Used for Cleaning Castings.

are frequently pickled in a weak acid solution and then rinsed in hot water. Large castings, which are difficult to handle, are often cleaned by hydraulic means. The casting is placed on a rotating table, and streams of water under considerable pressure wash away the sand.

In addition to these cleaning processes, many castings require a certain amount of chipping or grinding to remove surface and edge defects. Stand, portable, and swing-frame grinders are all used for this work. A swing-frame grinder is shown in Figure 18. Fast free-cutting abrasive wheels, operating at a cutting speed of around 9500 feet per minute, are recommended for this type of grinding. Swing-frame grinders are used in steel mills for removing defects on ingots and are widely employed also in steel and iron foundries.

Review Questions

1. What is the difference between cast iron, steel, and wrought iron?
2. What are the raw materials and products of a blast furnace?
3. List the principal iron ores, and give the chemical symbol for each.
4. Sketch a cupola, and label the essential parts.
5. Describe the procedure of charging a cupola.

6. Why is a fluxing material added to the charge of a cupola?
7. How much air is required to melt a ton of iron?
8. For what purpose is an air furnace used?
9. What different kinds of iron are produced?
10. How are malleable-iron castings made?
11. How is nodular cast iron made?
12. List the elements in cast iron, and state the influence on each.
13. In what forms does carbon exist in cast iron?
14. What is steel? How are steel castings classified?
15. What furnaces are used in the production of steel castings?
16. How is steel produced in a converter?
17. Describe the operation of a Wheelabrator Tumblast.
18. What various methods are used in cleaning castings?
19. What is the difference between brass and bronze?
20. Describe the kind of furnace used for nonferrous casting.
21. What elements are found in casting aluminum?
22. What is Dowmetal, and for what purpose is it used?

References

Alloy Cast Irons, American Foundrymen's Association.

BENNETT, J. S., "Essentials in the Production of Sound Steel Castings," *Foundry Trade Journal*, April 11, 1935, pp. 253, 256.

BRIGGS, C. W., and R. A. GEZELIUS, "Studies on Solidification and Contraction in Steel Castings," *Transactions AFA*, Vol. 43, pp. 274–302, 1935.

CAMPBELL, H. L., *Metal Castings*, John Wiley & Sons, 1936.

CAMPBELL, J. S., JR., *Casting and Forging Processes in Manufacturing*, McGraw-Hill Book Company, 1950.

Cast Metals Handbook, 3d edition, American Foundrymen's Association, 1944.

CHARNOCK, G. F., and F. W. PARTINGTON, *Mechanical Technology*, Constable & Company, London, 1934.

MAREK, C. T., *Fundamentals in the Production and Design of Castings*, John Wiley & Sons, 1950.

MASSARI, S. C., "The Properties and Uses of Chilled Iron," *ASTM Transactions*, Vol. 38, part 2, pp. 217–34, 1938.

Metals Handbook, American Society for Metals, 1948.

Steel Castings Handbook, Steel Founders' Society of America, 1950.

WENDT, R. E., *Foundry Work*, 4th edition, McGraw-Hill Book Company, 1942.

CHAPTER
5

SPECIAL CASTING METHODS

Castings from various types of sand molds probably have fewer limitations than those produced by any other casting processes. All metals may be cast in sand molds, and there is no limitation as to size. However, sand molds are single-purpose molds, being completely destroyed after the metal has solidified. Quite obviously, the use of a *permanent mold* would effect considerable saving in labor cost. Great strides have been made in this field, particularly in the die casting of nonferrous alloys. *Centrifugal casting* is another promising method, in which the molds may be either of single-purpose or permanent materials. Of the nonmetallic molds, the *"lost-wax"* process and the *plaster-of-Paris* molds for precision castings have gained a new importance through wartime research. A summary of the various special casting methods which will be discussed in this chapter is as follows:

1. Casting in metallic molds
    (a) Gravity or permanent-mold casting.
    (b) Slush casting.
    (c) Pressed or Corthias casting.
    (d) Die casting
        (1) Hot-chamber machines.
        (2) Cold-chamber machines.
2. Casting in nonmetallic molds
    (a) Centrifugal casting
        (1) True centrifugal.
        (2) Semicentrifugal.
        (3) Centrifuge.
    (b) Precision casting
        (1) "Lost-wax" method.
        (2) Plaster molds.
        (3) Mercast process.
        (4) Croning process.
    (c) Molds of wood, paper, rubber, and the like.
3. Continuous casting
    (a) Reciprocating molds.
    (b) Draw casting.
    (c) Stationary molds.
    (d) Direct sheet casting.

Methods of Casting in Metallic Molds

Permanent molds must be made of metals capable of withstanding high temperatures. Because of their high cost they are recommended only when many castings are to be produced. Although permanent molds would be impractical for large castings and alloys of high melting temperatures, they can be used advantageously for small and medium nonferrous castings that are manufactured in large quantities.

Gravity or permanent-mold casting.   This method consists of filling a metal mold as in sand casting.   No pressure is used except that obtained from the head of metal in the mold.   The process is used successfully for both ferrous and nonferrous casting, although the latter

Courtesy Eaton Manufacturing Company.

Fig. 1.   Multistation Machine for Permanent-Mold Casting.

type does not present so many problems as ferrous castings because of the lower pouring temperatures.   The simplest type of permanent mold hinges at one end of the mold with provision for clamping the halves together at the other.   Some production machines, as illustrated in Figure 1, are circular in arrangement and have molds placed at a number of stations.   The cycle of events consists of pouring, cooling, and ejecting the casting, blowing out the molds; coating them, and, in some cases, setting the cores.   Both metal and dry-sand cores can be used in molds of this type.   If metal cores are used, they are withdrawn as soon as the metal starts to solidify.

A typical mold is shown in Figure 2.   Molds are made of either cast iron or steel and should be of such composition as to resist the high temperature of the metal. They are usually coated with a refractory wash and then lampblack which reduces the chilling effect on the metal and facilitates the removal of the casting. At the start of a run, the molds should be heated to the proper temperature by being filled with hot metal several times. As the proper temperature is obtained, surface defects disappear, and there is no longer any evidence of excessive chilling. Further control is obtained by regulating the rate at which castings are produced or by cooling the molds with air or

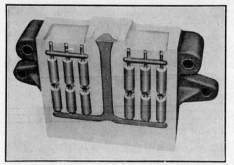

Courtesy Eaton Manufacturing Company.

FIG. 2.   Coated Mold Half for Permanent-Mold Casting.

water. Castings are frequently removed before they are completely solidified to prevent cracks from developing as a result of shrinkage strains.

Permanent molds produce castings free from sand and with good finish and surface detail. They are especially adapted to the quantity production of small and medium-size castings and are capable of maintaining tolerances ranging from 0.0025 to 0.010 inch. The high initial cost of equipment and the cost of mold maintenance might be listed as disadvantages of the process. Aluminum pistons, cooking utensils, refrigerator parts, electric irons, and small gear blanks are examples of this process.

Slush casting. Slush casting is a method of producing hollow castings in metal molds without the use of cores. Molten metal is poured into the mold, which is turned over immediately so that the metal, remaining liquid, can run out. A thin-walled casting results, the thickness depending on the chilling effect from the mold and the time of the operation. The casting is removed by opening the halves of the mold. This method of casting is used only for ornamental objects, statuettes, toys, and other novelties. The metals used for these objects are lead, zinc, and various low-melting alloys. Parts cast in this fashion are either painted or finished in a way to represent bronze, silver, or other more expensive metals.

Pressed or Corthias casting. This method of casting resembles both the gravity and slush processes but differs somewhat in the manner in which the operation is performed. A definite amount of metal is poured into an open-ended mold, and a close-fitting core is forced into the cavity. This causes the metal to be forced into the mold cavities with some pressure. The core is removed as soon as the metal sets, leaving a hollow thin-walled casting. This process, developed in France by Corthias, is limited in use mainly to ornamental casting of open design.

Die casting. Die casting, as practiced in the United States, refers to the forcing of molten metal under pressure into a metal die. The term *die* used in this process implies a metallic mold which is filled under pressure. Pressures vary according to the kind of metal being cast and numerous other factors, ranging from 80 to 40,000 pounds per square inch. Regardless of the amount, the pressure is maintained until solidification is completed.

Die casting, the most widely used of any of the permanent-mold processes, is done by two different methods: the *hot-chamber method* and the *cold-chamber method*. In the former, a melting pot is included with the machine, and the injection cylinder is immersed in the molten metal at all times, the injection cylinder being actuated by either air or hydraulic pressure which forces the metal into the dies to complete the casting. Machines using the cold-chamber process have a separate melting furnace, and metal is introduced into the injection cylinder by hand or mechanical means. Hydraulic pressure then forces the metal into the die.

The first machines developed for the production of miscellaneous castings were limited to low-melting alloys and were hand-operated. Some machines of this type are still in operation but are confined to small-production runs and to castings of rather simple design. Most production machines of today are either semiautomatic or completely automatic. The essential parts of a die casting machine using the hot-chamber method are the container for molten metal, a heating chamber, means for forcing the metal into the die, stationary and movable dies, a mechanism for opening and closing dies, an ejector mechanism for removing the casting, and the necessary framework for the machine. Various modifications will be discussed in connection with typical designs.

Metal is forced into the mold and pressure maintained during solidification by either of two common methods: (1) *plunger,* or (2) *compressed air.* Both methods are shown diagrammatically in Figure 3. The plunger-type machine, shown in the upper part of the figure, is hydraulically operated for both the metal plunger and the mechanism for opening and closing the die. In this machine the

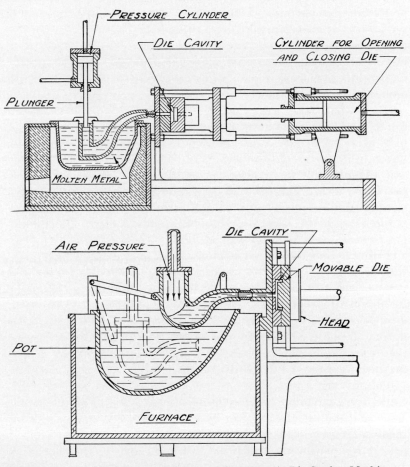

Fig. 3. Diagrammatic View of Plunger and Pneumatic Die-Casting Machine.

plunger operates in one end of a gooseneck casting which is submerged in the molten metal. With the plunger in the upper position, metal flows by gravity into this casting through several holes just below the plunger. On the down stroke these holes are closed by the plunger, and pressure is applied on the entrapped metal, causing it to be forced into the die cavity. Pressures over 5000 pounds per square inch are used in some machines of this type, resulting in castings of dense structure. As soon as the casting is solidified the pressure is relieved, the dies are forced open, and the casting is ejected by means of knock-out pins. The sprue is removed with the runner and the castings.

Plunger-type machines are used with low-melting alloys because of the difficulties encountered in plunger fits at higher temperatures and increased corrosion of the parts. Alloys of zinc, tin, and lead are particularly adapted to these machines.

Air-operated machines, such as the one shown in the lower part of Figure 3, have a gooseneck casting that is operated by a lifting mechanism. In the starting position that casting is submerged in the molten metal and is filled by gravity. It is then raised, so that the nozzle is in contact with the die opening, and locked in position. Compressed air, at pressures ranging from 80 to 600 pounds per square inch, is applied directly on the metal, thus forcing it into the die. When solidification is about complete, the air pressure is turned off and the gooseneck lowered into position to receive more metal. The operation of opening the dies, withdrawing cores, and ejecting the castings is the same as for the plunger-type machine. Frequently this operation is controlled by a hydraulic cylinder which produces smoother action than compressed air.

A small plunger-type hot-chamber machine is shown in Figure 4. This machine is primarily used for zinc and has a capacity of 1½ pounds per shot with air pressure ranging from 100 to 125 pounds per square inch. In operation it is similar to the plunger machine shown in the top half of Figure 3. Molten metal enters the gooseneck casting in the melting pot and is forced into the dies by pressure exerted from the plunger. As the dies open, the castings are automatically ejected. The entire casting cycle of this machine is automatic.

In the hot-chamber process there are limitations in the kinds of metal that can be used and the maximum pressure that can be exerted on the molten metal. Since many metals have an affinity for iron, only those that do not attack the immersed metal parts can be used. The alloys of zinc, tin, and lead are recommended for the process. Metals that require extremely high pressure to obtain desired densities are cast in cold-chamber machines.

The die casting of brass, aluminum, and magnesium requires higher pressures and melting temperatures and necessitates a change in the melting procedure from that previously described. These metals are not melted in a self-contained pot, as the life of the pot would be very short. The usual procedure is to heat the metal in an auxiliary furnace and ladle it to the plunger cavity next to the dies. It is then forced into the dies under hydraulic pressure. Machines operating by this method are built very strong and rigid to withstand the heavy pressures exerted on the metal as it is forced into the dies. Two types of machines are in general use: in one, the plunger is in a vertical position; in the other, horizontal.

A diagrammatic sketch illustrating the operation of horizontal-plunger cold-chamber machines is shown in Figure 5. In the first

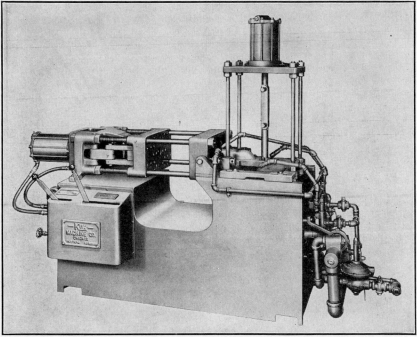

Courtesy Kux Machine Company.

Fig. 4. Plunger-Type Hot-Chamber Die-Casting Machine.

figure the dies are shown closed, with cores in position, and the molten metal ready to be ladled in. As soon as the ladle is emptied, the plunger moves to the left and forces the metal into the two cup-shaped molds. After the metal solidifies, the cores are first withdrawn, and then the dies are opened. In the third figure the dies are opening, and the casting is shown as ejected from the stationary half. To complete the process of opening, an ejector rod comes into operation and ejects the casting from the movable half of the die. This operating cycle is used in a variety of machines (made by the Reed-Prentice Corporation) which operate at pressures ranging from 5600 to 22,000 pounds per square inch. These machines are fully hydraulic and semiautomatic. After the metal is ladled in, the rest of the operations are automatic.

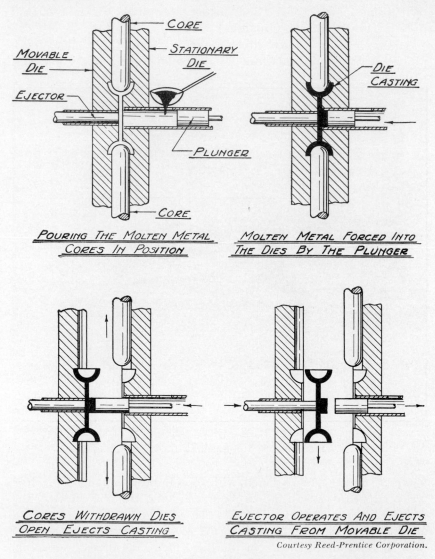

POURING THE MOLTEN METAL
CORES IN POSITION

MOLTEN METAL FORCED INTO
THE DIES BY THE PLUNGER

CORES WITHDRAWN DIES
OPEN EJECTS CASTING

EJECTOR OPERATES AND EJECTS
CASTING FROM MOVABLE DIE

Courtesy Reed-Prentice Corporation.

FIG. 5. Die Casting of Brass, Aluminum, and Magnesium.

The hydraulically operated machine shown in Figure 6 is equipped with a hand-ladling injection unit for brass, aluminum, and magnesium die casting. On casting, metal from a near-by furnace is ladled to the well opening on the plunger injection unit located to the rear of the stationary die plate. Aside from the ladling procedure, the operation of the machine is the same for hot-chamber machines. The hand-ladling injection unit on this machine can be readily replaced by a plunger-gooseneck unit for casting low-melting alloys. The production rate on this machine is 400 shots per hour, and aluminum castings up to 2.3 pounds can be made.

Courtesy Reed-Prentice Corporation.

FIG. 6. Cold-Chamber Die-Casting Machine for Brass, Aluminum, and Magnesium.

The manufacture of brass die castings is a comparatively recent achievement. The difficulties of the high temperatures involved and the resulting rapid oxidation of the steel dies have been largely overcome by improvements in die metals and by casting at as low a temperature as possible. A machine developed in Czechoslovakia, known as the Polak machine, is used successfully for the production of these castings by the Titan Metal Manufacturing Company of the United States. This machine is designed to use metal in a semiliquid or plastic state to permit operation at lower temperatures than those used for liquid metal. To protect the dies further from overheating, water is circulated through plates adjacent to the dies. Metal is maintained under close temperature control and is ladled by hand to the compression chamber. The pressure used in this machine is 9800 pounds per square inch while 100 to 200 shots per hour can be made, depending on the size of the machine.

Two variations of this process, each with the injection plunger in a vertical position, are diagrammatically illustrated in Figure 7. In the lower figure the compression chamber, into which the plastic metal is ladled, is separate from the dies. The metal is poured into this cavity onto a spring-backed plunger. As the ram descends, this

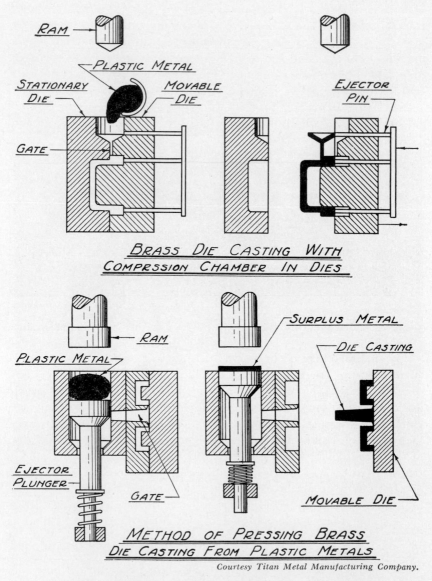

RAM →

PLASTIC METAL

STATIONARY DIE   MOVABLE DIE   EJECTOR PIN

GATE

BRASS DIE CASTING WITH
COMPRESSION CHAMBER IN DIES

PLASTIC METAL   RAM   SURPLUS METAL   DIE CASTING

EJECTOR PLUNGER   GATE   MOVABLE DIE

METHOD OF PRESSING BRASS
DIE CASTING FROM PLASTIC METALS

Courtesy Titan Metal Manufacturing Company.

FIG. 7.   Construction of Dies for Pressing Brass Die Castings.

plunger is forced down until the gate opening is exposed, permitting the metal to be forced into the die cavity. As the ram returns to its upper position, the ejector plunger also moves upward, carrying with it any surplus metal. As the die opens up, the casting is ejected.

A variation of this machine, with the compression chamber a part of the die, is shown in the upper part of the figure. Metal is poured into this chamber at the upper part of the die and forced by pressure into the die cavity as the ram descends. As soon as the ram moves up, the dies open, and the casting is ejected by means of the ejector pins. The sprue and excess metal are trimmed off in the finishing operation.

Die-casting dies. Dies for both the hot- and cold-chamber machines are similar in construction as there is little difference in the method

Courtesy Aluminum Corporation of America.

FIG. 8. Close-up of Die in Cold-Chamber Machine just before the Ejection of the Casting.

of holding and operating the dies. They are made in two sections to provide means of removing the castings and are usually equipped with heavy dowel pins to keep the halves in proper alignment. Metal enters the stationary side when the die is locked in closed position. As the die opens, the ejector plate in the movable half of the die is advanced so that pins project through the die half and force the casting from the cavity of fixed cores. The dies are provided with a separate mechanism for moving the ejector plate or movable cores.

A close-up of a die in a cold-chamber machine is shown in Figure 8. A movable core has just been withdrawn from one end of the casting before being ejected from the mold. These molds are made of an alloy steel capable of resisting high temperatures and erosion of the molten metal. The life of these molds depends on the metal cast and may range from 10,000 fillings if brass castings are made to several million if zinc is used.

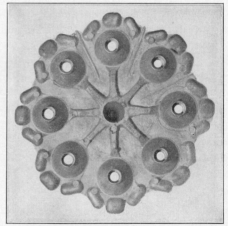

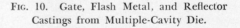

Courtesy
The New Jersey Zinc Company.

Courtesy The New Jersey Zinc Company.

FIG. 9. Gate and Casting
from Single-Cavity Die.

FIG. 10. Gate, Flash Metal, and Reflector
Castings from Multiple-Cavity Die.

It is always desirable to provide vents and small overflow wells (See Figure 10) on one side of a die to facilitate the escape of air and to catch surplus metal that has passed through the die cavity. In spite of this provision, there is always a certain amount of flash metal which must be trimmed off in the finishing operation.

For large or complex castings a single-cavity mold is used. The casting and gate from such a mold is shown in Figure 9. If the quantity of castings to be produced is large and they are relatively small in size, a multiple-cavity die can be used. Figure 10 shows a number of castings with the flask, gates, and sprue from such a die. A combination die is one that has two or more cavities, each of which is different. Dies of this type are frequently made up of insert blocks that can be removed so that other die blocks can be substituted if desired. Most dies are provided with channels for water cooling to keep the die at correct temperature for rapid production.

Advantages and disadvantages of die casting. One of the main advantages of die castings over sand castings is the rapidity of the process, since both molds and cores are permanent. This feature alone is sufficient to warrant its consideration in the mass production of castings. However, it has other advantages. The metal molds give die castings a smooth surface which not only greatly improves their appearance but also minimizes the work required to prepare them for plating or other finishing operations. By this method, size is so accurately controlled that little or no machining is necessary. Because of the uniformity in wall thickness, less material is required in die castings than in sand castings. Furthermore, there are no possibilities for sand inclusions, and a strong dense metal structure is obtained. Finally, because of the accurate tolerance that can be maintained, the process eliminates such machining operations as drilling and certain types of threading. Die-casting tolerances vary according to the size of the casting and the kind of metal used. For small castings the tolerance ranges from ±0.002 to 0.010 inch. The closest tolerances are obtained when zinc alloys are die-cast.

One of the limitations of die casting is the high cost of the equipment and dies. This is not an important factor in mass production, but it does eliminate its use in short-run jobs. There is also a rapid decrease in the life of the dies as the metal temperature increases. In some cases there is an undesirable chilling effect on the metal unless high temperatures are maintained. Metals having a high coefficient of contraction must be removed from the mold as soon as possible because of the inability of the mold to contract with the casting. There are certain limitations in the shape of die castings, and the process is not adapted to the production of large castings. For these reasons, die casting has, to a large extent, been limited to low-melting alloys, but, with a gradual improvement of heat-resisting metals for dies, this process can now be used for numerous alloys.

Die-Casting Alloys

A relatively wide range of nonferrous alloys can be die-cast. The principal base metals used, in order of commercial importance, are as follows: zinc, aluminum, copper, magnesium, lead, and tin. Virtually all of the usable alloys are covered by ASTM specifications while most of them are also included in SAE specifications.

The alloys may be further classified as low-temperature alloys and high-temperature alloys; those having a casting temperature below 1000 F, such as zinc, tin, and lead, are in the low-temperature class. The latter have the advantages of lower cost of production and lower die-maintenance costs. As the casting temperature increases, alloy and other special steels in the best treated condition are required to resist the erosion and heat checking of die surfaces. The destructive effect of high temperature on the dies has been the principal factor in retarding the development of high-temperature die castings.

Another factor governing the choice of alloy is the erosive or solvent action of the molten metal on the respective machine parts and dies. This action increases with temperature, although it is more pronounced with some alloys than with others. Aluminum, in particular, has a destructive action on ferrous metals and, for this reason, is seldom melted in the machine, while the copper-base alloys are never melted in the machine.

Other considerations that influence alloy selection are the mechanical properties required, weight, machinability, resistance to corrosion, surface finish, and, of course, cost. Obviously, the lowest-cost alloy that will give satisfactory service should be selected.

Zinc-base alloys. Over 75% of die castings produced are the zinc-base type. This alloy casts easily with a good finish, has considerable strength, is low in cost, and can be cast at fairly low temperatures. The purest grades of commercial zinc, 99.99+% zinc, known as Special High Grade, should be used, since such elements as lead, cadmium and tin are impurities that cause serious casting and aging defects unless properly alloyed for a specific purpose. The usual elements alloyed with zinc are aluminum, copper, and magnesium; all are held within close limits. Aluminum in amounts around 4% greatly improves the mechanical properties of the alloys and, in addition, reduces the tendency of the metal to dissolve iron. Copper increases the tensile strength, ductility, and hardness. Magnesium, which is usually held to an optimum of 0.04%, is used because of the beneficial effect it has in making the castings permanently stable.

The most widely used zinc alloy is ASTM XXIII, which corresponds to SAE 903 and to the New Jersey Zinc Company's alloy, Zamak 3.* This alloy has 4.10% aluminum, 0.04 magnesium, and the remainder Special High Grade zinc. The melting point of the alloy is 727.9 F. Average tensile strengths of 41,000 pounds per square inch are obtained from cast specimens 6 months after casting. Another important alloy, ASTM XXV (SAE 905 or Zamak 5), contains 4.1% aluminum, 2.70 copper, and 0.04 magnesium, with the remainder Special High Grade

* *Zamak Alloys for Zinc Die Castings*, The New Jersey Zinc Company.

zinc. Both these alloys are somewhat similar in general properties. Zamak 3 is distinguished by excellent retention of impact strength and dimensions. Zamak 5 has greater hardness and tensile strength and displays somewhat better resistance to corrosion under adverse conditions, but it suffers loss of impact strength when used at elevated temperatures. At normal temperature and under mild exposures, there is little choice between Zamak 3 and Zamak 5.

Zinc alloys are widely used in the automotive industry and for other high-production markets such as washing machines, oil burners, refrigerators, radios, phonographs, television, business machines, parking meters, small machine tools, and literally hundreds of other kindred products.

Aluminum-base alloys. A wide variety of die castings are made of aluminum alloys because of their lightness in weight and resistance to corrosion. However, compared to zinc alloys, they are lower in physical properties and more difficult to die-cast. Typical die castings made from aluminum alloys are shown in Figure 11.

Since molten alloys of aluminum will attack steel if kept in continuous contact with it, the cold-chamber process generally is used in casting. Although more expensive to operate than the air-injection type of machine formerly used, it has the advantage of producing sounder castings. The melting temperature of aluminum alloys is around 1185 F.

The principal elements used as alloys with aluminum are silicon, copper, nickel, and magnesium. Silicon increases the hardness and corrosion-resisting properties; copper improves the mechanical properties slightly; nickel improves surface appearance; and magnesium increases the lightness and resistance to impact. ASTM S5 (SAE 305 or Alcoa 13) contains 0.6% copper, 12.0% silicon, 0.5% nickel, and the remainder aluminum. This specification permits iron up to 2%, whereas ASTM S9 limits iron to 1.3% and is somewhat more ductile than S5. Alloy S9 ranks high in corrosion and salt-water resistance and resistance to attack by acids. Both alloys are generally considered to be the best all-around aluminum alloys for large, intricate, thin-walled die castings.

ASTM has recently adopted two alloys, SG2 and SG3, which are modifications of the high-silicon alloy in that the silicon content is 10% maximum and 0.5% magnesium is added. These alloys have better mechanical properties than S5 or S9, but the primary improvement lies in the effect of magnesium in overcoming the formation of eutectic chill flakes.

Alloy SC6, containing 3 to 4% copper and 7.5 to 9.5% silicon, is

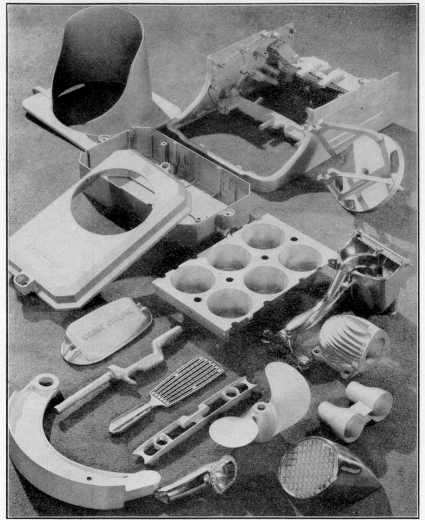

Courtesy Aluminum Company of America.

FIG. 11.   Die Castings from Aluminum Alloys.

an outgrowth of World War II, being based on the use of aircraft scrap, most of which contains about 4% copper.   After most of the magnesium has been removed and the necessary silicon added, the alloy has worked out well for die casting.   It possesses good casting characteristics and good mechanical properties and serves as a general-purpose alloy that is low in cost.

ASTM alloy G2 contains 8% magnesium as the only alloying

ingredient. This alloy, which is the lightest of all the aluminum-base alloys, also has the highest impact strength and is the easiest to machine. Other mechanical properties are excellent, and corrosion resistance is also good, but casting is somewhat more difficult than with the alloys containing silicon.

Copper-base alloys. Die castings of brass and bronze have presented more of a problem in pressure casting because of their high casting temperatures. These temperatures range from 1600 to 1900 F and make it necessary to use heat-resisting alloy steel for the dies to reduce their rapid deterioration. Because of these high temperatures copper-base alloys are melted in an auxiliary furnace and ladled to the machine in either a liquid or a plastic state. The latter method is used a great deal, as it permits operating at temperatures considerably lower than the melting temperatures of the molten metal. A plunger-type cold-chamber machine is used in this work.

Two of the copper alloys covered by ASTM specifications, alloy A and alloy B, have a copper content around 60, with the remainder zinc, since this mixture is economical and has good casting qualities. Both these alloys are very similar to the commercial yellow brasses and contain, in addition to copper and zinc, small percentages of tin, lead, manganese, and aluminum. The tensile strength of alloy A is about 45,000 pounds per square inch, whereas that of alloy B is about 50,000 pounds per square inch.

A third alloy, C, contains around 80% copper and 4% silicon, in addition to small percentages of the other constituents shown in alloys A and B. This alloy is used extensively in the machines previously described and is cast in the plastic state. It is characterized by considerably higher mechanical properties than the other two alloys.

Copper-base alloys have extensive use in miscellaneous hardware; electric-machinery parts; small gears; marine, aircraft, and automotive fittings; chemical apparatus; and numerous other small parts. These alloys are used principally where high strength or resistance to corrosion is required.

Magnesium-base alloys. Magnesium is alloyed principally with aluminum but may contain small amounts of silicon, manganese, zinc, copper, and nickel. Its alloys are the lightest in weight of all die-cast metals, being about two-thirds the weight of alloys of aluminum. Although the price per pound is slightly higher than for aluminum, the extra cost is compensated for by light weight and improved machinability.

The corrosion resistance of the magnesium alloys is inferior to that of the other die-casting alloys, especially in moist or sea atmospheres, and usually necessitates a chemical treatment as well as the subsequent application of a special priming coat shortly after the casting is produced.   These treatments, however, render the casting suitable for a wide range of applications.

ASTM Specification B94, alloy AS 100 (Dowmetal K), is one of the principal die-casting alloys, having good casting characteristics and fairly high mechanical properties.   This alloy contains about 10% aluminum, 0.30% zinc, 0.10% manganese, 1.00% silicon, and the remainder magnesium.   By decreasing aluminum, as in alloy AZ 91A (Dowmetal R), it is possible to secure somewhat better mechanical properties.   With both alloys it is desirable that the copper and nickel be kept low to minimize corrosion.

Magnesium alloys are cast in much the same manner as aluminum alloys and require a casting temperature between 1200 and 1300 F. Best results are obtained in so-called cold-chamber machines, and it is necessary to ladle the alloy from a crucible which is hooded and keeps the metal covered by a nonoxidizing atmosphere.   The lightness of these alloys, combined with good mechanical properties and excellent machinability, fits them admirably for aircraft, motor and instrument parts, portable tools, textile machinery, household appliances, and many other similar applications.

Lead-base alloys.   Pure lead, which melts at 621.3 F, will melt at around 470 F when alloyed with about 16% antimony.   This element is the principal one used with lead, and its percentage ranges from 9.25 to 16.   Antimony hardens lead and reduces its shrinkage value. Lead alloys have low mechanical properties but are inexpensive and easily cast.   Their use is principally for light-duty bearings, weights, battery parts, X-ray shields, and applications requiring a noncorrosive metal.   ASTM Standard Specifications B-102 give no. 5 with 10.75% antimony content and remainder lead with copper held to 0.50% maximum and arsenic to 0.15% maximum.

Tin is also used as an alloying element with lead and antimony. Tin increases the fluidity, hardness, and strength of the alloys, thus improving their use for bearing purposes.   The ASTM Standard Specifications B-102 includes a lead–tin–antimony alloy, no. 4, with a nominal tin content of 5%.

Tin-base alloys.   Die-casting alloys based on tin are in about the same category as the lead alloys as far as mechanical properties are concerned, but are high in price.   On the other hand, the tin alloys are high in corrosion resistance, and some of them are well suited for use in contact with foods and beverages.   Also tin alloys have excellent bearing properties and can be cast within remarkably close dimensional tolerances. This fact, together with high corrosion resistance, accounts for their use in small parts such as number wheels, especially where contact with corrosive inks may be involved. Bearings were once die-cast in large quantities from tin alloys, but cheaper as well as better methods of making bearings have resulted in substantial if not complete elimination of die-cast bearings. Tin alloys can also be used for low-cost jewelry, and certain grades are classed as pewter.

There are several tin alloys that can be die-cast, three of which are covered by ASTM Specifications B-102. Antimony is used in most if not all tin alloys, usually in amounts of 4 to 16%, and up to 19% lead is common, although it should be eliminated where the die casting remains in contact with foods or beverages. The low melting point and low solidification shrinkage of the tin alloys favor their use in die casting and promote long die life. Because the use for tin-alloy die castings is very limited and because die casters cannot afford the risk of contaminating zinc alloys with tin, the number of suppliers is few. Applications are so restricted that the total output has become of little significance to the industry.

Methods of Casting in Nonmetallic Molds

Nonmetallic molds are not restricted to either high or low temperatures. Each mold material has its own temperature limitations as to the kind of metal for which it is suitable. In many cases nonmetallic molds are used in precision casting, as the dimensional accuracy obtained with accompanying smooth-surface finish tends to offset the higher costs. Centrifugal casting is included under this heading although castings are made by this process in both metal and nonmetallic molds.

Centrifugal casting.* Centrifugal casting is the process of rotating a mold while the metal solidifies, so as to utilize centrifugal force to position the metal in the mold. The metal is forced against the walls of the mold with much greater pressure than that obtained by static pressure in ordinary sand casting. Greater detail on the surface of the casting is obtained, and the dense metal structure has superior physical properties. Castings of symmetrical shape lend themselves particularly to this method, although many other types of castings can be produced. The methods of centrifugal casting may be classified as follows:†

* Acknowledgment is given to the Centrifugal Casting Company for supplying certain illustrations used in this discussion.

† S. D. Moxley, "Centrifugal Casting of Steel," *Mechanical Engineering*, October 1944.

1. True centrifugal casting.
2. Semicentrifugal casting.
3. Centrifuging.

True centrifugal casting is used for pipe, liners, and symmetrical objects which are cast by rotating the mold about its horizontal or vertical axis. The metal is held against the wall of the mold by centrifugal force, and no core is required to form a true cylindrical

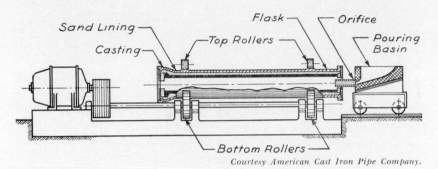

Courtesy American Cast Iron Pipe Company.

FIG. 12.   Centrifugal Casting Machine for Casting Steel or Cast-Iron Pipe.

cavity on the inside. This method is illustrated by the casting machine shown in Figure 12 designed for the production of steel or cast-iron pipe. The wall thickness of the pipe produced is controlled by the amount of metal poured into the mold.

Another example of true centrifugal casting is shown in Figure 13, which illustrates two methods that may be used for casting radial-engine cylinder barrels. The horizontal method of casting is similar to the process followed in casting pipe lengths, and the inside diameter is a true cylinder requiring a minimum amount of machining. In vertical castings the inside cavity takes the form of a paraboloid as illustrated by the figure. The slope of the sides of the paraboloid depends on the speed of rotation, the dotted lines at *A* representing a higher rotational speed than shown by the paraboloid *B*. In order to reduce the inside-diameter differences between the top and bottom of the cylinder, spinning speeds are higher for vertical casting than for horizontal casting. Radial-engine cylinder castings produced by this process are shown in Figure 14 and illustrate the rough casting, the cylinder after rough machining, and the finished cylinder with its cooling fins.

As the name implies, *semicentrifugal* casting is the rotating of the mold about its vertical axis. In this method the center of the casting is usually solid, and the center cavity is machined out later

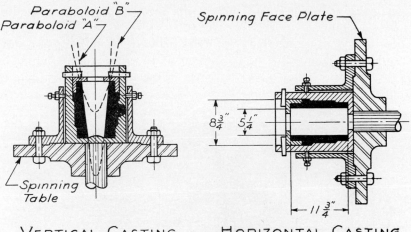

VERTICAL CASTING   HORIZONTAL CASTING

Courtesy American Cast Iron Pipe Company.

FIG. 13. True Centrifugal Method of Casting Radial-Engine Cylinder Barrels.

or is formed by the metal passing down around the outside of a core. This method, often used in stack molding, is illustrated in Figure 15, where five track wheels are cast solid in one mold. The number of

FIG. 14. Radial-Engine Cylinder Barrels Shown Before and After Machining.

castings made in a mold depends on the size of the casting and the convenience in handling and assembling the molds. Rotational speeds for this form of centrifugal casting are not so great as for the true centrifugal process. The process produces a dense structure at the outer circumference where it is needed, while the center metal is machined out.

In the *centrifuge* method several casting cavities are located around the outer portion of a mold, and metal is fed to these cavities by radial sprues or gates from the center of the mold.   Either single or

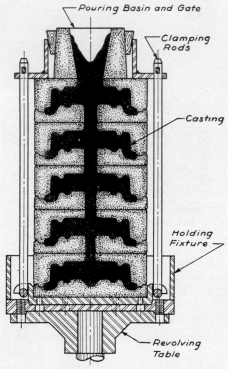

Courtesy American Cast Iron Pipe Company.

FIG. 15.   Semicentrifugal Stack Molding of Track Wheels.

stack molds can be used.   The mold cavities are filled under pressure from the centrifugal force of the metal as the mold is rotated.   In Figure 16 are shown five castings made in one mold by this process. The internal cavities of these castings are irregular in shape and are formed by dry-sand cores.   The centrifuge method, not limited to symmetrical objects, can produce castings of irregular shape such as bearing caps or small brackets.   For many years the dental profession has used this process for the casting of gold inlays.

The average rotational speed* for miscellaneous centrifugal cast-

* G. E. Stedman, "Unique Centrifugal Steel Casting Method," *Metals & Alloys,* August 1944.

ings approximates 600 surface feet per minute, although for cast-iron pipe the speeds may be as high as 1250 feet per minute. Too great a speed may result in surface cracks caused by high stresses set up in the mold. The rotational speed depends on the kind of mold used (whether sand or metal), the manner of rotation (whether horizontal or vertical), the size of casting, and the kind of metal being cast.

FIG. 16. Centrifuged Castings with Internal Cavities of Irregular Shape.

Centrifugal casting reduces cost by its advantages over other methods. Cores in cylindrical shapes and risers or feedheads are both eliminated. The castings have a dense metal structure with all impurities forced back to the center where frequently they can be machined out. Because of the pressure exerted on the metal, thinner sections can be cast than would be possible in static casting. Finally, any metal can be cast by this process. It must be remembered, however, that all castings cannot be made centrifugally, since there are definite size and shape limitations.

"Lost-wax" casting process. This process* derives its name from the fact that the wax pattern used in the process is subsequently melted from the mold, leaving a cavity having all the details of the original pattern. The process as originally practiced by artisans in the 16th century consisted of forming the object in wax by hand. The wax object or pattern was then covered by a plaster investment. When this plaster became hard, the mold was heated in an oven, melting the wax and at the same time further drying and hardening

* J. D. Wolfe, "Precision Castings for Ordnance and Aircraft," *Metals & Alloys*, Vol. 18, October 1943.

the mold. The remaining cavity, having all the intricate details of the original wax form, was then filled with metal. Upon cooling, the plaster investment was broken away leaving the desired casting. One advantage of this process was that intricate forms having under-cuts could be reproduced, since the mold did not have to be opened

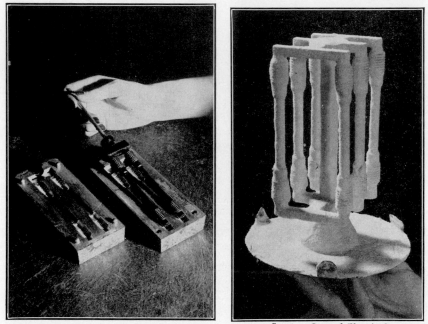

Courtesy General Electric Company.

FIG. 17. Split Lead-Alloy Mold Shown with a Wax Pattern Being Lifted from It.   FIG. 18. Wax-Pattern Assembly Is Shown Precoated with Silica Flour Suspended in Suitable Binder.

for the pattern to be removed. In large castings, such as statuary,* plaster cores were used to provide relatively thin walls in the casting.

The procedure followed in this process is first to prepare one or more master patterns of steel or brass which are replicas of the part to be cast. Using these patterns a bismuth- or lead-alloy split mold is cast, similar to the one shown in Figure 17. The mold is properly finished and gated and is then ready for use in forming the wax patterns. In the forming operation, the mold is held in a water-cooled vise, and the heated wax is injected into it under considerable

* Benvenuto Cellini's famous chapter on the casting of his bronze statue, Perseus, contains much interesting information on methods of molding used during the Renaissance. Cellini used a form of "lost-wax" process.

pressure. Thermoplastic polystyrene resin is sometimes used in place of wax. Upon solidification, the wax patterns are removed from the mold and are ready for final assembly.

In this operation several patterns are usually assembled together with necessary gates and risers and by heating the contact surfaces (wax welding) with a hot wire held to correct temperature by electrical resistance. The patterns are then ready to be placed in a metal flask and surrounded by a refractory plaster. This may be done by pouring into the flask a finely ground refractory material thinned by some mixing agent as alcohol or water. However, the procedure is generally to dip or spray the patterns first with a fine silica-flour mixture to insure having a smooth surface on the castings (see Figure 18), and then fill the flask with a coarser plaster mixture. After the plaster sets, the mold is placed upside down and heated in an oven for several hours to melt out the wax and to dry the mold. The final casting can be produced by gravity, vacuum, pressure, or centrifugal casting. Pressures ranging from 3 to 30 pounds per square inch are generally used in the casting operation. When the mold has cooled, the plaster is broken away. After gates and feeders are cut off, the castings are finally cleaned by grinding, sand blasting, or other finishing operations.

Plaster-mold casting. The use of plaster as a casting investment has had limited use for many years, but recent improvement in its ability to dry quickly with sufficient porosity has greatly accelerated its use as a modern casting material. Compared with sand molds, it has a higher molding cost, but the advantages gained by close tolerance, fine detail, and good surface finish enable it to be economically used in short and medium production runs. The molds are not permanent, being destroyed in the process of removing the castings.

Patterns are made of a free-machining brass and are held to a close tolerance. They are assembled on bottom plates of standard-size flasks (usually 10 by 18 by 3 inches and 12 by 18 by 4 inches), as shown in Figure 19. Before receiving the plaster, they are sprayed with a parting compound. The plaster, which is made of gypsum with added strengtheners and settling agents, is dry mixed, and water is added. It is then poured over the patterns, and the mold is vibrated slightly to insure the plaster filling all small cavities. The plaster sets in a few minutes and is removed from the flask by a vacuum head. All moisture is driven from the molds by baking them in an oven conveyor at a temperature around 1500 F. These molds are shown in Figure 20 as they are emerging from the drying oven. After pouring, the castings are removed by breaking up the mold, any surplus plaster being removed by a washing operation.

Mold porosity for the removal of any gases developed in the mold is controlled by the water content of the plaster. When the mold is dried, the water driven out leaves numerous fine passageways which act as vents. The amount of water added originally is in excess of what is needed for setting of the plaster and provides the excess of voids needed for venting. In addition to having adequate porosity,

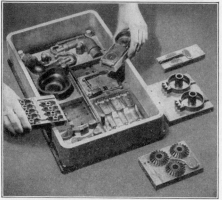

Courtesy Universal Castings Corporation.

FIG. 19.   Assembling Metal Patterns in Flask.

plaster molds have the necessary structural strength for casting, plus enough elasticity to allow some contraction of the metal during its cooling.

Plaster molds are suitable only for nonferrous alloys having casting temperatures not much over 2100 F. While plaster has proved to be an excellent mold material for yellow brass, certain bronzes and aluminum alloys may also be used. The wide variety of small-size castings made by this process includes miscellaneous airplane parts, small gears, cams, handles, pump parts, small housings, and numerous other intricate castings.

One of the principal advantages of plaster-mold casting is the resulting high degree of dimensional accuracy. This, coupled with the smooth surface obtained, enables the process to compete favorably with sand casting in producing parts requiring a considerable amount of machining. Because of the low thermal conductivity of plaster, the metal does not chill rapidly, and very thin sections may be cast. There is little tendency towards internal porosity in plaster-mold castings, and no difficulty is experienced with sand or other inclusions. In general, the process competes more successfully with die casting using the high-temperature alloys such as brass rather than metals such as zinc and aluminum. At high temperatures, metal molds have a relatively short life; with plaster molds, which are used only once, the temperature is no problem.

A tolerance of ±0.005 inch can be maintained for simple castings; slightly more is required if the dimension crosses the parting line. The process can be used for both small and quantity production runs.

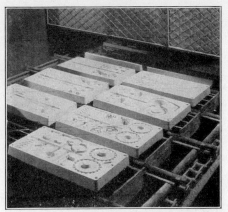

Courtesy Universal Castings Corporation.

Fig. 20. Finished Plaster Molds Coming from Drying Oven.

Molds from mercury patterns. A casting process utilizing frozen mercury and known as the Mercast process* has been developed for the production of precision castings. A metal mold or die is first made of the part to be cast with the necessary gates and sprue hole. When assembled and ready for pouring, it is partially immersed in a cold bath and filled with acetone which acts as a lubricant. As the mercury is poured into the mold, the acetone is displaced. Freezing takes place in a liquid bath held at around −76 F and is complete in about 10 minutes.

The patterns are then removed from the mold and invested in a cold ceramic slurry by repeated dippings until a shell about ⅛ inch thick is built up. Mercury is melted and removed from the shell at room temperature, and, after a short drying period, it is fired at a high temperature resulting in a hard permeable form. The shell is then placed in a flask, surrounded by sand, preheated, and filled with metal. Casting is usually done by the centrifugal method.

* Process controlled by the Mercast Corporation, New York.

Castings produced by this method are accurate in detail, have a smooth surface, and, for small castings, maintain a tolerance of ±0.002 inch per inch. Both ferrous and nonferrous metals can be cast by this process, the maximum pouring temperature being around 3000 F. Wide commercial use of this process is limited by the high cost of the castings.

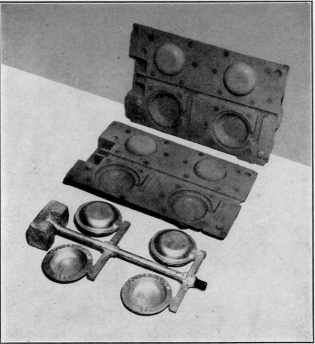

Courtesy Bakelite Division, Union Carbide & Carbon Corporation.

FIG. 21. Two Half Molds of Sand and Phenolic Resin Binder and the Castings Made from Them by the Croning Process.

Croning process.* The mold in this process is made up of a mixture of sand and phenolic resin formed into two thin half-mold shells which are clamped together for pouring. The half-mold shells, shown in the upper part of Figure 21, are made in a molding machine on a hot metal pattern and baked in an oven for 1 to 2 minutes for additional hardening. After the two mold halves are assembled, they are placed in a flask and surrounded by steel shot or similar material to give the shell mold adequate support to resist the pressure of the

* Process developed by Johannes Croning of Hamburg, Germany. U. S. patents controlled by Crown Casting Associates, Boston.

liquid metal.   Metal is poured into the mold in the usual manner, and the casting, upon solidification, is easily removed from the shell.   No special venting is required as the gases readily escape through the shell mold.

Castings produced by this method are clean and smooth and require little subsequent finishing, and tolerances of 0.002 to 0.003 inch per inch can be maintained.   Metals that have been cast by this process include brass, bronze, aluminum, cast iron, and steel.

Molds of other materials.   Various materials such as rubber, paper, and wood can be used for molds for casting of low-melting-temperature metals.   Costume jewelry and similar small items are successfully cast in rubber molds.*   A two-piece rubber casing is vulcanized over a mold or pattern which, when complete, serves as the mold.   Casting is by centrifugal means, and metal temperatures up to 600 F can be used.   The flexibility of the mold permits intricate designs with under-cuts, but close dimensional accuracy cannot be maintained.   An alloy of 98% tin, 1% copper, and 1% antimony is frequently used in this work.

Full-page newspaper type is cast in a mold (called a "mat") upon which the type and illustration impressions have been made on damp paper.   The type metal is poured into the mold after the paper is dry.   End-grain wood may also be used as a mold material for low-melting alloys where only a limited number of simple castings are desired.

Continuous Casting

Research and experimental work has proved that there are many opportunities for saving in the continuous casting of metals.   Briefly the process consists of continuously pouring molten metal into a mold which has the facilities for rapidly chilling the metal to the point of solidification and then withdrawing it from the mold.   The following processes are typical of those in use or in the process of development.

Reciprocating mold process.†   In the process shown in Figure 22 a reciprocating water-cooled copper mold is used, the down stroke being synchronized with the discharge rate of the slab.   Molten metal is poured into the holding furnace shown and is discharged to the mold through a 1/2-inch tube at the rate of 20,000 pounds per hour. The molten metal is distributed across the mold from a submerged

* Lupke, Paul, Jr., "Making Cast Models in Rubber Molds," *Mechanical Engineering*, June 1945.

† Process used by the Scovill Manufacturing Company and a development of the Junghans-Rossi process.

horizontal cross piece, the level of the metal being held constant at all times. The pouring rate of the molten metal is controlled by a needle valve through the top of the holding furnace. As the metal becomes chilled in the lower part of the mold, it is discharged at a constant rate and enters the withdrawing rolls. These are synchronized with the downward movement of the mold and are mounted

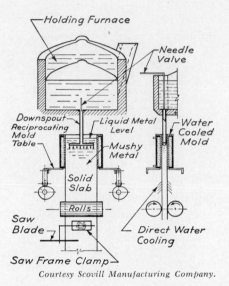

Courtesy Scovill Manufacturing Company.

Fɪɢ. 22. Reciprocating-Mold Process of Continuous Slab Casting.

just above a circular saw which cuts the slab to desired lengths. Brass slabs produced by this process are further processed by cold rolling into sheets and strips.

Asarco process.* The Asarco process, shown in Figure 23, differs from other continuous processes in that the forming die or mold is integral with the furnace and there is no problem of controlling the flow of metal. The metal is fed by gravity into the mold from the furnace as it is continuously solidified and withdrawn by the rolls below. An important feature of this process is the water-cooled graphite forming die which is self-lubricating, has excellent resistance to thermal shock, and is not attacked by copper-base alloys. The upper end, being in the molten metal, acts as a riser and compensates for any shrinkage taking place during solidification while simultaneously

---

* This process in its present stage is the product of the work of a number of collaborators. It has been developed by the American Smelting & Refining Company.

acting as an effective path for the dissipation of evolved gases. These dies are easily machined to desired shapes, and products may be produced ranging from $\frac{7}{16}$ to $5\frac{1}{8}$ inches in diameter. Multiple production from a single die permits casting the small section rods.

In starting the process, a rod of the same shape as that to be cast is placed between the drawing rolls and inserted into the die. This rod is tipped with a short length of the alloy to be cast. As the molten

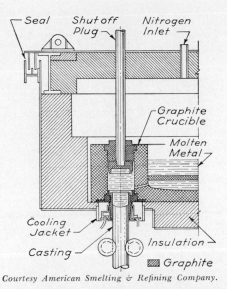

Courtesy American Smelting & Refining Company.

Fig. 23. Asarco Process for Continuous Cast Shapes (J. S. Smart, Jr., and A. A. Smith, Jr., "Asarco Continuous Cast Shapes," *Iron Age*, September 22, 1949).

metal enters the die, it melts the end surface of the rod forming a perfect joint. The casting cycle is then started by the drawing rolls, and the molten metal is continuously solidified as it is chilled and withdrawn from the die. As the casting leaves the furnace, it ultimately reaches the sawing floor where it is cut to desired lengths while still in motion. A tilting receiver takes the work and drops it to a horizontal position, and from there it goes to inspecting and straightening operations.

The process has proved successful for phosphorized copper and many of the standard bronzes. The alloy compositions may be produced, with satisfactory commercial finish, as rounds, tubes, squares, or special shapes. Physical properties are superior to permanent-mold and sand castings.

Williams continuous-casting process.* Developed for continuous casting of carbon and alloy steels, this process utilizes thin-walled brass molds having cross-sectional areas up to 45 square inches. These molds are preferably oval in cross section. A small stream of metal is poured into the mold from an electric holding furnace at a rate controlled by the metal level in the mold. The mold must of necessity be constructed of a material having a high heat conductivity and one that is not easily wetted by the liquid metal. Rapid mold cooling is essential for the success of this process, and results in improved mold life, less segregation, smaller grain structure, and a better surface. Actually the metal next to the mold wall solidifies only a few inches below the top surface and shrinks slightly from the mold sides. As the cast section leaves the cooled mold, it passes through a section that controls the rate of cooling, then to the drawing and straightening rolls. Below this point it is cut to desired lengths by an oxyacetylene torch and finally lowered to a horizontal position. Steel blooms and billets produced by this process have good crystalline structure, little segregation, uniform section, and a size close to that required for many rolling mills.

Alcoa direct-chill process.† This process consists of pouring molten aluminum from a holding furnace through a refractory trough into shallow stationary molds, the bottoms of which rest on a hydraulic elevator. When the metal at the bottom of the mold becomes chilled, the elevator drops at a rate of 2 to 5 inches per minute. As the ingots descend, they are sprayed with water to complete their solidification. This process is shown diagrammatically in Figure 24 although, in actual practice, three ingots are usually cast instead of two as shown. The shallow molds used are made in sizes of 12 by 36 and 12 by 48 inches and are rectangular in shape, although other sizes and circular shapes can be cast if desired. The length of the ingots is regulated to give a convenient size for rolling and is usually 136 inches. This process leaves a rough surface on the ingots which must be removed by milling before they can be further processed in the rolling mill. Most of the aluminum used in the United States is cast by this process.

Direct casting of sheet (Hazelett process).‡ Much work has been done in the attempt to cast various metals into sheet form between water-cooled rolls, as is done in the manufacture of glass by the con-

---

* Original patents on this process by E. R. Williams. Process now being developed jointly by Republic Steel Corporation and Babcock & Wilcox Tube Company.

† Based on patent of W. T. Ennor, November 3, 1942. Process developed and used by Aluminum Company of America.

‡ C. W. Hazelett, *Mechanical Engineering*, Vol. 61, 1939, p. 923.

tinuous method. So far this process has not proved commercially successful, owing to the fact that the metal solidifies faster at the edges of the strip than at the center and, consequently, builds up a greater thickness at the edges than is desired. This forces the cooling rolls

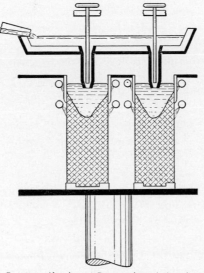

Courtesy Aluminum Corporation of America.

Fig. 24. Casting Aluminum Ingots by the Direct-Chill Process.

apart which changes the sheet thickness. Also, in casting solid-solution alloys, the process is affected by segregation problems resulting ultimately in wide variations of metal analysis. Some progress has been made in the elimination of these difficulties by increasing rolling speeds and reducing the contact area that the metal has with the rolls.

Review Questions

1. Describe the process of permanent-mold casting.
2. For what type of work is slush casting used?
3. Define "die casting."
4. What are the advantages of the die-casting process over sand casting?
5. Distinguish between hot- and cold-chamber methods of die casting.
6. What is the difference between a multiple-cavity die and a combination die?
7. What are the limitations of the hot-chamber method of die casting?
8. What metals are usually die-cast by the cold-chamber process?
9. List the principal metals or alloys used in die casting.
10. What group of alloys are most widely used in die casting?
11. Describe how mercury patterns are used in making castings.
12. What advantages are claimed for the Croning process?

13. State the differences between true centrifugal casting, semicentrifugal casting, and centrifuging.

14. How is cast-iron pipe made? Illustrate by sketch.

15. What is the average rotational speed for centrifugal casting, and on what does the speed depend?

16. State the advantages of centrifugal casting over other methods.

17. Describe the "lost-wax" casting process.

18. What alloys may be cast in plaster molds?

19. Compare the reciprocating-mold and draw-casting processes of continuous casting.

20. Why are ferrous metals difficult to cast continuously?

References

ANDERSON, E. A., and G. L. WERKY, *Zamak Alloys for Zinc Alloy Die Casting,* New Jersey Zinc Company, 1944.

BOLZ, R. W., (*a*) "Plaster-Mold Casting," *Machine Design,* December 1949. (*b*) "Die-Casting," *Machine Design,* November 1949.

CADY, E. L., *Precision Investment Castings,* Reinhold Publishing Company, 1948.

CHARNOCK, G. F., and F. W. PARTINGTON, *Mechanical Technology,* Constable & Company, London, 1934.

CHASE, HERBERT, (*a*) *Die Casting,* John Wiley & Sons, 1934. (*b*) "Which Form of Non-Ferrous Casting," *Metals & Alloys,* September 1944.

HARVILL, H. L., *High Pressure Die Casting,* H. L. Harvill Manufacturing Company, 1945.

LIPPERT, T. W., "Continuous Casting of Semi-finished Steel," *Iron Age,* August 19, 1948.

MOXLEY, S. D., "Centrifugal Casting of Steel," *Mechanical Engineering,* 1944.

SAGER, ALFRED, "Permanent Mold Castings," *Metals & Alloys,* April 1945.

SMART, J. S., JR., and A. A. SMITH, JR., "Continuous Casting—The Asarco Process," *Iron Age,* August 26, 1948, and September 22, 1949.

WILKINS, W. G., "Plaster-Mold Castings," *Machine Design,* June 1949.

CHAPTER
6

HEAT TREATMENT OF STEEL

Heat treatment is the operation of heating and cooling a metal or alloy in its solid state. Steel responds to this treatment in a unique fashion: its physical properties can be greatly changed according to the procedure involved. Therefore, the purpose of heat treating is to enhance certain desired properties in steel. For example, a tool that has been machined can be made hard to resist cutting action and abrasion, whereas another part, already hard, can be softened so that further machine work can be done. With the proper treatment, internal stresses may be removed, grain size reduced, toughness increased, or a hard surface produced on a ductile interior. To use the correct treatment for desired properties, the analysis of the steel must be known; for small percentages of certain elements, notably carbon, greatly change the physical properties.

The following discussion applies principally to the ordinary commercial steels known as carbon steels, in which carbon is the controlling element. Alloy steels are those that owe their properties in a marked degree to the presence of one or more elements other than carbon. The elements used in the manufacture of alloy steels include nickel, chromium, manganese, molybdenum, tungsten, silicon, vanadium, copper, and cobalt. Their greatly improved physical properties enable alloy steels to fulfill many important commercial applications not possible with carbon steels.

The treatments discussed in this chapter apply only to steel. Bronze given similar treatments will not react the same, because of the nature of the elements it contains. For example, if the bronze were in a hardened state from cold working, it could be softened by heating followed by any rate of cooling. For steel, on the other hand, the rate of cooling is a controlling factor. Rapid cooling from above the critical point results in a hard structure, whereas very slow cooling has the opposite effect. To understand these changes, a knowledge of the structure of steel and its various constituents is necessary.

Iron–Iron-Carbide Diagram

Under conditions of equilibrium, the knowledge of steel and its structure is best summarized in the iron–iron-carbide diagram shown in Figure 1.   If a piece of 0.20% carbon steel is slowly and uniformly

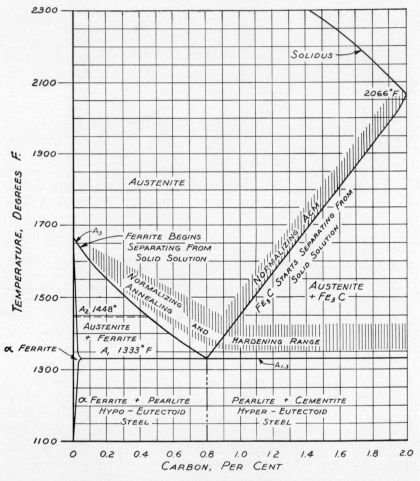

FIG. 1.   Partial Iron–Iron-Carbide Phase Diagram.

heated and its temperature recorded at definite intervals of time, a temperature–time curve similar to Figure 2 will be obtained.   From this curve there are three temperatures where the heating rate changes. These same three points will occur if the steel is slowly cooled from a temperature above 1600 F but will also occur at slightly lower temperatures. These points are known as *critical points* where structural changes occur and are designated by the symbols Ac_1, Ac_2, and Ac_3. The letter c is the initial letter of the French word *chauffage*, meaning "heating." The points on the cooling curve are designated by Ar_1, Ar_2, and Ar_3, the r being taken from the word *refroidissement*, meaning "cooling."

Certain changes which take place at these critical points are called *allotropic changes*. Although the chemical content of the steel remains

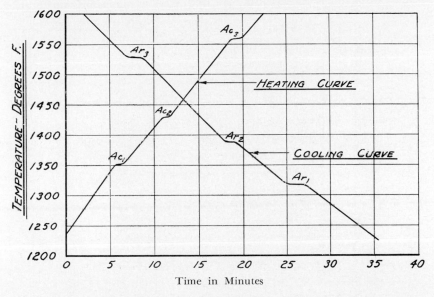

FIG. 2. Time–Temperature Heating Curve for SAE 1020 Steel.

the same, its properties are changed. Principal among these are changes in electrical resistance and atomic structure and loss of magnetism. By definition, an allotropic change is a reversible change in the atomic structure of the metal with a corresponding change in the properties of the steel. These critical points should be known, as most heat-treating processes require heating the steel to a temperature above this range. Steel cannot be hardened unless it is heated to a temperature within or above the upper critical range.

If a series of time–temperature heating curves are made for steels of different carbon contents and the corresponding critical points plotted on a temperature–per-cent carbon curve, a diagram similar to Figure 1 would be obtained. This diagram, which applies only under slow cooling conditions, is known as a partial iron–iron-carbide diagram.

Consider again the piece of 0.20% C steel which has been heated to a temperature around 1600 F. Above the Ar_3 point this steel is a solid solution of carbon in gamma iron and is called *austenite*. The iron atoms lie in a face-centered cubic structure and are nonmagnetic. Upon cooling this steel, the iron atoms start to form a body-centered cubic lattice below the Ar_3 point. This new structure that is being formed is called *ferrite* or alpha iron and is a solid solution of carbon in alpha iron. The solubility of carbon in alpha iron is very much less than in gamma iron. At the Ar_2 point the steel becomes magnetic, and, as the steel is cooled to the Ar_1 line, additional ferrite is formed. At the Ar_1 line the austenite that remains is transformed to a new

Fig. 3. Structure of SAE 1095 Steel Furnace-Cooled from 1550 F. Etched in 5% Picral Showing Lamellae of Cementite and Ferrite in Pearlite. Magnification ×1200.

structure called *pearlite*. This constituent is lamellar in appearance under high magnification, the lamellae being alternately ferrite and iron carbide. It is called pearlite because of its "mother of pearl" appearance. It is shown under high magnification in Figure 3.

As the carbon content of the steel increases above 0.20%, the temperature at which the ferrite is first rejected from the austenite drops until, at about 0.80% carbon, no ferrite is initially rejected from the austenite. This steel is called *eutectoid* steel and consists of 100% pearlite in structure composition. The eutectoid point in any metal is the lowest temperature at which changes occur in a solid solution. If the carbon content of the steel is greater than the eutectoid, a new line is observed in the iron–iron-carbide diagram labeled *Acm*. This line denotes the temperature at which iron carbide is first rejected from the austenite instead of ferrite. The iron

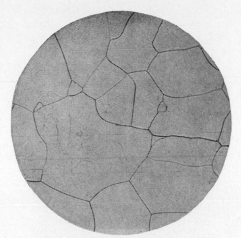

A. High-Purity Iron

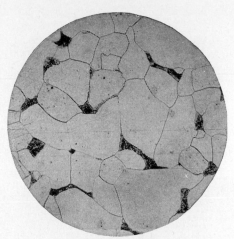

B. 0.12% Carbon

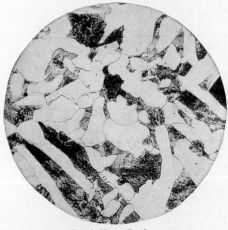

C. 0.40% Carbon

D. 0.62% Carbon

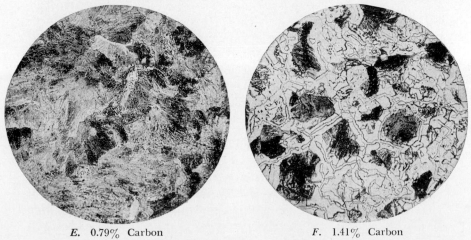

E. 0.79% Carbon

F. 1.41% Carbon

Courtesy Bureau of Standards.

Fig. 4. Microphotographs of Iron–Carbon Alloys Showing the Effect of Increasing Amounts of Carbon on the Structure of the Metal.

carbide (Fe_3C) is known as *cementite* and is extremely hard and brittle. Steels containing less carbon than the eutectoid are known as *hypoeutectoid* steels, and those with more carbon are called *hypereutectoid* steels.

These in structure are shown in the series of microphotographs in Figure 4. The first figure shows pure iron or ferrite. As the carbon content increases to 0.79% carbon, the dark areas of the pearlite form and increase in size while the white background area of ferrite decreases. At 0.79% carbon the sample is all pearlite. In the sample containing 1.41% carbon the pearlite area is smaller and the white background area is now cementite. These iron–carbon alloys have all been cooled slowly to produce the constituents just described.

Hardening

Hardening is the process of heating a piece of steel to a temperature within or above its critical range and then cooling it rapidly. If the carbon content of the steel is known, the proper temperature to which the steel should be heated may be obtained by reference to Figure 1, the iron–carbon diagram. However, if the composition of the steel is unknown, a little preliminary experimentation may be necessary to determine the range. A good procedure to follow is to heat and quench a number of small specimens of the steel at various temperatures and observe the results, either by hardness testing or by microscopic examination. When the correct temperature is obtained, there will be a marked change in hardness and other properties.

In any heat-treating operation the rate of heating is important. Heat flows from the exterior to the interior of steel at a definite maximum rate. If the steel is heated too fast, the outside becomes hotter than the interior, and uniform structure cannot be obtained. If a piece is irregular in shape, a slow rate is all the more essential to eliminate warping and cracking. The heavier the section, the longer must be the heating time to achieve uniform results. Even after the correct temperature has been reached, the piece should be held at that temperature for a sufficient period of time to permit its thickest section to attain a uniform temperature.

The hardness obtained from a given treatment depends on the quenching rate, the carbon content, and the work size. In alloy steels the kind and amount of alloying element also have an influence on the hardness.

A very rapid quench is necessary to harden low- and medium-carbon steels. Quenching in a bath of water is considered to be rapid cooling and is common practice for low- and medium-carbon steels. For high-carbon and alloy steel, oil is generally used as the quenching medium, because its action is not so severe as that of water. Various commercial oils, such as mineral oil, have different cooling speeds and, consequently, impart different hardnesses to steel on quenching. For extreme cooling, brine or water spray is most effective. Certain alloys can be hardened by air cooling, but for ordinary steels such a cooling rate is too slow to give an appreciable hardening effect. Large parts are usually quenched in an oil bath. This quenching medium has the advantage of cooling the part down to ordinary temperatures rapidly and yet is not too severe. It should be remembered that the temperature of the quenching medium must be kept uniform to achieve uniform results. Any quenching bath used in production work should be provided with means for cooling.

Steel with low carbon content will not respond appreciably to hardening treatments. The predominating constituent of such steel is ferrite, which is soft and not changed by the treatment. As the carbon content increases up to the eutectoid point, the ability of the steel to be hardened also increases. Above this point the hardness can be increased only slightly, because steels above the eutectoid point are made up entirely of pearlite and cementite in the annealed state. Pearlite responds best to heat-treating operations; any steel composed mostly of this constituent can be transformed into a hard steel.

As the size of parts to be hardened increases, the surface hardness decreases, even though all other conditions have remained the same. This is evident if it is remembered that there is a limit to the rate of heat flow through steel. No matter how cool the quenching medium may be, if the heat in the inside of a large piece cannot escape faster than a certain critical rate, there is a definite limit to the hardness that may be obtained. For similar reasons it is evident that the inside of a piece of steel would be softer than the outside.

Alloys make it possible to harden small pieces uniformly from the outside to the interior. Also, much greater surface hardness is obtained on alloy steel than on similar sizes of carbon steel. Finally, alloy steel has greater hardenability; that is, it will harden at a slower cooling rate than carbon steel. Therefore, it may be quenched in oil instead of water.

Constituents of hardened steel. It has been previously stated that austenite is a solid solution of iron carbide in gamma iron. All carbon steels are composed entirely of this substance above the upper (Ac_3) critical point. The appearance of austenite under the microscope is shown in Figure 5 at a magnification of 100. Extreme quenching of a steel from a high temperature will preserve some of the austenite at ordinary temperatures. This constituent is about one half as hard as martensite but has excellent wear-resisting properties and is non-magnetic.

If a hypoeutectoid steel is cooled down slowly, the austenite is transformed into ferrite and pearlite. Steel having these constituents is soft and ductile. Faster cooling will result in a different constituent, and the steel will be harder and less ductile. A rapid cooling, as a water quench, will result in a martensitic structure, which is the

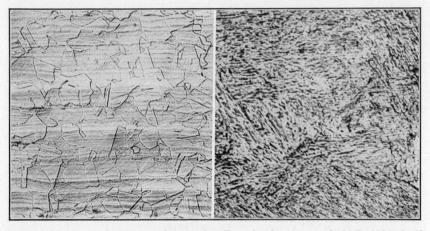

FIG. 5. Structure of 18–8 Stainless Steel Water-Quenched to Show Austenite. Lines Caused by Hot Rolling. Magnification ×125.

FIG. 6. Structure of SAE 1095 Steel Water-Quenched. Etched with Villella's Reagent to Show Martensite. Magnification ×562.

hardest structure that can be obtained. Cementite, although somewhat harder, is not present in its free state except in hypereutectoid steels and then only in such small quantities that its influence on the hardness of the steel can be ignored.

The essential constituent of any hardened steel is *martensite*. A. Martens, a German scientist, first recognized this constituent about 1878. Martensite is obtained by rapid quenching of carbon steels and is the transitional substance formed by the rapid decomposition of austenite. It is a mixture of very small crystals of alpha iron with carbon, which is probably in the form of cementite. Under the microscope it appears as a needlelike constituent, as may be seen in Figure 6. The hardness of martensite depends on the amount of carbide present and varies from Rockwell C45 to C67. It cannot be machined, is quite brittle, and is strongly magnetic.

If steel is quenched at a rate slightly less than the critical rate, a dark constituent with somewhat rounded outlines will be obtained. The name of this constituent is *fine pearlite*.   Under the microscope at usual magnifications, it appears as a dark unresolved mass, but at very high magnification a fine lamellar structure can be seen.   Fine pearlite is less hard than martensite, having a Rockwell C hardness varying from 34 to 45, but is quite tough and capable of resisting considerable impact.   As the quenching rate is still further reduced, the pearlite becomes coarser and is definitely laminated under high magnification at slow rates of cooling.

Maximum hardness of steel.   The maximum hardness obtainable in a given piece of steel depends on the carbon content.   Although various alloys such as chromium and vanadium increase the rate and

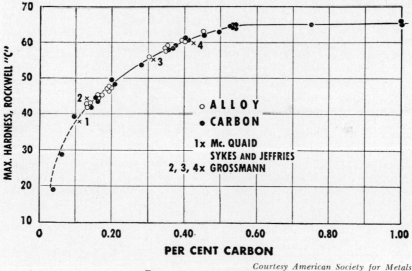

Courtesy American Society for Metals.
From "Quantitative Hardening," by J. L. Burns, T. L. Moore, R. S. Archer, *Transactions ASM*, Vol. XXVI, 1938.

FIG. 7.   Maximum Hardness versus Carbon Content.

depth-hardening ability of alloy steels, their maximum hardness will not exceed that of a carbon steel having the same carbon content. This fact is illustrated in the curve shown in Figure 7, where Rockwell C hardness is plotted against percentage of carbon.   This curve shows the maximum hardness that is possible for a given carbon percentage.   To obtain maximum hardness, the carbon must be completely in solution in the austenite when quenched.   The *critical quenching rate,* which is the slowest rate of cooling that will result in

100% martensite, should be used. Finally austenite must not be retained in any appreciable percentages, as it is considerably softer than martensite.

The curve in Figure 7 is made up of test points from both alloy and carbon steels, and it may be seen that there is little variation in the results. However, the same quenching rate cannot be used for both alloy and carbon steels of the same carbon content. The maximum hardness obtained in any steel represents the hardness of martensite and is approximately Rockwell C65.

Annealing

The primary purpose of *annealing* is to soften hard steel so that it may be machined or cold-worked. This is usually accomplished by heating the steel to a temperature slightly above the critical temperature, holding it there until the temperature of the piece is uniform throughout, and cooling at a slow rate. This process is known as *full annealing* because it wipes out all trace of previous structure and refines the crystalline structure in addition to softening the metal. Annealing also relieves internal stresses previously set up in the metal and removes gases trapped in the metal during the initial casting.

When hardened steel is reheated to above the critical range, the constituents are changed back into austenite, and slow cooling then provides ample time for complete transformation of the austenite into the softer constituents. For the hypoeutectoid steels these constituents are pearlite and ferrite. It may be noted by referring to the equilibrium diagram that the annealing temperature for hypereutectoid steels is lower, being slightly above the A_1 line. There is no reason to heat above the Acm line, as it is at this point that the precipitation of the hard constituent cementite is started. All martensite is changed into pearlite by heating above the lower critical range and slowly cooling. Any free cementite in the steel is unaffected by the treatment.

The temperature to which a given steel should be heated in this process depends on its composition, and for carbon steels it can be obtained readily from the partial iron–iron-carbide equilibrium diagram shown in Figure 1. The heating rate should be consistent with the size and uniformity of sections so that the entire part is brought up to temperature as uniformly as possible.

When the annealing temperature has been reached, the steel should be held there until conditions are uniform throughout. This usually takes about 45 minutes for each inch of thickness of the largest section. For maximum softness and ductility, the cooling rate should be very slow, such as allowing the parts to cool down with the furnace. The higher the carbon content, the slower must be this rate. Low-carbon steels may be cooled more rapidly.

Process annealing practiced in the sheet and wire industry between cold-working operations consists of heating the steel to a temperature a little below the critical range and then cooling slowly. This process is more rapid than the spheroidizing process and results in the usual pearlitic structure. It is similar to the tempering process but will

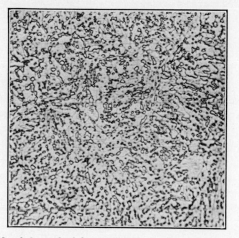

Fig. 8. SAE 1095 Steel Quenched from 1550 F and Tempered at 1250 F for 8 Hours. Structure is Spheroidized Cementite in a Ferritic Matrix. Magnification ×900.

not give so much softness and ductility as a full anneal. Also at the lower heating temperature there is less tendency for the steel to scale or decarburize.

Normalizing

The process of normalizing consists of heating the steel about 100 F above the critical range and cooling in still air to room temperature. This process is principally used with low- and medium-carbon and alloy steels to make the grain structure more uniform, to relieve internal stresses, or because the treatment results in desired physical properties. Most commercial steels are normalized after being rolled or cast.

Spheroidizing

Spheroidizing is the process of changing the lamellar cementite in pearlite to a spheroid structure as shown in Figure 8. If a steel is heated slowly to a temperature just below the critical range and held there for a prolonged period of time, this structure will be obtained.

It may also be accomplished by alternately heating and cooling between temperatures that are just above and below the Ac_1 range. The globular structure obtained by this treatment gives improved machinability to the steel. This treatment is particularly useful for hypereutectoid steels that must be machined.

Tempering

Steel that has been hardened by rapid quenching is brittle and not suitable for most uses. By *tempering* or "drawing," the hardness and brittleness may be reduced to the desired point for service conditions. As these properties are reduced, there is also a decrease in tensile strength and an increase in the ductility and toughness of the steel. The operation consists of the reheating of hardened steel to some temperature below the critical range, followed by any rate of cooling. Although this process softens steel, it differs considerably from annealing in that the process lends itself to close control of the physical properties and in most cases does not soften the steel to the extent that annealing would.

Tempering is possible because of the instability of the martensite, the principal constituent of hardened steel. At about 400 F this constituent will start to break down to the softer constituents. Low draws from 300 to 400 F do not cause much decrease in hardness and are used principally to relieve internal strains. As the tempering temperatures are increased, the breakdown of the martensite takes place at a faster rate, and at about 600 F the change to a structure called *sorbite* is very rapid. Although much softer than fine pearlite formed on direct cooling from austenite, sorbite is tough and has considerable resistance to impact. Increasing tempering temperatures to 1200 F causes a further decrease in hardness and increase in toughness.

In the process of tempering some consideration should be given to time as well as to temperature. Although most of the softening action occurs in the first few minutes after the temperature is reached, there is some additional reduction in hardness if the temperature is maintained for a prolonged time. Usual practice is to heat the steel to the desired temperature and hold it there only long enough to have it uniformly heated.

Interrupted Quenches

The conventional method of hardening and tempering steel just described is illustrated by the time–temperature curve shown in Figure 9. In another process, known as *martempering,* the steel is quenched from the austenite region to a temperature just above that where martensite starts to form. The steel is held at this temperature for a period of time long enough to enable the surface and the center of the piece being treated to come to the same temperature. When this occurs, the piece is usually cooled in air to room temperature, thus forming martensite. The temperature at which the steel is held varies with the carbon and alloy content, although for steels containing around 0.40% carbon the temperature is 400 F. The main purpose of martempering is to minimize distortion, cracking, and internal stresses that result from normal quenching in oil or water.

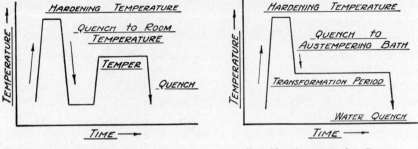

<table>
<tr><td>Fig. 9. Customary Quench and Temper Process.</td><td>Fig. 10. Austempering Process.</td></tr>
</table>

If the steel is quenched from the austenite region to a temperature of 600 to 800 F and the transformation allowed to occur as indicated in Figure 10, a new constituent, *bainite,* is formed. Under the microscope this structure is similar in appearance to martensite, etching somewhat darker. Although the steel is of the same hardness, it is tougher and more ductile than quenched and tempered steel. The steels that respond to this treatment are limited to those containing about 0.60% carbon.

Surface Hardening

Carburizing. The oldest known method of producing a hard surface on steel is case hardening or *carburizing.* This process, in brief, is merely heating iron or steel to a red heat in contact with some carbonaceous material. Iron, at temperatures close to and above its critical temperature, has an affinity for carbon. The carbon enters the metal to form a solid solution with iron and converts the outer surface into a high-carbon steel.

The steel used for this process is usually a low-carbon steel of about 0.15% carbon, which does not respond appreciably to heat treatment. In the course of the process, the outer layer is converted into a high-carbon steel with a content ranging from 0.9% to 1.2% carbon. By proper heat treatment such steel will have an extremely hard surface on the outside and a soft ductile center.

This process is merely one of changing the carbon content of the surface steel, which makes it possible to obtain different physical properties in a given piece of steel. A steel with varying carbon content, and, consequently, different critical temperatures, requires consideration in the heat-treatment procedure. The case has a much lower critical temperature than the interior. Since there is some grain growth in the steel during the prolonged carburizing treatment, the work should first be heated to the critical temperature of the core and cooled, which refines the core structure. The steel should then be reheated to the critical range of the case and quenched to produce a hard fine structure. A third tempering treatment may be used to reduce strains.

Nitriding. Nitriding is somewhat similar to ordinary case hardening, but it uses a different material and treatment to create the hard-surface constituents. In this process the metal is heated to a temperature of around 950 F and held there for a period of time in contact with ammonia gas. Nitrogen from the gas is introduced into the steel, forming very hard nitrides which are finely dispersed through the surface metal.

It has been found that nitrogen has greater hardening ability with certain elements than with others; hence, special nitriding alloy steels have been developed. Aluminum in percentages of 1 to 1½ has proved to be especially suitable in steel, as it combines with the gas to form a very stable and hard constituent. The temperature of heating ranges from 850 to 1200 F, although 960 to 975 F is the temperature range generally used.

The nitriding process develops extreme hardness in the surface of steel. This hardness ranges from 900 to 1100 Brinell, which is considerably higher than that obtained by ordinary case hardening. Nitriding steels, by virtue of their alloying content, are stronger than ordinary steels and respond readily to heat treatment. It is recommended that these steels be machined and heat-treated before nitriding, as there is no scale or further work necessary after this process. Fortunately, the structure and properties are not affected appreciably by the nitriding treatment; and, since no quenching is necessary, there is little tendency to warp, develop cracks, or change condition in any way. The surface effectively resists corrosive action of water, salt-water spray, alkalies, crude oil, and natural gas.

This process is used on many automotive, airplane, and Diesel-engine wearing parts, as well as on numerous miscellaneous parts, such as pump shafts, gages, drawing dies, gears, clutches, and mandrels. Its use is limited by the expense necessary for the treatment and the comparatively thin case obtained (0.001 to 0.005 inch).

Cyaniding. Cyaniding is a process combining the absorption of carbon and nitrogen to obtain surface hardness in low-carbon steels that do not respond to ordinary heat treatment. In this process the part to be case-hardened is immersed in a bath of fused sodium cyanide salts at a temperature of approximately 1600 F, the time of soaking depending on the depth of case desired. The part is then quenched in water or oil to obtain the desired hard surface. Case depths of 0.005 to 0.020 inch may be readily obtained by this process. Disadvantages of this process are the toxicity of the salts used and the size limitation of the parts that can be treated.

Induction hardening. Metals have been heated and melted by induced electric currents for some time. It is only recently, however, that this means of heating has been employed in surface hardening. This process here described is commonly known as the *Tocco process,** and it was developed for the purpose of surface-hardening crankshaft bearings and other similar wearing surfaces. It differs from ordinary case-hardening practice in that the analysis of the surface steel is not changed, the hardening being accomplished by an extremely rapid heating and quenching of the wearing surface which has no effect on the interior core metal. A surface hardness of approximately 58 to 62 Rockwell C is obtained.

An inductor block acting as a primary coil of a transformer is placed around, but not touching, the journal to be hardened. A high-frequency current, usually 2000 cycles, is passed through this block, inducing a current in the surface of the bearing. The heating effect is due to induced eddy currents and hysteresis losses in the surface material. As the steel is heated to the upper critical range, the heating effect of these losses is gradually decreased, thereby eliminating any possibility of overheating the steel. The inductor block surrounding the heated surface has water connections and numerous small holes in its inside surface, and, as soon as the steel has been brought up to the proper temperature, it is automatically spray-quenched under pressure.

An important feature of this method of hardening is its rapidity of action, since it requires only 5 seconds to heat the steel to a depth of ⅛ inch. Obviously, this procedure eliminates warping to a great extent and consequently necessitates only a small allowance for grind-

* Developed by The Ohio Crankshaft Company.

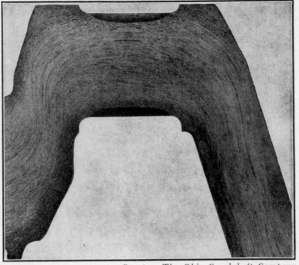

Courtesy The Ohio Crankshaft Company.

FIG. 11. Section of an Induction-Hardened Crankpin Bearing.

ing to the finished size. Medium-carbon steel has proved very satisfactory for parts treated in this manner, and the nature of the process has practically eliminated the necessity of using costly alloy steels. Figure 11 illustrates the local heating obtained in a hardened crankpin bearing which has been induction-hardened.

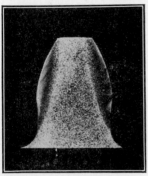

Courtesy The Linde Air Products Company.

FIG. 12. Section through a Gear Tooth Showing Structure Obtained by Flame Hardening.

Flame hardening. Flame hardening, like the induction-hardening process, is based on rapid heating and quenching of the wearing surface. The heating is accomplished by means of an oxyacetylene flame, which is applied for a sufficient length of time to heat the surface above the critical temperature of the steel. Integral with the flame head are water connections which cool the surface by spraying as soon as the desired temperature is reached. By proper control, the interior surface is not affected by the treatment, the depth of the case being a function of the heating time and flame temperature. Figure 12 shows an etched cross section of a gear tooth and the hardened areas.

Several methods are employed in this process. In the stationary method of spot hardening, both torch and work are stationary, and the effect is local. In progressive hardening the flame and work move with respect to one another, as, for example, in rail hardening. As the flame progresses, the work is immediately quenched behind the flame. Spinning or rapidly rotating circular work may be used, employing one or more flames. As soon as the work is brought up to the proper temperature, it is quenched while rotating. This method is usually applied to fairly small work when the heating time is short. Spinning may also be used in connection with a progressive movement of the torch along the side of the work.

The following advantages are claimed for this process: Hard surfaces with a ductile backing may be obtained, large pieces may be treated without heating the entire part, the case depth is easily controlled, the surface is free of scale, and the equipment is portable.

Grain Size

All steel is crystalline in structure, and the size of these crystals or grains has an important effect on the quality of the steel. Molten steel upon cooling starts solidifying at many small centers or nuclei, the atoms in each group orienting themselves in the same direction. The irregular grain boundaries seen under the microscope after polishing and etching are the outlines of each group of atomic cells that have the same orientation. The size of these grains depends on a number of factors, the principal ones being the composition of the steel and the heat treatment it has received.

It has long been known that coarse-grain steels are weaker and more brittle than those having a fine grain; however, they have better machinability and greater depth-hardening power. The fine-grained steels, in addition to being tougher, are more ductile and have less tendency to distort or crack during heat treatment. Control of grain size is possible through regulation of composition in the initial manufacturing procedure, but, after the steel is made, the control is through proper heat treatment.

When a piece of low-carbon steel is heated, there is no change in the grain size up to the Ac_1 point. As the temperature increases through the critical range, the ferrite and pearlite are gradually transformed to austenite, and, at the upper critical point Ac_3, the average grain size is a minimum. Further heating of the steel causes an increase in the size of the austenitic grains, which in turn governs the final size of the grains when cooled. Quenching from the Ac_3 point would result in a fine-grained structure, whereas slow cooling or quenching from a higher temperature would give a coarser structure.

The final grain size depends entirely on the prior austenitic grain size in the steel at the time of quenching.

All steels do not start growing large crystals immediately upon being heated above the upper critical range, and such steels can be heated to some higher temperature with little change in their structure. A temperature known as a *coarsening temperature* is eventually reached, and grain-size increase becomes rapid. This is characteristic of

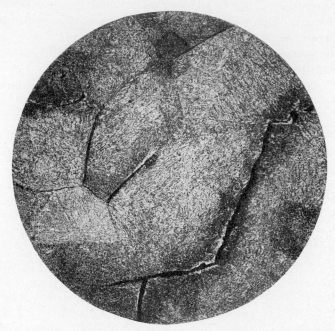

FIG. 13.   Crystalline Separation and Excessive Grain Size.   Magnification ×300.

medium-carbon steels, many alloy steels, and steels that have been deoxidized with aluminum. The coarsening temperature is not a fixed temperature and may be changed by prior hot or cold working and heat treatment.* Hot work on steel is started at temperatures well above the critical range with the steel in a plastic state and has the effect of refining the grain structure and eliminating any coarsening effect due to the high temperature. Hot forging or rolling should not continue below the critical temperature.

The principal method of determining grain size is by microscopic examination, although it may be roughly estimated by examination of a fracture. For microscopic determination it is necessary that the

* M. A. Grossman, "Grain Size in Metals with Special Reference to Grain Growth in Austenite," *Transactions ASM*, Vol. 22, no. 10, 1934.

grain boundaries be clearly outlined by some constituent. Low-carbon steels have ferrite precipitated from the austenite upon slow cooling, and the outline of these grains can be clearly brought out by polishing and etching. In estimating the former austenitic grain size for low-carbon steels, the area of the pearlite formed from the remainder of the austenite must also be considered. For medium-carbon steels the former austenitic grain size would be represented roughly by the pearlitic area plus one-half the surrounding ferrite. Hypereutectoid steels will have the grain boundaries outlined by the cementite that is precipitated.

An example of a large-grained steel is shown in the photomicrograph in Figure 13. This specimen has been heated to an excessively high temperature, resulting in large grain growth and some crystalline separation. Steel that has been "burnt" shows this separation owing to oxidation at the grain boundaries, and such structure cannot be remedied by heat treatment. It can be rendered fit for commercial use only by remelting.

Review Questions

1. What are the principal microconstituents found in all annealed steels?
2. Describe what takes place when an allotropic change occurs in steel.
3. What changes take place in steel at the critical points?
4. Describe the process known as hardening.
5. What is martensite? How does it appear under the microscope?
6. What determines the maximum hardness that can be obtained in a piece of steel?
7. What is meant by the following terms: eutectoid, pearlite, cementite, austenite, and alpha ferrite?
8. What microconstituents will be found in annealed 0.50% carbon steel? 1.2% carbon steel?
9. What is the purpose of annealing, and how is it done?
10. Distinguish between normalizing and spheroidizing.
11. How is martempering done, and why is it used?
12. What is the difference between austempering and ordinary tempering?
13. Describe the process of carburizing.
14. For what type of work is cyanizing used?
15. What is nitriding, and what advantages does the process have over carburizing?
16. How is induction hardening accomplished?
17. Describe the methods used in flame hardening.
18. How does a variation in grain size affect the properties of steel?

References

BULLENS, D. K., *Steel and Its Heat Treatment*, 5th edition, Vols. I and II, John Wiley & Sons, 1948.

CAMP, J. M., and C. B. FRANCIS, *The Making, Shaping, and Treating of Steel,* 5th edition, Carnegie-Illinois Steel Corporation, 1940.

COONAN, F. L., *Principles of Physical Metallurgy,* Harper & Brothers, 1943.

DAVENPORT, E. S., and E. C. BAIN, *Transformation of Austenite at Constant Subcritical Temperatures,* AIME Technical Publication 348, 1930.

DOAN, G. E., and E. M. MAHLE, *The Principles of Physical Metallurgy,* 2d edition, McGraw-Hill Book Company, 1941.

DOWDELL, R. L., H. S. JERABEK, A. C. FORSYTH, and C. H. GREEN, *General Metallography,* John Wiley & Sons, 1943.

HEYER, R. H., *Engineering Physical Metallurgy,* D. Van Nostrand Company, 1939.

KELLER, J. F., *Lectures on Steel and Its Treatment,* 2d edition, American Society for Steel Treating, 1930.

Metals Handbook, American Society for Metals, 1948.

NEWTON, J., *An Introduction to Metallurgy,* 2d edition, John Wiley & Sons, 1947.

ROSENHOLTZ, J. L., and J. F. OESTERLE, *The Elements of Ferrous Metallurgy,* 2d edition, John Wiley & Sons, 1938.

SACHS, G., and K. R. VAN HORN, *Practical Metallurgy,* American Society for Metals, 1940.

SISCO, F. T., *Modern Metallurgy for Engineers,* Pitman Publishing Company, 1948.

STOUGHTON, B., *The Metallurgy of Iron and Steel,* 4th edition, McGraw-Hill Book Company, 1934.

STOUGHTON, B., and A. BUTTS, *Engineering Metallurgy,* 3d edition, McGraw-Hill Book Company, 1938.

TEICHERT, E. J., *Ferrous Metallurgy,* 3 Vols., McGraw-Hill Book Company, 1944.

WILLIAMS, R. S., and V. HOMERBERG, *The Principles of Metallography,* 4th edition, McGraw-Hill Book Company, 1939.

WOLDMAN, N. E., *Materials Engineering of Metal Products,* Reinhold Publishing Corporation, 1949.

CHAPTER
7

WELDING AND ALLIED PROCESSES

Welding is the fusion or uniting of two pieces of metal by means of heat. Many welding processes have been developed which differ widely in the manner in which the heat is applied and in the type of equipment used. Some processes require hammering, rolling, or pressing to effect the weld; others bring the metal to a fluid state and require no pressure. Those processes that use pressure require bringing the surfaces of the metal to a temperature sufficient that cohesion takes place. This is nearly always a subfusion temperature. However, if the fusion temperature is reached, the molten metal must be confined by surrounding solid metal. No additional weld metal is required in welds of this type. Most welds are made at fusion temperature and require the addition of weld metal in some form. In the welding of dissimilar metals, it is often possible to make a satisfactory bond by bringing only one of the metals to a fusion temperature. Welds are also made by casting, in which case the metal is heated to a high temperature and poured into the cavity between the two pieces to be joined. In this method the heat in the weld metal must be sufficient to cause it to fuse properly with the parent metal.

Soldering is the uniting of two pieces of metal with a different metal, which is applied between the two in a molten state and at a temperature not exceeding 800 F. In this process some alloying with the base metal takes place, and additional strength is obtained by mechanical bonding. The usual metals for soldering are low-melting alloys of lead and tin. *Brazing* is a similar process in which the metal parts are joined by nonferrous metals, such as copper-zinc and silver alloys, having melting points below that of the parent metal but above 800 F. The filler metal is distributed between the joint surfaces by capillary attraction. Soldering is not considered a welding process, but brazing is now considered one.* Temperatures in this process range from 1100 to 1983 F which includes a wide selection of possible filler metals.

* *Welding Handbook,* American Welding Society.

Most of the developments of modern welding have taken place since the first World War as a result of the demands of industry for more rapid means of fabrication and assembly of metal parts. Welding processes are employed extensively in the manufacture of automobile bodies, aircraft, high-speed railroad cars, machine frames, structural work, tanks, and general machine-repair work. In the oil industry welding is extensively used at refineries and in pipe-line fabrication. During war the largest single use for welding has been in shipbuilding; in peacetime it is the fabrication of metal structures. The competition of welding has also been felt in the casting industry, as many machine parts that were formerly cast are now made up of steel members welded together. Such construction has the advantage of being lighter and stronger than cast iron. Gas cutting has likewise had its influence on forged products. Many parts are now accurately cut from thick steel plates, thus saving the cost of expensive dies. There is hardly an industry today that is not affected in some way by welding and cutting processes.

The first welding processes were all limited to low-carbon steel and wrought iron. All such materials are easily welded and have a wide welding range. As the carbon content increases or as alloying elements are added, the welding range decreases, and good welds become increasingly difficult. However, the development of new electrodes and new welding techniques has greatly altered our concept of what is weldable material. Practically all alloy steels can now be welded if proper equipment and materials are used. Cast iron at first presented serious difficulties, because of its low ductility, poor fusion, and tendency to crack on cooling. Most of these difficulties are now overcome by proper methods and the selection of suitable welding materials. Such nonferrous metals as brass, bronze, Monel metal, aluminum, copper, and nickel can all be successfully welded, although special precaution must usually be taken to prevent oxidation.

General Conditions for Welding

Welding is facilitated if surfaces are cleaned and freed from foreign matter by wire brushing, machining, or sand blasting. Impurities tend to weaken a weld, causing the metal to be either brittle or filled with gas and slag inclusions. They also cause poor cohesion of the metals.

Tendencies toward oxidation increase with temperature. At the high temperatures used in many welding processes, the oxidation of the weld metal is likely to have serious weakening effects in the weld. In some processes this influence is counteracted by the use of a flux which removes the oxides and permits perfect cohesion of the metals.

In the electric-arc process the flux is coated on the electrodes and, when melted, forms a protective coating of slag over the weld metal, as well as a nonoxidizing atmosphere. In gas welding and forge welding it is usually added in powder form. Other processes eliminate any oxidation tendencies by creating a nonoxidizing atmosphere at the point where the welding is done.

Inasmuch as oxidation takes place rapidly at high temperature, speed in welding is important. Some processes are naturally quicker than others, but in any event the work should be done as rapidly as possible.

Principal Welding Processes

The principal welding processes are listed in Table 4. Most of these are discussed briefly in the text matter that follows.

TABLE 4. WELDING PROCESSES *

I. Forge welding
    A. Manual.
    B. Machine
      1. Rolling.
      2. Hammer.
      3. Die.

II. Resistance welding
    A. Spot.
    B. Seam.
    C. Projection.
    D. Flash.
    E. Butt.
    F. Percussion.

III. Gas welding
    A. Air–acetylene.
    B. Oxyacetylene.
    C. Oxyhydrogen.
    D. Pressure.

IV. Braze welding
    A. Torch.
    B. Twin-carbon arc.
    C. Furnace.
    D. Induction.
    E. Resistance.
    F. Dip.
    G. Block.
    H. Flow.

V. Arc welding
    A. Carbon electrode
      1. Shielded.
      2. Unshielded.
    B. Metal electrodes
      1. Shielded
        (a) Shielded metal arc.
        (b) Impregnated tape.
        (c) Atomic hydrogen.
        (d) Inert gas.
        (e) Submerged arc.
        (f) Shielded stud.
      2. Unshielded
        (a) Bare metal.
        (b) Stud.

VI. Thermit welding
    A. Pressure.
    B. Nonpressure.

VII. Flow welding.

VIII. Induction welding.

IX. Cold welding.

* This table follows closely the chart prepared by The American Welding Society.

Welded Joints

The six principal types of joints used in most welding processes (see Figure 1) are butt, lap, edge, corner, plug, and tee. Some of

(a) Butt Weld $\left(\frac{4}{32}" \text{ to } \frac{1}{8}"\right)$ *(b) Single Vee* $\left(\frac{3}{16}" \text{ and over}\right)$

(c) Double Vee (Heavy Plates)   *(d) U-Shaped   (Heavy Casting)*

(e) Flange Weld (Thin Metal)   *(f) Single Strap Butt Joint*

(g) Lap Joint (Single or double fillet weld)   *(h) Joggled Lap Joint (Single or double weld)*

(i) Tee Joint (Fillet Welds)   *(j) Edge Weld (Used on thin plates)*

(k) Corner Welds (Thin Metal)   *(l) Plug or Rivet Butt Joint*

FIG. 1. Types of Welded Joints.

these types, such as butt welds, may be further subdivided, as they vary in form according to the thickness of the material. Joints for forge welding differ in their manner of preparation and do not resemble those shown in the figure. Lap and butt joints are the principal types used in resistance welding. In general, resistance-welded joints must be prepared more accurately and must be considerably cleaner than those used in other processes. Both gas and arc welding use the same types of joints.

Forge Welding

Forge welding was the first form of welding used and for many centuries the only one in general use. Briefly, the process consists of heating the metal in a forge to a plastic condition and then uniting it by pressure. The heating is usually done in a coal- or coke-fired forge, although modern installations frequently employ oil or gas furnaces. The manual process is naturally limited to light work, as all forming and welding is accomplished with a hand sledge. Before the weld is made, the pieces are first formed to correct shape, so that, when they are welded, they will unite at the center first. As they are hammered together from the center to the outside edges, any oxide or foreign particles will be forced out. The process of preparing the metal is known as *scarfing*.

Forge welding is naturally rather slow, and there is considerable danger of an oxide scale forming on the surface. The tendency to oxidize can be counteracted somewhat by using a thick fuel bed and by covering the surfaces with a fluxing material which dissolves the oxides. Many special fluxes have been prepared; however, borax in combination with sal ammoniac is commonly used. Heating must be slow on account of unequal section thickness. As soon as the desired uniform temperature is reached, the pieces are removed to the anvil and hammered together.

For this type of welding, low-carbon steel and wrought iron are recommended, as they have a large welding-temperature range. This range decreases rapidly as the carbon content increases. High-carbon steels and alloy steels require considerably more care in controlling temperatures and producing the welds.

Large work may be welded in hammer forges driven by air or steam. Such equipment is especially valuable for forming and shaping work in the plastic state and has the additional advantage of refining the grain size when worked above the critical temperature of the metal. Welded steel pipe is made mechanically by running the preheated steel strips through rolls which form the pipe to size and apply the necessary pressure for the weld, as discussed in Chapter 8.

Electrical-Resistance Welding

In this process a heavy electric current is passed through the metals to be joined, causing a local heating, and the weld is completed by the application of pressure. This process dates back to the latter part of the 19th century and was first used by Elihu Thompson. When the current passes through the metal, the greatest resistance is at the point of contact; hence, the greatest heating effect is at the point where the weld is to be made. Alternating current is generally used, coming to the machine with the usual commercial voltages. A transformer in the machine reduces the voltage to 4 to 12 volts and raises the amperage sufficiently to produce a good heating current. The amount of current necessary is 30 to 40 kva per square inch of area to be united, based on a time of about 10 seconds. For other time intervals the power varies inversely with the time. The necessary pressure to effect the weld will vary from 4000 to 8000 pounds per square inch.

Resistance welding is essentially a production process adapted to the joining of light-gage metals which can be lapped. Usually the equipment is suitable for only one type of job, and the work must be moved to the machine. The process is especially adapted to quantity production, and its use includes a large amount of the welding done at the present time. It is the only process that permits a pressure action at the weld, while allowing an accurately regulated heat application. Also, the operation is extremely rapid.

The weldability of a given metal depends to some extent on its melting point. Practically all metals can be welded by resistance welding, although some few, such as tin, zinc, and lead, can be welded only with great difficulty.

In all resistance welding the three factors that must be given consideration are expressed in the formula: Heat $= I^2RT$, where I is the welding current in amperes, R the resistance of the metal being welded, and T the time. The amperage of the secondary or welding current is determined by the transformer. To provide possible variation of the secondary current, the transformer is equipped with a regulator on the primary side to vary the number of turns on the primary coil. This may be seen in Figure 2. For good welds these three variables, current, resistance, and time, must be carefully considered and determined by such factors as material thickness, kind of material, type and size of electrode.

The timing of the welding current is very important. There should be an adjustable delay after the pressure has been applied until the weld is started. The current is then turned on by the timer and held a sufficient time for the weld. It is then stopped, but the pressure remains until the weld cools, thus eliminating any tendency for the electrodes to arc and also protecting the weld from discoloration. The pressure on the weld may be obtained manually, by mechanical means, by air pressure, by springs, or by hydraulic means. Its application must be controlled and co-ordinated with the application of the welding current.

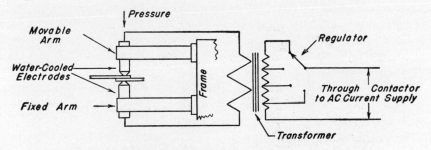

Fig. 2. Diagram of Spot Welder.

Resistance welding may be subdivided into six separate heads: (1) Spot welding, (2) projection welding, (3) seam welding, (4) butt welding, (5) flash welding, and (6) percussion welding.

Spot welding. In this form of resistance welding two or more sheets of metal are held between metal electrodes as shown in Figure 2. The welding cycle is started with the electrodes contacting the metal under pressure before the current is applied, and for a period known as the *squeeze time.* A low-voltage current of sufficient amperage is then passed between the electrodes causing the metal in contact to be rapidly raised to a welding temperature. As soon as the temperature is reached, the pressure between the electrodes squeezes the metal together and completes the weld. This period, usually 3 to 30 cycles, is known as the *weld time.* Next, while the pressure is still on, the current is shut off for a period called the *hold time,* during which the metal regains some strength by cooling. The pressure is then released, and the work is either removed from the machine or moved so that another portion can be welded. This is the *off time.* All times are measured in terms of current cycles and usually range from 3 to 60 (1 cycle = $\frac{1}{60}$ sec).

Spot welding is probably the simplest form of resistance welding and for ordinary sheet steel does not present much of a problem. However, good welds require sheet steel which is free from scale or foreign substances. Such films cause variations in surface resistance and tend to increase the heating effect of metal in contact with the electrodes. Surface imperfections, variations in weld strength, and electrode pickup are defects to be expected if sheet surfaces are not properly prepared. It may be noted that in spot welding there are three zones of heat generation: one at the surface between the two sheets, and the other two at the contact surfaces of the sheets with the

Courtesy The Taylor Winfield Corporation.   *Courtesy Thompson-Gibbs Electric Welding Company.*

FIG. 3. Air-Operated Rocker-Arm Spot Welder, 15-Kva Capacity.   FIG. 4. Direct-Pressure Spot-Welding Machine.

electrodes. The center surface reaches a fusing temperature first, since the heat is rapidly conducted from the outside surfaces by the water-cooled electrodes.

Machines for spot welding are made in three general types: stationary single-spot, portable single-spot, and multiple-spot machines. Stationary machines may be further classified as rocker-arm and direct-pressure types. The rocker-arm type, shown in Figure 3, is the simplest and cheapest but is generally limited to machines of small capacity. This machine is so designated because the motion for applying pressure and raising the upper electrode is made by rocking the upper arm. The larger machines usually employ direct straight-line motion of the upper electrode. This arrangement permits them to be used also for projection welding. A 250-kva air-operated machine of this type is shown in Figure 4.

As assemblies to be welded increase in size, it is not always possible to bring them to a machine. Portable spot welders, connected to the transformer by long cables, and capable of being moved to any desired position, are then used. Welding jig assemblies where all welds cannot be made by a single machine setup are also served best by portable welders. A wide variety of portable welding guns is made, as indicated

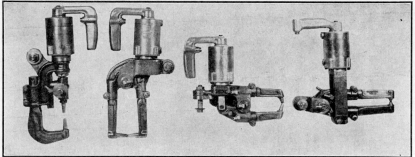

Courtesy Progressive Welder Company.

Fig. 5. Different Types of Welding Guns. All May Be Operated by Either Air or Hydraulic Means.

in Figure 5, the principal differences among them being in the manner of applying the pressure and the shape of the tips. Pressure is applied manually, pneumatically, or hydraulically, depending on the size and type of gun.

For production work, multiple-spot-welding machines have been developed which are capable of producing two or more spots simultaneously. In machines of this type several direct welds can be made from either one or more transformers. In some cases a system known as *indirect welding* is used, where two electrodes are in series, and the current passes through a heavy plate underneath the sheets and between the electrodes.

Figure 6 shows a high-production welding machine consisting of 16 hydraulically operated guns controlled by air valves. A mechanism actuates groups of four guns (in series) through the air valve in rapid sequential welding. The mufflers, made of 0.040-inch galvanized steel, are welded at the rate of 480 mufflers per hour. This is a special-purpose machine and typical of those designed for multiple-spot-welded production jobs. Gun welding machines normally operate at 100 to

360 spot welds per minute although speeds up to 720 have been attained.

Spot welding lends itself readily to production work because of its simplicity and the rapidity with which welds can be made. Most ferrous and nonferrous alloys may be spot-welded, but each metal

Courtesy The Taylor Winfield Corporation.

Fɪɢ. 6. Multiple-Spot Gun-Type Machine Welding Baffles in Automobile Muffler.

requires special manipulation and current regulation. Spot welding has a wide application, from thin foils in which low currents are used to heavy plates requiring high current and long time. Theoretically, any material of reasonable thickness can be spot-welded; however, as the thickness increases, the required tremendous force necessary becomes a limiting factor. One-half inch is the usual upper limit. Spot welding is widely used in the manufacture of automobiles, refrigerators, and metal toys, and in numerous other metal-stamping assemblies.

Projection welding. Projection welding is similar to spot welding and is illustrated in the line diagram shown in Figure 7. Projection welds are produced at localized points in work pieces held under pressure between suitable electrodes. Sheet metal to be welded in this manner is first put through a punch press, which presses small projections or buttons into the metal. These projections are made with a diameter on the face equal to the thickness of the stock and project above the stock about 60% of its thickness. Such projection spots or ridges are made at all points where a weld is desired. This process is also used for cross-wire welding and for parts where the ridges are produced by machining. One advantage of this form of welding is that a number of welds can be made simultaneously, the only limit to

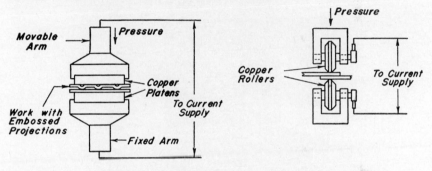

FIG. 7. Projection Welding.   FIG. 8. Seam Welding.

the number being the ability of the press to furnish and distribute equally to the work the correct current and pressure. Results are generally uniform, and weld appearance is often better than in spot welding. Electrode life is long, since only flat surfaces are used and little maintenance is required.

In actual welding the sequence of operation is identical with that of spot welding. The current per weld is slightly less than for spot welds, but, because multiple welds are made, greater current and pressure capacity must be available. Only press-type machines are recommended for this process. It is possible to weld all metals by this method as readily as by other resistance-welding processes.

Seam welding. Seam welding, shown in Figure 8, consists in making a continuous weld or joint on two overlapping pieces of metal. Such welds are made by passing the metal between two electrode rollers or dies which transmit current and to which mechanical pressure is applied. In some cases only a single roller is used in conjunction with a flat track. This method is, in effect, a continuous spot-welding process, as the current is not on continuously but is regulated by the timer on the machine. The spots can be spaced close together to form a continuous seam or can be regulated so that they are several inches apart.   The welding time is measured in cycles, and electronic-tube controls are used to provide current interruptions.   To produce a pressure-tight seam requires 5 to 14 spots per inch, depending on the type and gage of the material.   This type of welding is limited to thicknesses ranging from 0.010 to ⅛ inch.

Courtesy Sciaky Bros.

FIG. 9.   Electrical-Resistance Rocker-Arm Seam-Welding Machine.

An air-operated rocker-arm-type seam and roll-spot-welding machine is shown in Figure 9.   The maximum pressure obtainable between the electrodes runs as high as 3500 pounds at an air pressure of 90 pounds per square inch.   Continuous rotation of the upper wheel can be adjusted up to 6 rpm, or intermittent rotation can be obtained if desired.   This machine is capable of producing 858 spot welds per minute on two 0.040-inch thicknesses, which is 66 inches per minute with 13 spots per inch.

Other machines are designed with the roller electrodes mounted so that the work is fed into the machine at right angles to the welder throat.   These machines are used for producing either circumferential or transverse welds.

Seam welding is used a great deal in the manufacture of metal containers, automobile mufflers, stove pipes, refrigerator cabinets, and gasoline tanks. Advantages of this type of fabrication include neater design, saving of material, tight joints, and low cost of construction.

Butt welding. This form of welding, illustrated in Figure 10, consists in gripping together two pieces of metal that have the same cross section and pressing them together while heat is being generated in the contact surface by electrical resistance. Although pressure is maintained while the heating takes place, at no time is the temperature sufficient actually to melt the metal. The joint is upset somewhat by the process, but this defect can be eliminated by subsequent rolling

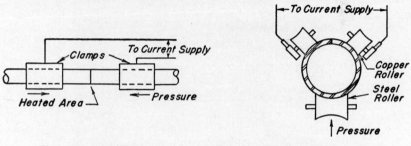

FIG. 10. Butt-Welder.   FIG. 11. Continuous Butt Welding of Pipe.

or grinding. Both parts to be welded should be of the same resistance in order to have uniform heating at the joint. If two dissimilar metals are to be welded, the metal projecting from the die holders must be in proportion to the specific resistance of the materials to be welded. The same treatment must be used where materials of different cross section are butt-welded.

In actual operation, the work is first clamped in the machine and a pressure is applied on the joints. The welding current is then started, and heating takes place, the rate depending on the pressure, the material, and the condition of surfaces. Since the contact resistance varies inversely with the pressure, the pressure is less at the start and is then increased to whatever is necessary to effect the weld (2500 to 8000 pounds per square inch) when the welding temperature is reached. As soon as the weld is completed, the current is cut off and the work unclamped from the machine. This process differs from flash-butt welding in that there is no flashing or arcing at the joint during the operation.

Practically all metals that can be spot- or projection-welded can also be butt-welded, with the strength of the weld being about equal to the strength of the metal being welded. This type of welding is especially adapted to rods, pipes, small structural shapes, and many other parts of uniform section.   Areas up to 70 square inches have been successfully welded, but generally the process is limited to small areas because of current limitations.   Figure 11 illustrates a special type of butt-seam welding used in pipe manufacture.

Flash welding.   Butt and flash-butt welding are similar in their application but differ somewhat in the manner of heating the metal. Figure 12 illustrates diagrammatically the operation of this type of welding machine.   The stock is clamped by dies as in ordinary butt welding.   As soon as the metal is clamped, the current is turned on, and the two joints are brought together by means of the cam control.

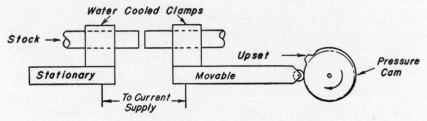

FIG. 12.   Principle of Butt-Flash Welding.

As the two parts are lightly contacted, there is vigorous arcing which melts down any unevenness of the surface and rapidly brings it to a plastic state.   The operating cam is adjusted so that the upset portion engages the moving platen at the proper time, and the two surfaces are forced together under high pressure (5000 to 25,000 pounds per square inch), thus completing the weld.   This system requires a very heavy current but takes a relatively short time.   A small fin or projection left at the joint can be easily removed.   An important advantage of the flash-welding process is that the plate edges do not have to be specially prepared.

Welding of small areas is usually done by the butt-welding method and those of large area by the flash-butt method; however, there is no clear demarcation between the two.   The shape of the piece and the nature of the alloy are frequently the determining factors.   Areas ranging from 0.002 to 50 square inches have been successfully welded by flash welding.   In this process, less current is required than in ordinary butt welding; there is less metal to remove around the joints; the metal that forms the weld is protected from atmospheric contamination; the operation consumes little time; and end-to-end welding of sheets is possible.   Because of these advantages, flash welding is more widely used than the ordinary butt or upset process.   Many nonferrous metals can be flash-welded satisfactorily; however, alloys containing high percentages of lead, zinc, tin, and copper are not recommended for this process. Flash welding is widely used for tubular furniture, rear-axle housings, steel rims, sheets in body manufacture, steel forgings, and rolled sections.

Percussion welding. This is a recent development in welding, and, like the flash-weld process, relies on arc effect for heating rather than on the resistance in the metal. Pieces to be welded are held apart, one in a stationary holder and the other in a clamp mounted in a slide and backed up against heavy spring pressure. When the movable clamp is released, it moves rapidly, carrying with it the piece to be welded. When the pieces are about $1/16$ inch apart, there is a sudden discharge of electric energy, causing intense arcing over the surfaces and bringing them to a high temperature. The arc is extinguished by the percussion blow of the two parts coming together with sufficient force to effect the weld.

The electric energy for the discharge is built up in one of two ways. In the electrostatic method, energy is stored in a capacitor, and the parts to be welded are heated by the sudden discharge of a heavy current from the capacitor. The electromagnetic welder uses the energy discharge caused by the collapsing of the magnetic field linking the primary and secondary windings of a transformer or other inductive device. In either case intense arcing is created, which is followed by a quick blow to make the weld.

The action of this process is so rapid (about 0.1 second) that there is little heating effect in the material adjacent to the weld. Heat-treated parts may be welded without being annealed. Parts differing in thermal conductivity and mass can be successfully joined, as the heat is concentrated only at the two surfaces. Some applications are welding Stellite tips to tools, copper to aluminum or stainless steel, silver contact tips to copper, cast iron to steel, lead-in wires on electric lamps, and zinc to steel. Butt welds are made without any upset or flash at the joint. The principal limitation of the process is that only small areas (up to $1/2$ square inch) of nearly regular sections can be welded. Thin sheets of equivalent area cannot be joined by this process. The equipment is expensive, since it must be extremely rugged, provided with accurate holding fixtures, and equipped with elaborate electric timing devices and large transformer capacity.

Gas Welding

Gas welding includes all the processes in which gases are used in combination to obtain a hot flame. Those commonly used are acetylene, natural gas, and hydrogen in combination with oxygen. Oxyhydrogen welding was the first gas process to be commercially developed. The maximum temperature developed by this process is 3600 F. The most-used combination is the oxyacetylene process, which has a flame temperature of 6300 F.

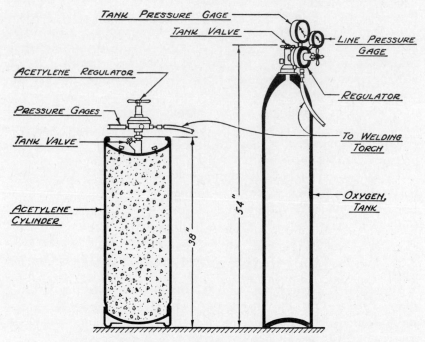

Fig. 13.   Cylinders and Regulators for Oxyacetylene Welding.

Oxyacetylene welding.   An oxyacetylene weld is produced by heating with a flame obtained from the combustion of oxygen and acetylene and with or without the use of a filler metal.   In most cases the joint is heated to a state of fusion, and no pressure is used; however, in some cases pressure may be applied.

Oxygen is produced by two main processes: electrolysis and liquefying air.   Electrolysis separates water into hydrogen and oxygen by passing an electric current through it.   Most of the commercial oxygen is made by liquefying air and separating the oxygen from the nitrogen.   It is stored in steel cylinders, as shown in Figure 13, at a pressure of 2000 pounds per square inch.   *Hydrogen* is produced either by the electrolysis of water or by passing steam over coke.

Acetylene gas (C_2H_2) is obtained by dropping lumps of calcium carbide in water.   The gas bubbles up through the water, and the remainder of the calcium carbide is converted into slaked lime. The reaction that takes place in an acetylene generator is

$$CaC_2 + 2H_2O = Ca(OH)_2 + C_2H_2$$

Calcium carbide   Water   Slaked lime   Acetylene gas .

The calcium carbide used for making this gas is a hard gray stonelike material formed by smelting calcium with coal in an electric furnace. This material is crushed, sized, and stored in air-tight steel drums before its use. Acetylene gas can be either obtained from acetylene generators, which generate the gas by mixing the carbide with the water, or purchased in cylinders ready for use. Because this gas may not be safely stored at pressure much over 15 pounds per square inch, it is stored in combination with acetone. Acetylene cylinders are filled with a porous filler saturated with acetone in which the acetylene gas can be compressed. These cylinders hold 300 cubic feet of gas at pressures up to 250 pounds per square inch.

A cross section of a typical welding torch is shown in Figure 14A. It consists of a series of brass tubes through which and into which the gases are conducted and finally mixed, valves for controlling the volumes of acetylene and oxygen, and a copper tip from which the gas mixture is burned. Regulation of the proportion of the two gases is of extreme importance, as the characteristics of the flame may be varied.

Three types of flame that can be obtained are *reducing, neutral,* and *oxidizing.* Of the three, the neutral flame has the widest application in welding and cutting operations. This flame occurs with approximately a one-to-one mixture of oxygen and acetylene. There are two sharply defined zones, an inner luminous cone surrounded by an outer envelope flame which is only faintly luminous and slightly bluish in color. The maximum temperature of 6300 F is obtained at the tip of the inner luminous cone.

When there is an excess of acetylene used, there is a decided change in the appearance of the flame. In this flame there will be found three zones instead of the two just described. Between the luminous cone and the outer envelope there is an intermediate cone of whitish color, the length of which is determined by the amount of the excess acetylene. This flame, known as a reducing or carbonizing flame, is used in the welding of Monel metal, nickel, certain alloy steels, and many of the nonferrous, hard-surfacing materials, such as Stellite and Colmanoy.

If the torch is adjusted to give excess oxygen, a flame similar in appearance to the neutral flame is obtained, except that the inner luminous cone is much shorter, and the outer envelope appears to have more color. This, the oxidizing flame, may be used in fusion welding of brass and bronze, but it is undesirable in other applications.

The advantages and uses of oxyacetylene welding are numerous. The equipment necessary for welding is comparatively inexpensive and requires little maintenance. It is portable and can be used with equal facility out in the field and in the factory. With proper technique practically all metals may be welded. There is also the added advantage that the equipment can be used for cutting as well as welding. The process is especially adapted to the welding of sheet metal, to flame hardening, and to the application of many hard-facing materials.

Oxyhydrogen welding. Since oxyhydrogen burns at a much lower temperature (3600 F) than oxygen and acetylene, it is used primarily for welding thin sheets and low-melting alloys and in some brazing work. The same equipment can be used for both processes; however, flame adjustments are more difficult in hydrogen welding, as there is no distinguishing color to judge the gas proportions. A reducing atmosphere is recommended, and the process is characterized by the absence of oxides formed on the surface of the weld. The quality of these welds is equal to that obtained by other processes.

Air–acetylene welding. The torch used in this process is similar in construction to a Bunsen burner—air is drawn into the torch as required for proper combustion. Since the temperature attained is lower than those attained by other gas processes, this type of welding has limited use. Principal applications of the process include lead welding and low-temperature brazing or soldering operations.

Pressure gas welding. In pressure gas welding, welds are produced by heating abutting areas of parts to be joined with oxyacetylene flames to a welding temperature (around 2200 F), followed by the application of pressure. It is a butt-welding process and similar to the resistance method except that heat is applied by a gas flame instead of by electrical resistance. Two methods are in common use. In the first, known as the closed-joint method, the surfaces to be joined are held together under pressure during the heating period. Multiflame water-cooled torches, designed to go completely around the joint, are used in this operation. During the heating operation the torches are oscillated slightly back and forth to eliminate excessive local heating. As the heating progresses, the ends, which are prepared with a slight bevel, close up, and, when the correct temperature is reached, an additional upsetting pressure is applied. For low-carbon steel the initial pressure is below 1500 pounds per square inch and the upsetting

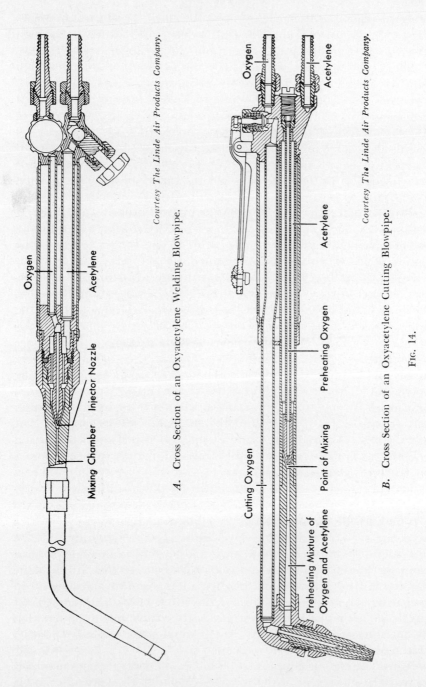

Oxygen

Acetylene

Mixing Chamber   Injector Nozzle

Courtesy The Linde Air Products Company.

A. Cross Section of an Oxyacetylene Welding Blowpipe.

Oxygen

Acetylene

Acetylene

Preheating Oxygen

Point of Mixing

Cutting Oxygen

Preheating Mixture of
Oxygen and Acetylene

Courtesy The Linde Air Products Company.

B. Cross Section of an Oxyacetylene Cutting Blowpipe.

Fig. 14.

pressure around 4000 pounds per square inch. Pressures, however, vary with the material and for high-carbon steel and many alloys a constant pressure is applied throughout the entire welding cycle.

The second or open-joint method employs a flat multiflame torch which is placed between the two surfaces to be joined. This torch uniformly heats these surfaces until there is a film of molten metal over each of them. The torch is then quickly withdrawn and the two surfaces are forced together and held under pressure (around 4000 pounds per square inch) until solidification takes place. The appearance of this joint is similar to that obtained by flash welding, whereas the closed-joint method produces a joint with a bulging appearance.

This process is successfully used in the welding of rods, tubes, railroad rails, and pipe lines. Dissimilar metals can be joined, such as high-speed steel to carbon shanks in the manufacture of certain tools. No filler metal is used, and the quality of the weld is determined by the properties of the metal being joined.

Oxyacetylene torch cutting. The cutting of steel with a flame-cutting torch has developed into a very important production process. A simple hand torch for flame cutting is shown in Figure 14*B*. It differs from the welding torch in that it has several small holes for preheating flames surrounding a central hole through which pure oxygen passes. The preheating flames are exactly like the welding flames and are intended only to preheat the steel before the cutting operation. The principle on which flame cutting operates is that oxygen has an affinity for iron and steel. At ordinary temperatures this action is slow, but eventually an oxide in the form of rust materializes. As the temperature of the steel is increased, this action becomes much more rapid. If the steel is heated to a red color and a jet of pure oxygen is blown on the surface, the action is almost instantaneous, and the steel is actually burned into an iron oxide slag-like appearance. About 1.3 cubic feet of oxygen is required to burn up 1 cubic inch of iron. This action is illustrated in Figure 15 where a square steel billet is being cut with a portable machine. In the operation shown, the blowpipe starts and finishes at an angle, while a constant clearance is maintained at all times between the cutting nozzle and the billet. A similar cutting operation is shown in Figure 16 in preparing plate edges for welding fabrication. Cuts in several planes can be made simultaneously, with accuracy comparable to preparation by machine tools, but at less cost. Metal plates up to 30 inches thickness can be cut by this process.

Many cutting machines have been developed that automatically control the movement of the torch to cut any desired shape. Such a machine is shown in Figure 17 cutting four parts simultaneously. Motion is transferred from the tracing unit to the blowpipe by means of two carriages. The lower carriage runs on rails along the edges of the tracing table, while the upper carriage moves on rails above the

Courtesy The Linde Air Products Company.

FIG. 15. Cutting a Square Billet with a Portable Bar-Cutting Machine.

lower carriage and provides the transverse movement. Electrically driven, the drive unit automatically controls the movement of the machine at a proper cutting speed in accordance with the template shape. Another example of multiple cutting is shown in Figure 18 where four tank sprockets are cut simultaneously. This machine operates on the pantograph principle so that one or several cutting torches are made to conform exactly to the movement of the tracing device. The latter may be a hand guide, or a spindle roller which is held against the templet by the operator.

Most cutting torches use acetylene in combination with oxygen to provide the necessary flame for preheating. This is not essential, however, as hydrogen, natural gas, or propane can be used if desired.

Hydrogen gas is recommended for underwater cutting, while the others are often used because of lower cost.

Many parts that previously required shaping by forging or casting are now cut to shape by this process. Flame-cutting machines, replacing many machining operations where accuracy is not paramount, are widely used in the shipbuilding industry, structural fabrication,

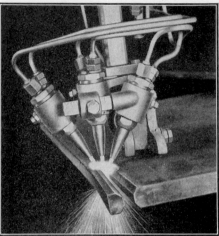

Courtesy The Linde Air Products Company.

FIG. 16. Preparing Plate Edges for Subsequent Welded Fabrication.

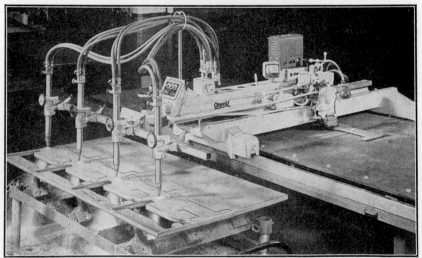

Courtesy The Linde Air Products Company.

FIG. 17. Shape-Cutting Machine Cutting Four Parts Simultaneously.

maintenance work, and the production of numerous items made from steel sheets and plates. Cast iron, nonferrous alloys, and high-manganese alloys are not readily cut by this process.

Courtesy Air Reduction Sales Company.

FIG. 18. Multiple Cutting of Tank Sprockets.

Flame machining.* Flame machining is the term used to describe the operation of removing metal with a cutting blowpipe. It differs from ordinary flame cutting in that it does not sever the main body of metal but merely removes metal as is done in machining operations. The torch is held at a small angle to the work surface and, as it progresses, cuts out a groove instead of penetrating. The process is rapid and requires no power, and the work setup need not be rigid. On the other hand, the surface finish is not good and close dimensional accuracy cannot be attained. However, for many rough machining

* E. L. Cady, "Flame Cutting and Machining Methods," *Metals & Alloys,* May 1945.

operations involving the removal of a large amount of metal, this method of cutting should be considered.

Arc Welding

Arc welding is a welding process in which coalescence is obtained by heat produced from an electric arc between the work and an electrode. The electrode or filler metal is heated to a liquid state and deposited into the joint to make the weld. Contact is first made between the electrode and the work to create an electric circuit, and then, by separating the conductors, an arc is formed. The electric energy is converted into intense heat in the arc, which attains a temperature of over 7000 F.

Either direct current or alternating current may be used for arc welding, direct current being preferred for most purposes. A d-c welder (see Figure 19) is simply a motor-generator set of constant-energy type (constant potential may also be used), having the necessary characteristics to produce a stable arc. There should not be too great a current surge when the short circuit is made, and the machine should compensate to some extent for varying lengths of the arc. D-c machines are built in capacities up to 600 amperes having an open-circuit voltage of 40 to 95 volts. A 200-ampere machine has a rated current range of 40 to 250 amperes, according to the standard of the National Electrical Manufacturers Association. While welding is going on, the closed-circuit voltage is 18 to 25 volts. In *straight polarity* the electrode is the negative terminal, whereas in *reverse polarity* the electrode is the positive terminal.

Carbon-electrode welding. The first methods of arc welding employed only carbon electrodes; however, this type of welding is still in use to some extent for both manual and machine operation. The carbon arc is used only as a source of heat, and the torch is handled in a fashion similar to the way it is in gas welding. Filler rods supply weld metal if additional metal is necessary. The twin-carbon-arc method was one of the first used, the arc being between the two electrodes and not with the work. In operation the arc is held ¼ to ⅜ inch above the work, and best results are obtained with the work in a flat position. The use of this method is limited to brazing and soldering.

A second process, utilizing a single carbon electrode of negative polarity, is considerably simpler. In this case the arc is created between the carbon electrode and the work, and any weld metal needed is supplied by a separate rod. Such an arc is easy to start, as there is no tendency for the electrode to stick to the metal. Straight polarity

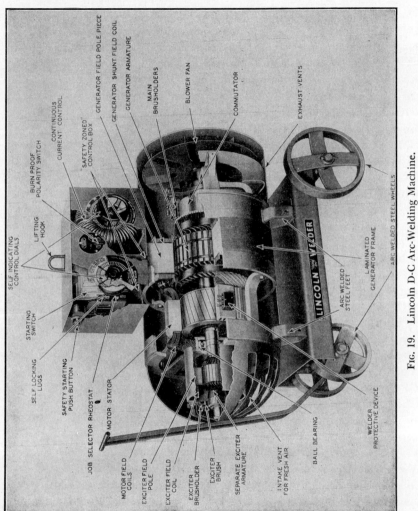

FIG. 19.   Lincoln D-C Arc-Welding Machine.

must always be used, as a carbon arc is unstable when held on the positive terminal.

Most carbon-arc welding of this type is done with the use of automatic welding equipment where the arc voltage and current, rate of travel, and rate of feeding the filler rod are all properly controlled. Since a carbon arc is easily affected by magnetic fields, a separate magnetic field is built into the electrode holder to stabilize the arc and control its direction. Protection of the metal can be obtained by introducing either inert gases or slag-forming fluxes into the arc. Carbon-arc welding is used for welding cast iron, steel, copper, bronze, galvanized iron, and aluminum. It may also be used effectively for rough cutting of metals.

Metal-electrode welding.   Shortly after the development of carbon-electrode welding, it was discovered that, by the use of a metal electrode with the proper current characteristics, the electrode itself could be melted down to supply the necessary weld metal. A basic patent for this process was issued to Charles Coffin in 1889, and it is this process that is in general use today. In actual operation, an arc is started by striking the work with an electrode and quickly withdrawing it a short distance. As the electrode end is melted by the intense heat, most of it is transferred across the arc in the form of small globules to a molten pool. A small amount is lost by being vaporized, and some globules are deposited alongside of the weld as spatter. The arc is maintained by uniformly moving the electrode toward the work at a rate that compensates for that portion of it which has been melted and transferred to the weld. At the same time the electrode is gradually moved along the joint being welded.

For ordinary welding there is little difference in the quality of the welds made by a-c and d-c equipment. The a-c machines consist principally of static transformers which are simple pieces of equipment having no moving parts. Their efficiency is high, their loss at no load is negligible, and their maintenance and initial costs are low. Welders of this type are built in six sizes specified by NEMA, and are rated at 150, 200, 300, 500, 750, and 1000 amperes. For welding requiring 750 amperes or higher, a-c equipment is preferred. The fact that there is less magnetic flare of the arc or "arc blow" with a-c than with the d-c equipment is important in the welding of heavy plates or fillet welding. For jobs requiring medium- or small-amperage current loads the a-c equipment is limited by the type of electrodes required. Most of the nonferrous metals and many of the alloys cannot be welded with a-c equipment, because electrodes have not been developed for this purpose.

If we compare a-c and d-c welders, the welding speed, the quality
of the welds, and the ease in welding are the same. However, d-c
machines are still to be preferred, as this type of machine permits the
selection of the proper polarity for the welding electrode. Because
the alternating current is continually reversing with every cycle, the
correct polarity is being used only half the time. This eliminates

Courtesy General Electric Company.

FIG. 20.   Arc-Welding Travel Carriage with Welding Head and Control Mounted.

the successful use of carbon electrodes and many of the metal electrodes.
Also, a-c welders operate at slightly higher voltages, and hence the
danger of shock to the operator is increased.   In spite of these limitations, there is a growing demand for the a-c type of welder in
fabrication and maintenance shops, sheet-metal work, and jobbing
machine shops.
   Much metal electrode welding is now being done by machine or
automatic units.   Such welding is essentially the same as manual
welding, except that machine units are supplied with controls that feed
the wire as it is consumed and move either the welding head or work
along at a proper welding rate.   The rate of feed is controlled by the
voltage of the arc, which varies as its length changes.   Automatic
welding heads are available for both bare and coated electrodes.

Prerequisites* for economic machine welding are (1) a sufficient volume of production to justify expensive equipment and (2) a uniform product. Assemblies must fit together readily, and each piece must be of the same size and similar in contour. Often jigs and handling devices are necessary to position the work. If these conditions are fulfilled, machine welding will be economical. The use of automatic-welding machines results in increased welding speed and uniform quality of the weld. In addition, the operator is relieved of tedious work, since he does not have to maintain the proper arc length and travel speed.

A thyratron-controlled automatic arc-welding unit is illustrated in Figure 20. Either alternating or direct current, up to 600 amperes, can be used as the source of power for this unit. When welding is going on, the coiled-wire electrode is fed by means of rollers which are controlled to keep the arc voltage at its preset value. Automatic units of this general type are widely used in production welding of both straight and circumferential seams.

Electrodes. The three types of metal electrodes (or "rods") are *bare, fluxed,* and *heavy coated.* Bare electrodes have a limited use for the welding of wrought iron and mild steel. Straight polarity is generally recommended. Improved welds may be made by applying

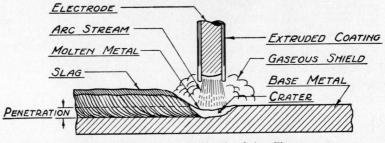

Fig. 21. Diagrammatic Sketch of Arc Flame.

a light coating of flux on the rods by a dusting or washing process. The flux assists both in eliminating undesirable oxides and in preventing their formation. However, the heavily coated arc electrodes are by far the most important ones used in all types of commercial welding. Over 95% of the total manual welding that is being done today is with coated electrodes.

Figure 21 is a diagrammatic sketch showing the action of an arc using a heavy-coated electrode. In the ordinary arc with bare wire

*R. F. Wyer, "Progress in Automatic Arc Welding," *Machinery,* November–December 1944.

the metal is affected to some extent by the oxygen and nitrogen in the air. This causes oxides and nitrides to be formed in the weld metal, both of which are undesirable. The effect of heavy coatings on electrodes is to provide a gas shield around the arc to eliminate such conditions and also to cover the weld metal with a protective slag coating which prevents oxidation of the surface metal during cooling. Welds made from rods of this type have superior physical characteristics. Manufacturers' recommendations should always be followed in the selection of an electrode for a given job.

Electrode coatings. Electrodes coated with slagging or fluxing materials are particularly necessary in the welding of alloys and nonferrous metals. Some of the elements in these alloys are not very stable and are lost if there is no protection against oxidation. Heavy coatings also permit the use of larger welding rods, higher current, and greater welding speeds. In summary, the coatings do the following things:

1. Provide a protecting atmosphere.
2. Provide slag of suitable characteristics to protect the molten metal.
3. Facilitate overhead and position welding.
4. Stabilize the arc.
5. Add alloying elements to the weld metal.
6. Perform metallurgical refining operations.
7. Reduce spatter of weld metal.
8. Increase deposition efficiency.
9. Remove oxides and impurities.
10. Influence the depth of arc penetration.
11. Influence the shape of the bead.
12. Slow down the cooling rate of the weld.

These functions are not common to all coated electrodes, since the coating put on a given electrode is largely determined by the kind of welding it has to perform. It is interesting to note that the coating composition is also a determining factor in electrode polarity. By varying the coating, rods may be used with either the positive or the negative terminal or may work equally well either positive or negative. Properly coated electrodes make possible a weld metal having physical properties equal with the base metal.

Many coating compositions have been developed to accomplish these results. In general, they may be classified as organic and inorganic coatings, although in some cases both types might be used. Inorganic coatings can be further subdivided into flux compounds

and slag-forming compounds.   These are some of the principal constituents used:

1. Slag-forming constituents: SiO_2, MnO_2, and FeO. Al_2O_3 is
   sometimes used, but it makes the arc less stable.
2. Constituents to improve arc characteristics: Na_2O, CaO, MgO,
   and TiO_2.
3. Deoxidizing constituents: graphite and wood flour.
4. Binding material: sodium silicate and asbestos.
5. Alloying constituents to improve strength of weld: V, U, Ce, Co,
   Mo, Al, and Zr.

Impregnated-tape metal-arc welding.   This form of welding utilizes
a tape impregnated with materials that have a shielding effect on the
arc when they are consumed, similar to the results obtained from
using a heavy-coated electrode.   This procedure is used only in automatic machine welding, in which case the tape is wrapped around
the bare wire just ahead of the arc.   Excellent welds are made in this
fashion and are of a quality equal to those obtained when a heavy-
coated rod is used.

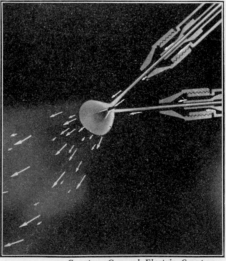

Courtesy General Electric Company.

FIG. 22.   Atomic-Hydrogen Welding Arc Drawn to Show Flow of Gas and Heat.
Electrode Holder Shown in Longitudinal Section.

Atomic-hydrogen arc welding.   In this process a single-phase a-c
arc is maintained between two tungsten electrodes, and hydrogen is
introduced into the arc as shown in Figure 22.   As the hydrogen enters

the arc, the molecules are broken up into atoms which recombine into molecules of hydrogen outside the arc. This reaction is accompanied by the liberation of an intense heat, attaining a temperature of about 11,000 F. Weld metal may be added to the joint in the form of welding rod, the operation being very similar to the oxyacetylene process. The atomic-hydrogen process differs from other arc-welding processes in that the arc is formed between two electrodes rather than

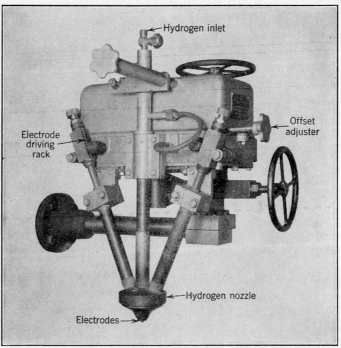

Courtesy General Electric Company.

FIG. 23. Automatic Atomic-Hydrogen Arc-Welding Head.

between one electrode and the work. This makes the electrode a rather mobile tool, as it can be moved from place to place without being extinguished.

Automatic atomic-hydrogen welding units, as shown in Figure 23, are used on production jobs that do not require the addition of filler rod. A thyratron panel provides control of the arc, thus regulating the heat output and length of arc that burns between the two tungsten electrodes. Provision is also made to offset the electrodes so that the flat fan-shaped arc is in line with the seam being welded. Automatic welding is rapid and particularly useful for applications having long straight or circumferential seams.

The outstanding advantage of this process over others is its ability to provide high heat concentrations. In addition, the hydrogen also acts as a shield and protects the electrodes and molten metal from oxidation. Metal of the same analysis as the metal being welded can be used with both manual and automatic equipment, and many alloys, difficult to weld by other processes, can be successfully treated. The welds are clean, smooth, and free from scale, and they respond to heat treatment in the same way as the parent metal when weld metal of the same composition is used. The process has wide use in die repair; it successfully welds heat-resisting alloys; it has proved to be an excellent means of applying carbides and many other hard-surfacing alloys; and it is widely used in production work where special ferrous and nonferrous alloys are used.

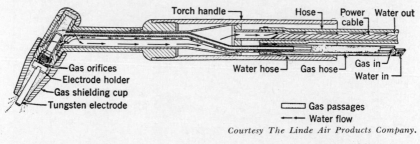

Courtesy The Linde Air Products Company.

Fig. 24. Hand-Welding Torch for Inert-Gas-Shielded Arc Welding.

Inert-gas-shielded arc welding. In this process, coalescence is produced by heat from an arc between a metal electrode and the work which is shielded by an atmosphere of either argon or helium. Two methods of welding are employed: one using a tungsten electrode with filler metal added as in gas welding, and the other using consumable metal wire as the electrode. Both methods are adaptable to either manual or automatic machine welding, and no flux or wire coating is required for protection of the weld.

A hand torch using a tungsten electrode is shown in Figure 24. This torch is water-cooled and constructed with a gas nozzle surrounding the tungsten electrode so that the gas, as it leaves the nozzle, completely envelops the tip of the electrode and the work beneath it. Either alternating or direct current can be used, the selection being determined by the kind of metal to be welded. Direct current with straight polarity is required for welding copper alloys and stainless steel, whereas reverse polarity is used for magnesium. Alternating current is more versatile in its application and is used for steel, cast iron, and aluminum, as well as those metals mentioned above.

The process using a consumable metal electrode is quite recent and differs considerably in operation from the previous method. Figure 25 shows the equipment required for manual welding which includes the welding gun and carriage containing the wire reel, feed motor, and control. In addition, a d-c generator is used as a source of current supply. Bare wire is fed through the gun at a rate controlled by the arc voltage and is consumed in the same fashion as electrodes in

Courtesy Air Reduction Company.

FIG. 25. Equipment for Manual Operation of Inert-Gas-Shielded Metal Arc-Welding Unit Consisting of Gun and Carriage Assembly.

ordinary arc welding. A high-density current is supplied permitting wire feeds of 100 to 300 inches per minute. This process has the characteristic of an automatic process and can be used manually in all welding positions. It is especially adapted for welding aluminum alloys, but most other metals can be welded by it as well.

An interesting application of inert-gas arc welding is the making of spot welds by an argon-shielded electric arc using a tungsten electrode. To effect a weld, a special welding gun with pistol grip is held tightly against the work to be welded. As the trigger is released, the argon valve is opened, and the current is allowed to pass through the electrode for a preset interval (1 to 2 sec), and then both are shut off. The main advantage of this equipment is its ability to make spot welds on thin sheets from one side of the work only. It is also useful in spot welding large or irregular-shaped assemblies that are difficult to spot-weld with resistance equipment.

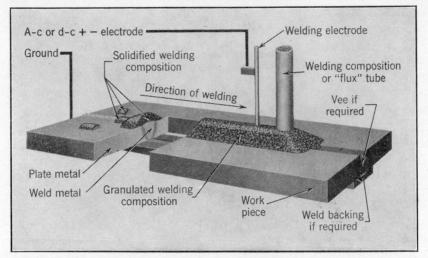

Submerged-Arc Welding.

Courtesy The Linde Air Products Company.

A Single-Vee Weld Made by This Process.

FIG. 26.

Submerged-arc welding. This process is so named because the metal arc is shielded by a blanket of granular fusible flux during the welding operation. Aside from this feature, its operation is quite similar to other automatic arc-welding methods. In operation, a bare electrode is fed through the welding head into the granular material, as shown in Figure 26. This material is laid down along the seam to be welded, and the entire welding action takes place beneath it. The arc is started either by striking beneath the flux on the work or by initially placing some conductive medium such as steel wool beneath the electrode. The intense heat of the arc immediately produces a pool of molten metal in the joint and at the same time melts a portion of the granular flux. This material floats on top of the molten metal forming a blanket which eliminates spatter losses and protects the welded joint from oxidation. Upon cooling, the fused slag solidifies and is easily removed—granular material not fused is recycled and used again.

This process is limited to flat welding although welds can be made on a slight slope or on circumferential joints. It is advisable to use a backing strip of steel, copper, or some refractory material on the joint to avoid losing some of the molten metal. The process uses high currents, 300 to 4000 amperes, which permits high rates of metal transfer and welding speeds. Deep penetration is obtained, and most commercial thicknesses of plate metal can be welded with one pass. As a result, thin plates can be welded without any preparation, whereas only a small vee is required on most others. Most submerged-arc welding is done on low-carbon and alloy steels, but it may also be used on many of the nonferrous metals.

Stud arc welding. Stud welding is a d-c arc-welding process developed to end-weld metal studs to flat surfaces. It is accomplished with a pistol-shaped welding gun which holds the stud or fastener to be welded. When the trigger of the gun is pressed, the stud is lifted to create an arc and then forced against the molten pool by a backing spring. The entire operation is controlled by a timer which is preset according to the size of the stud being welded. Shielding of the arc is usually accomplished by surrounding it with a ceramic ferrule. This ferrule also confines the metal to the weld area and protects the operator from the arc. Stud welding has much use in ship construction as well as in many industrial applications involving the use of metal fasteners.

Thermit Welding

Thermit welding is the only welding process employing an exothermal chemical reaction for the purpose of developing a high temperature and is based on the fact that aluminum has a great affinity for oxygen and can be used as a reducing agent for many oxides. The

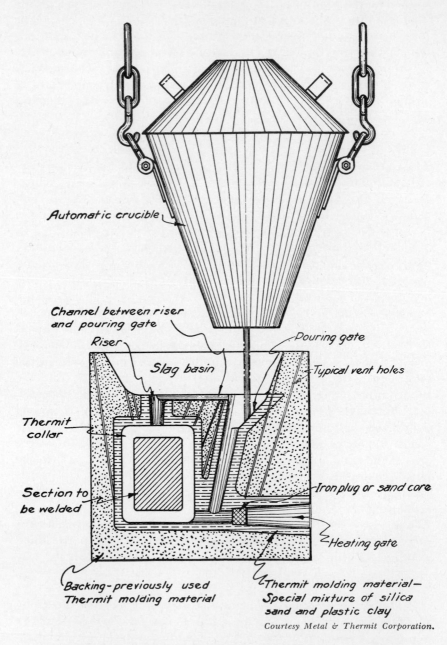

Automatic crucible

Channel between riser
and pouring gate

Riser

Pouring gate

Slag basin

Typical vent holes

Thermit
collar

Section to
be welded

Iron plug or sand core

Heating gate

Backing-previously used
Thermit molding material

Thermit molding material—
Special mixture of silica
sand and plastic clay

Courtesy Metal & Thermit Corporation.

FIG. 27.   Line Drawing of Mold and Crucible for a Thermit Weld.

usual Thermit mixture or compound consists of finely divided aluminum and iron oxide, mixed at a ratio of about 1 to 3 by weight. The iron oxide is usually in the form of roll mill scale. This mixture is not explosive and can be ignited only at a temperature of about 2800 F. A special ignition powder is used to start the reaction. The chemical reaction requires only about 30 seconds and attains a temperature of around 4500 F. The mixture reacts according to the chemical equation:

$$8Al + 3Fe_3O_4 = 9Fe + 4Al_2O_3$$

The resultant products are a highly purified iron (actually steel) and an aluminum oxide slag, which floats on top and is not used. Other reactions also take place, as most Thermit metal is alloyed with manganese, nickel, or other elements.

Figure 27 illustrates the method of preparing the material for such a weld. Around the break where the weld is to be made, a wax pattern of the weld is built up. Refractory sand is packed around the joint, and necessary provision is made for riser and gates. A preheating flame is used to melt and burn out the wax, to dry the mold, and to bring the joints to a red heat. The reaction is then started in the crucible, and, when it is complete, the metal is tapped and allowed to flow into the mold. As the weld-metal temperature is approximately twice the melting temperature of steel, it readily fuses in the joint. Such welds are sound, because the metal solidifies from the inside toward the outside, and all air is excluded from around the mold.

In Thermit pressure welds, the ends of joints to be welded are pressed tightly together, and a mold is built around a joint. After the reaction starts, the slag is poured in first to form a glasslike surface around the joint, and then the superheated metal is added. When the heat from the slag and metal bring the joint up to welding temperature, the weld is made by pressure, similar to the procedure followed in resistance butt welding.

There is no limit to the size of welds that can be made by Thermit welding. It is used primarily for the repairs of large parts which would be difficult or uneconomical to weld by other processes.

Cold-Pressure Welding

Cold-pressure welding is a method of joining nonferrous metals by applying pressure and causing the metals to flow in a manner necessary to produce a weld. The type of bond obtained is shown by the micrograph in Figure 28. Before a weld is made, the surfaces or parts to be joined must be wire-brushed thoroughly at a surface speed of around

3000 feet per minute.   This removes oxide films on the surface which
must be eliminated before a weld can be made.   Other methods of
cleaning seem to be unsatisfactory.   In making a weld, the pressure
is applied over a narrow strip so that the metal can flow away from the
weld on both sides.   It may be applied either by impact or with a

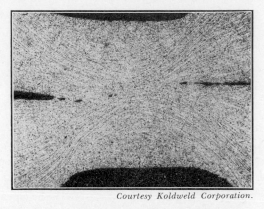

Courtesy Koldweld Corporation.

FIG. 28.   A Micro Section of an Aluminum Cold Weld, Showing Lines of Flow.

slow squeezing action, both methods being equally effective.   Pressure
required for aluminum ranges from 25,000 to 35,000 pounds per square
inch.   Spot welds are rectangular in shape and in terms of gage thickness are approximately $t \times 5t$ in size.   In addition, both ring welds
and continuous seam welds can be made.   The greatest success of this
method of welding has been with aluminum and copper; however,
lead, nickel, zinc, and Monel can also be joined by this method.

Brazing and Soldering

The processes of brazing and soldering, which unite metals by means
of a different metal, are shown in Table 5.   In these processes, joints

TABLE 5.   BRAZING AND SOLDERING

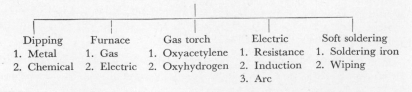

Dipping	Furnace	Gas torch	Electric	Soft soldering
1. Metal	1. Gas	1. Oxyacetylene	1. Resistance	1. Soldering iron
2. Chemical	2. Electric	2. Oxyhydrogen	2. Induction	2. Wiping
			3. Arc	

are made without pressure, the joining metal merely being introduced
into the joint in a liquid state and allowed to solidify.   Both these

processes have wide commercial use in the uniting of small assemblies and electrical parts.

Brazing. In the process of brazing, a nonferrous alloy is introduced in a liquid state, between the pieces of metal to be joined, and allowed to solidify. The filler metal has a melting temperature of over 800 F, but lower than the melting temperature of the parent metal, and is distributed between the surfaces by capillary attraction. Braze welding is similar to ordinary brazing except that the filler metal is not distributed by capillary attraction. In both cases special fluxes are required to remove surface oxide and to give to the filler metal the fluidity necessary to wet the joint surfaces completely. The brazing metals and alloys commonly used are as follows:

1. Copper: melting point 1982 F.
2. Copper alloys: brass and bronze alloys having melting points ranging from 1600 F to 2250 F.
3. Silver alloys: melting temperatures ranging from 1165 to 1550 F.*
4. Aluminum alloys: melting temperatures ranging from 1025 F to 1785 F.†

In the brazing of two pieces of metal, the joint must first be cleaned of all oil, dirt, or oxides, and the pieces properly fitted together with appropriate clearance for the filler metal. Mechanical or chemical cleaning may be necessary in the joint preparation in addition to the flux used during the process. Borax, either alone or in combination with other salts, is commonly used as a flux.

According to Table 5 there are four methods used in heating the metal to complete a joint. They are:

1. *Dipping* the assembled parts in a bath of filler metal or flux. When dipped in a flux bath, which is held at a temperature sufficient to melt the filler metal, the assembly must be held together securely in a jig and the joint preloaded with the brazing alloy.

2. In *furnace brazing* the assemblies are held in position by jigs and are introduced into a controlled-atmosphere furnace maintained at the proper temperature to melt the brazing metal. These furnaces can be either gas- or electric-heated, and of the batch or continuous type.

3. *Torch brazing* is similar to oxyacetylene welding. Heat is applied locally by an oxyacetylene or oxyhydrogen torch, and the filler

* *Metals Handbook,* American Society for Metals, 1948, p. 80.

† *Welding and Brazing of Alcoa Aluminum,* Aluminum Company of America, p. 99.

metal, in wire form, is melted into the joint. Flux is applied by immersing the wire.

4. In *electric brazing* the heat may be applied by resistance, by induction, or by an arc. Of these methods, the first two are most often used because of their speed and accurate temperature control.

To facilitate speed in brazing, the filler metal is frequently prepared in the form of rings, washers, rods, or other special shapes, to fit the joint being brazed. This insures having the proper amount of filler metal available for the joint as well as having it placed in the correct position.

Joints in brazing may be of the lap, butt, sleeve, or scarf types, or of various shapes obtained by curling, upsetting, or seaming processes. The strength of the joint* is determined principally by the strength of the brazing material used, although other influencing factors are strength of the parent metal, amount of clearance, cleanness of the joint, and method of heating and cooling.

Advantages of the brazing process include its ability to effect joints in materials difficult to weld, in dissimilar metals, and in exceedingly thin sections of metal. In addition, the process is rapid and results in a neat-appearing joint requiring a minimum of finishing. Brazing is used for the fastening of pipes and fittings, tanks, carbide tips on tools, radiators, heat exchangers, electrical parts, and the repair of castings.

Soldering. Soldering differs from brazing in that lower-temperature filler metals (below 800 F) are used in the joint. Lead and tin alloys having a melting range of 300 to 700 F are principally used in soldering, and the strength of the joint is determined by the adhesive qualities and the strength of these alloys. Although any heating method used in brazing can be employed in this process, much soldering is done with the common soldering iron which is especially suitable for small parts and light-gage metal. Heat is supplied by the iron, and solder is fed to the joint in the form of wire. Cleaning of the joint surface is equally as important in soldering as in brazing, and a flux is necessary. Electric connections, wire terminals, and similar small parts are typical of the joints made by soft soldering. A form of soldering known as *wiping* is used in making connections of lead pipe.

Hard Surfacing

Hard surfacing is applying to a wearing surface some metal or treatment that renders the surface highly resistant to abrasion. Such processes vary a great deal in their technique. Some apply a hard

* *Materials and Processes*, edited by J. F. Young, John Wiley & Sons, 1944, p. 438.

surface coating by fusion welding; in others no material is added, and the surface metal is changed by heat treatment or by contact with other materials. With the development of the processes, many new hard-surfacing materials were discovered. The research for these hard materials has been especially keen during recent years, owing to the great demand of industry for longer-life products.

The several properties required of materials subjected to severe wearing conditions are hardness, abrasion resistance, and impact resistance. Hardness is easily determined by several known methods, and an accurate comparison of metals for this property can be obtained readily. Tests for wear or abrasion resistance have not been standardized, and it is difficult to obtain comparative results. In general, experience has shown that, to obtain proper results, wear testing must simulate the service conditions for each type of hard-facing material. The statement that "the wear resistance of a material is a function of the method by which it is measured" has been confirmed by both practical experience and research. If we consider all the factors involved, hardness is probably the best criterion of wear resistance. Ability to withstand wear and abrasion usually increases as the hardness of the metal increases.

Table 6 is a classification of the various processes used for obtaining a hard surface. Obviously, there is a great difference in the hardness that can be obtained from these methods. The classification does not include heat-treating methods which produce a hard interior surface.

Where thick coatings of hard materials are required, it is necessary to use some form of welding. The hard-facing materials used as electrodes or filler rods are classified roughly as "overlay" and "diamond-substitute" types. The overlay materials include such metals as high-carbon steel, ferrous alloys of chromium and manganese, and numerous nonferrous alloys containing principally cobalt, manganese, and tungsten. The hardness of these materials varies considerably, ranging from around Rockwell C40 to 70. According to the Mohs scale, the hardness seldom exceeds 8. The "diamond substitutes" are such materials as tungsten, boron, tantalum carbides, and chromium boride. These materials are among the hardest available and on the Mohs scale fall between 8.5 and 9.5. They cannot be applied by self-fusion but must be bonded to the parent metal with some lower-melting alloy.

High-carbon welding rod with a carbon content ranging from 0.9 to 1.1% is the most economical hard-facing material to apply from the standpoint of initial cost. Such rods form a tough surface of moderate hardness, ranging from Rockwell C30 to 45. Hardest surfaces are obtained by rapid quenching; and, as with all martensitic deposits, not much additional hardness can be obtained by cold working. Their corrosion resistance is poor, but such coatings have a wide application where wear resistance is desired.

TABLE 6. METHODS OF PRODUCING HARD SURFACES

I. Heat treatment
  A. Carburizing—heating in contact
    1. With solids as charcoal.
    2. With liquids as KCN.
    3. With gases as CO.
  B. Special case-hardening processes
    1. Nitriding—contact with NH_3 gas.
    2. Chapmanizing—contact with liquid containing N and C.
    3. Dry cyaniding—contact with gases.
    4. Ni-carbing—contact with gases.
  C. Induction hardening—electric heating and rapid quenching.
  D. Flame hardening—heating with torch and rapid quenching.

II. Metal spraying—applying with air pressure
  A. High-carbon steel.
  B. Stainless steel.
  C. Other alloys.

III. Metal plating—electrolytic deposit of chromium and other hard elements.

IV. Fusion welding processes
  A. Overlay process—welding with
    1. Ferrous alloys
      (a) High-carbon steel.
      (b) Steel alloys.
    2. Nonferrous alloys
      (a) Chiefly of chromium, cobalt, molybdenum, and tungsten.
  B. Diamond substitutes
    1. Cemented, cast, or sintered carbides of tungsten and other elements
      (a) Inserts.
      (b) Screen sizes in tubes.
      (c) Screen sizes and binder cast into rods.
      (d) Screen sizes loose or with gelatin binder.
      (e) "Sweat-on"—paste containing very fine hard particles.
  C. Casting or spinning process—chiefly nickel borides.

Increased hardness and wear resistance can be obtained by alloying steel with such elements as nickel, manganese, molybdenum, and chromium. The limit of hardness for such coatings is around Rockwell C55, and, since many of the alloys result in austenitic deposits, their hardness can be increased by cold working. Corrosion resistance of most of these materials is good, as well as their resistance to impact, and no heat treatment is required after application.

In the nonferrous group are included all rods that are made up of elements other than iron, but in some cases small percentages of iron may be present. The principal elements in this group are tungsten, chromium, molybdenum, and cobalt. The average room-temperature hardness of this group is about the same as that of the ferrous-alloy group. A high percentage of this hardness is retained while the rods are at red heat, which adds greatly to their wear-resisting power. In severe abrasive work considerable heat is developed by friction, which acts on the minute areas of particles in contact. The effect of this heat is to soften the metal on these areas and cause them to wear away. However, if the metal in contact can retain a hardness at a relatively high temperature, it has a much greater resistance to wear than metals that do not have this property. In such cases the initial hardness is not a true criterion of the wear-resisting ability of the metal.

Both the electric-arc and oxyacetylene processes can be used in applying this material, the latter process being preferred. Better control of the deposit is obtained, and there is less dilution of the rod with the parent metal. There is also no loss of the expensive rod material by volatilization and spattering. Practically any carbon or alloy steel can be hard-surfaced with this material, and it is especially adapted for coating surfaces subject to severe abrasion and impact, such as valve seats and oil-drilling tools.

The so-called diamond substitutes constitute the hardest materials that are available for hard surfacing. These materials, generally spoken of as cemented carbides, include tungsten carbide, tantalum carbide, titanium carbide, boron carbide, and chromium boride, or a combination of these and other carbides with a suitable cementing agent. In tungsten carbide, which is one of the most common of the group, the usual analysis by percentage is tungsten 81.4%, cobalt 12.7%, carbon 5.3%, and iron 0.6%. The cobalt serves as a binder and adds to the ductility of the carbide. It may vary in percentage from 5 to 13. Tantalum carbide is 87% TaC, with 13% of some binder. Usually the binder is either a combination of molybdenum and iron or of tungsten carbide and cobalt. Boron carbide contains about 78.2% boron and 21% carbon, with a trace of silicon and iron. It is usually known by the symbol B_4C. Many similar carbide materials are manufactured under special trade names, the compositions of which are not generally known and vary with manufacture.

Carbide material cannot be applied as other hard-surfacing materials because of its high melting temperature and is therefore furnished either in the form of small inserts or in screen sizes. Inserts can be applied by a brazing or sweating-on process or placed in melted or puddled metal and then surrounded by metal from a steel or hard-surfacing welding rod. Screen sizes of crushed carbide particles can be applied conveniently by putting the particles in steel tubes. The steel sheath melts like an ordinary welding rod and fuses to the metal. The carbide particles do not melt but are distributed through the molten metal and are held fast when the metal cools. Screen sizes can also be applied by mixing the particles with a suitable binder and casting them into rods. These rods can be used conveniently like other hard-surface welding rods.

These materials all have hardnesses approaching that of a diamond, and on the Mohs scale they range from 9 to 9.5. This hardness is maintained to a large extent at a red heat. Because of such extreme hardness and brittleness, diamond substitutes do not have a high strength rating and are not suitable where severe shock and impact conditions exist. This difficulty is partially eliminated by the elements being properly supported with a tough binding material. Another characteristic of these surfacing materials is that they do not respond to heat treatment or cold working and retain their initial hardness under all conditions. They are not suitable for casting, although a few hard materials, principally boron alloys with an iron base, can be processed in this manner.

Metal Spraying

The spraying of molten metal, a comparatively recent development, is rapidly becoming an important process in industry. Any metal obtainable in wire form can be applied in this manner. The wire is fed into the spray gun at a definite rate, where it is melted by an oxyacetylene flame and then blown by compressed air to the surface being coated. A typical layout of metal-spraying equipment is shown in Figure 29.

Because the bond between the sprayed metal and the parent metal is entirely mechanical, it is important that the surface of the metal be properly prepared before spraying. The usual method of cleaning and preparing the surface is by blasting with sharp silica sand or angular steel grit. Cylindrical objects may be prepared by machining small grooves on the surface followed by rolling over the tops of these grooves with a tool similar to a knurling tool.

Either of these methods roughens the surface and provides the necessary interlocking surfaces or keys to make the plastic metal adhere to the surface. The molten metal is blown with considerable force against the surface, causing it to flatten out and interlock with surface irregularities and the adjacent metal particles. The sprayed metal itself provides a suitable surface for successive coatings and permits building up a layer of considerable thickness.

Obviously there is some change in the physical properties of metal applied in this manner. There is an increase in porosity and a corresponding decrease in the tensile strength of the material. The reason

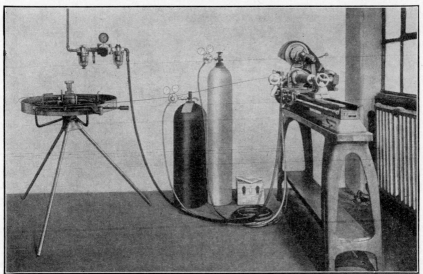

Courtesy Metallizing Engineering Company.

FIG. 29.   Arrangement of Equipment for Metal-Spraying a Cylindrical Object on a Lathe.

for this is that the bond is mechanical and not fusile, as for welding. The compressive strength is high, and there is some increase in hardness. Stainless-steel and high-carbon deposits will develop a Scleroscope hardness of 70 to 75, which corresponds to a Brinell hardness of 500 to 550. The wearing quality of sprayed metal is good, as evidenced by its wide use in building up worn shafts and other moving parts. All deposits can be finished satisfactorily by usual machining or grinding methods. In general, the metals retain most of their original properties.

The success of this process is due largely to its economy and the rapidity with which the metal can be applied. There is no distortion in the parts being surfaced, nor are any internal stresses developed. Practically any metal can be applied to any other commercial metal and even to other base surfaces such as wood and glass.

Metal Plating

Electroplating has long served as a means of applying decorative and protective coatings on metals. For wear or abrasive resistance, the outstanding metal for plating metallic surfaces is chromium. For this use, coatings are seldom less than 0.002 inch thick and may be considerably more. Coatings of this nature are plated not on a soft base metal but directly onto the hard parent metal. If plated on a soft base metal, as copper or nickel, they would have greater corrosion-resisting power, but their resistance to abrasion and deformation would be much less. Hence, any measure of hardness or abrasive resistance is to some extent a function of the metal on which it is plated as well as of the chromium deposit itself.

The process, electrolytic, consists in passing an electric current from an anode to a cathode (the cathode being the object on which the metal is deposited) through a suitable chromium-carrying electrolytic solution in the presence of a catalyst. The catalyst does not enter into the electrochemical decomposition. A solution of chromic acid with a high degree of saturation is used as the electrolyte. The surfaces must be thoroughly polished and cleaned before operations start; and, since the rate of deposition is fairly slow, the work must remain in the tanks several hours for heavy plating.

Chromium has proved very satisfactory for wear-resisting parts because of its extreme hardness, which exceeds most other commercial metals. According to the Brinell scale, the hardness of plated chromium ranges from 500 to 900. This wide variation is due not to the metal but to methods and equipment used.

Review Questions

1. What is the difference between soldering and brazing?
2. What factors must be given careful consideration in resistance welding?
3. List the cycle of events in making a spot weld.
4. Describe indirect welding as applied to spot welding.
5. What advantages are claimed for projection welding?
6. Describe the process of resistance seam welding.
7. Distinguish between butt welding and flash welding.
8. How is percussion welding accomplished?
9. How is oxygen made? Will pure oxygen ignite?
10. Give the reaction that takes place in an acetylene generator.
11. What are the advantages of oxyacetylene welding?
12. For what type of work is oxyhydrogen welding used?
13. Describe two methods of pressure gas welding.
14. Why is steel cut so readily with a torch?
15. What is meant by straight polarity?

16. Briefly compare a-c and d-c arc welding.
17. What are the prerequisites for automatic machine welding?
18. How is the arc length controlled in automatic machine welding?
19. Why are electrodes coated with fluxing materials?
20. What are the advantages claimed for atomic-hydrogen welding?
21. Describe the two methods of inert-gas-shielded arc welding that are in commercial use.
22. How is submerged-arc welding accomplished?
23. For what type of work is Thermit welding used?
24. How are cold pressure welds made?
25. What methods of surface preparation are used for metal spraying?

References

Arc Welding Manual and Operators Training Course, Hobart Brothers Company, 1941.

BEGEMAN, M. L., "Hard-Surfacing Processes and Materials," *Mechanical Engineering,* Vol. 60, December 1938.

CADY, E. L., "Flame Cutting and Machining Methods," *Metals & Alloys,* May 1945.

CHAFFEE, W. J., *Arc Welding and How to Use It,* 3d edition, Hobart Brothers Company, 1938.

Design for Welding, James F. Lincoln Arc Welding Foundation, 1947.

KERWIN, H., *Arc and Acetylene Welding,* McGraw-Hill Book Company, 1944.

MAMPLE, A. Z., "Soldering with Tin-Lead Alloys," *Metals & Alloys,* May 1945.

Procedure Handbook of Arc Welding Design and Practice, 9th edition, Lincoln Electric Company, 1950.

Properties of Haynes Stellite, Haynes Stellite Company, 1936.

Recommended Practices for Resistance Welding, American Welding Society, 1950.

Resistance Welding Manual, Resistance Welder's Manufacturing Association, 1948.

SHAPIRO, C. H., "Oxy-Acetylene Application of Hard Facing Materials to Oil Well Drilling Bits," *Metal Progress,* Vol. 35, April 1939.

SINGLETON, R. C., "Electric Arc Stud Welding," *Welding Journal,* December 1947.

The Oxwelder's Handbook, 15th edition, Linde Air Products Company, 1939.

The Welding Encyclopedia, 11th edition, Welding Engineer Publishing Company, 1943.

Welding Handbook, 3d edition, American Welding Society, 1950.

Welding and Cutting Manual, Linde Air Products Company, 1949.

WYER, R. F., "Some Developments in Gas-Shielded Arc Welding," paper presented at Philadelphia Chapter of American Welding Society, May 1944.

CHAPTER 8

HOT FORMING OF METALS

The mechanical working of metal is the shaping of metal in either the cold or the hot state by some mechanical means. This does not include the shaping of metals by machining or grinding, in which processes metal is actually machined off, nor does it include the casting of molten metal into some form by use of molds. In mechanical working processes, the metal is shaped by pressure—actually forging, bending, squeezing, drawing, or shearing to its final shape. In these processes the metal may be either cold- or hot-worked. For cold working of steel, normal room temperature is used; however, temperatures up to critical are included in this range. Hot working of steel takes place at temperatures above the critical range. At such high temperatures the metal is in a plastic state and is readily formed by pressures. The properties of the metal are actually improved by mechanical working, since grain refinement is caused by the process. Little grain refinement takes place below the critical range, the action there being principally one of grain distortion. Both hot and cold working produce a structure elongated in the same direction as rolling, drawing, or other form of mechanical work.

Metals which are cast from the furnace into ingot molds must be reduced to commercial shapes by mechanical force. This force is applied to the metal while it is hot, for the following reasons: to shape the product more easily into some commercial article, to improve the physical properties of the metal, and to impart a fine crystalline structure to the metal. Principal methods of hot-working metals are:

1. Rolling.

2. Forging
   (a) Hammer or smith forging.
   (b) Drop forging.
   (c) Machine or upset forging.
   (d) Press forging.
   (e) Forging rolls.
   (f) Swaging.

3. Pipe welding
   (a) Butt welding of heated strips.
   (b) Butt welding by electrical resistance.
   (c) Lap welding.
   (d) Hammer welding.

4. Piercing.

5. Drawing or cupping.

6. Spinning.

7. Extrusion.

Hot-Working Processes

Before metals are mechanically worked, they are first cast into ingot molds of suitable form for subsequent operations. The mold

Courtesy Bethlehem Steel Company.

FIG. 1. Steel Being Poured in Molds to Make Ingots for Subsequent Rolling.

may be either square or round in cross section, and the final casting may vary in size from a few hundred pounds to several tons. The kind of metal cast and the product desired* are the principal factors in determining the ingot size. The operation of pouring ingot molds with steel from an open-hearth furnace is shown in Figure 1. The steel remains in these molds until solidification is about complete, and then the molds are removed. While still hot, the ingots are placed in gas-fired furnaces called *soaking pits,* where they remain until they have attained a uniform working temperature throughout and then are taken to the rolling mill.

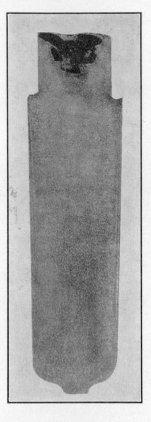

Courtesy Drop Forging Association.

Longitudinal Section of
Steel Ingot.

Cross Section of Medium-Carbon
Killed-Steel Ingot Showing Crystalline Structure.

Fig. 2.

The structure of the steel *ingot* is very coarse, because the grains grow while the metal is slowly cooling from a liquid to a solid state. This is illustrated in Figure 2, which shows a longitudinal and cross section of a medium-carbon killed-steel* ingot. The coarse dendritic crystalline structure may be clearly seen in the cross section. This coarse structure will be subsequently eliminated by the effects of hot

* Steel that has been deoxidized to the extent that gases are evolved during the process of solidification is known as "killed" steel.

working. The impurities in ingots tend to segregate in the shrink head during the process of solidification. Cutting off the end of the ingot, either before the rolling starts or shortly after it has started, largely eliminates this defect.

Rolling. After the ingot has remained in the soaking pit at a temperature around 2200 F for a sufficient time to become uniformly heated, it is then removed by an overhead crane and placed on the

Courtesy Bethlehem Steel Company.

FIG. 3. Hot Ingots Are First Rolled in the Blooming Mill until Reduced to Desired Size.

rolling-mill table. Because of the large variety of finished shapes to be made, ingots are first rolled into such intermediate shapes as *blooms, billets,* or *slabs.* These shapes all have rounded corners and vary principally in cross-sectional area. A *bloom* has a square cross section with a minimum size of 6 by 6 inches. Figure 3 shows an ingot being rolled in a blooming mill. This mill is a two-high reversing mill, permitting the metal to pass back and forth through the rolls. At frequent intervals it is turned 90 degrees on its side to keep the section uniform and to refine the metal throughout. About 20 passes are required to reduce a large ingot into a bloom. Grooves are provided in both the upper and lower rolls to accommodate the various reductions in cross-sectional area.

A *billet* is smaller than a bloom, and may have any square section from 1½ by 1½ inches up to the size of a bloom. Although billets could be rolled to size in a large blooming mill, this is not usually done for economic reasons. Frequently they are rolled from blooms

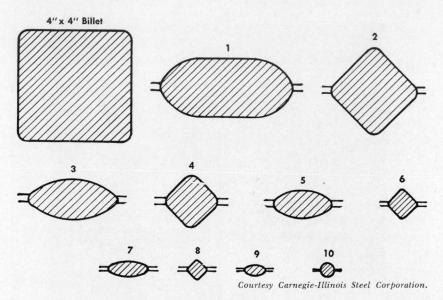

Courtesy Carnegie-Illinois Steel Corporation.

Fig. 4. Diagram Illustrates Number of Passes and Sequence in Reducing the Cross Section of a 4-by-4-Inch Billet to Round Bar Stock.

in a continuous billet mill consisting of about eight rolling stands in a straight line. The steel makes but one pass through the mill and emerges with a final billet size of approximately 2 by 2 inches. The billet is the raw material for many final shapes such as bars, tubes, and forgings. The diagram in Figure 4 illustrates the number of passes and sequence in reducing the cross section of a 4-by-4-inch billet to round bar stock.

Slabs may be rolled from either an ingot or a bloom. They have a rectangular cross-sectional area with a minimum width of 10 inches and a minimum thickness of 1½ inch. Slabs constitute the material from which plates, skelp, and thin strips are rolled.

Various arrangements of rolls used in rolling machines are shown in Figure 5. Those that have four or more rolls use the extra ones for backing up the two that are doing the rolling. In addition, many

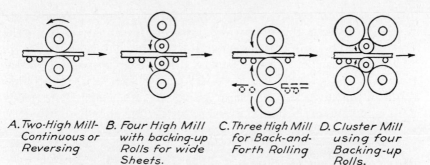

A. Two-High Mill-
Continuous or
Reversing

B. Four High Mill
with backing-up
Rolls for wide
Sheets.

C. Three High Mill
for Back-and-
Forth Rolling

D. Cluster Mill
using four
Backing-up
Rolls.

FIG. 5. Various Roll Arrangements Used in Rolling Mills.

special rolling mills take the intermediary products just described and fabricate them into such finished articles as rails, structural shapes, plates, and bars. Such mills usually bear the name of the prod-
uct being rolled and in appearance are similar to mills used for
rolling blooms and billets.

Hammering or smith forging.
This type of forging consists of
hammering the heated metal
either with hand tools, or between flat dies in a steam hammer. Hand forging as done by
the blacksmith is the oldest form
of forging. It is largely used in
repair or maintenance work and
in the production of numerous
small parts such as hooks, crow-
bars, chisels, cutting tools, U
bolts, and similar articles, where
only small quantities are involved. Much of this type of work
is now done in power forges
called steam or smith hammers.
Machines of this type have an
open-frame construction to allow
plenty of room around the flat
dies as shown in Fig. 6. The force

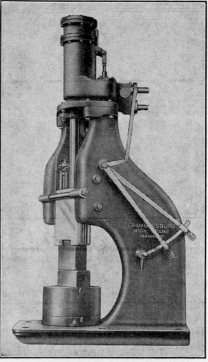

Courtesy Chambersburg Engineering Company.

FIG. 6. High Frame Steam Hammer.

of the blow is closely controlled by the operator, and the work done is generally for the purpose of reducing the cross section of the metal.

Drop forging. Drop forging differs from smith forging in that closed-impression rather than open-face dies are used. The forging is produced by impact or pressure which compels the plastic metal to conform to the shape of the dies. In this operation there is drastic flow of the metal in the dies caused by the repeated blows on the metal. The ram, operating in a vertical plane, carries one half of the dies and the other half is held stationary on the anvil block. Both are held in perfect alignment.

Steps in the forging of a connecting rod are illustrated in Figure 7. The first step in the manufacture of this part is to shear off bar stock to proper length and bring it up to forging temperature in a furnace adjacent to the forge. The dies used in this operation, shown at A, contain impressions for several operations. Preliminary hot working first proportions the metal for forming the connecting rod; then the fillering operation, illustrated at B, reduces the cross-sectional area of the center while the edging gathers metal for the two ends of the rod. The blocking operation, which forms the rod into a definite shape, is shown at C.

The appearance of the connecting rod after several blows in the finishing die is shown at D. Flash around the edges of the finished forging is removed in a separate press by trimmer dies immediately after the finishing operation is completed. The completed connecting rod, ready for heat treatment, is shown at E. At F is a macroetched cross section of a connecting-rod forging, showing the flow lines of the metal and the fiber structure obtained by the hammering action.

The two principal types of drop-forging hammers are the *steam hammer* and the *board hammer*. In the former the ram and hammer are lifted by steam, and the force of the blow is controlled by throttling the steam. These hammers work rapidly: over 300 blows a minute can be obtained. The capacities of steam hammers range from 500 to 50,000 pounds. Steam hammers are usually of double-housing design and resemble in appearance the board hammer shown in Figure 7, except that they have an overhead steam cylinder assembly for supplying the power. In the board drop hammer several boards are attached to the ram, the lifting of which is accomplished by several friction rollers contacting the boards on both sides, as shown by the line diagram insert in Figure 8. When the top of the stroke is reached, the rollers are spread apart, allowing the boards and ram to fall by gravity. The force of the blow is dependent on the weight of the ram or head assembly, which seldom exceeds 8000 pounds. A modification of the board hammer is now available in which the board has been replaced by a rod and piston.

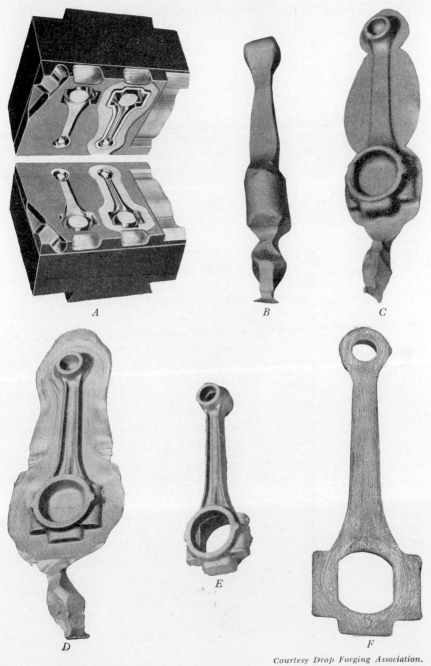

A   *B*   *C*

D   *E*   *F*

Courtesy Drop Forging Association.

FIG. 7. Steps in Drop-Forging Connecting Rod.

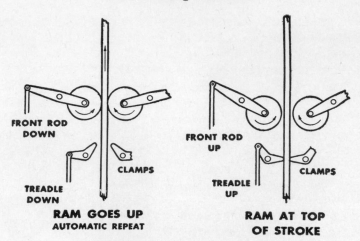

FRONT ROD DOWN

CLAMPS

TREADLE DOWN

RAM GOES UP
AUTOMATIC REPEAT

FRONT ROD UP

CLAMPS

TREADLE UP

RAM AT TOP OF STROKE

Courtesy Chambersburg Engineering Company.

FIG. 8.   Board Drop Hammer.

In this machine the hammer is lifted by air or steam, but a gravity drop is used to do the work. A faster lifting speed is obtained with a consequent increase in the number of blows per minute, and there is less maintenance required in replacing rods than boards.

The drop-forging process is advantageous in that the physical properties of the metal are improved by the severe mechanical working, the operation is rapid, many complicated parts can be forged to shape, a minimum amount of machining is necessary, and internal defects are eliminated. This method of fabrication is adapted to both carbon and alloy steels, wrought iron, copper-base alloys, aluminum alloys, and magnesium alloys. A limitation is the cost of the equipment and dies, which necessitates the making of a large number of parts. Casting or flame cutting may be employed if the advantages by hot working are not a paramount consideration.

Press forging. Press forging employs a slow squeezing action in deforming the plastic metal, as contrasted with the rapid-impact blows of a hammer. The squeezing action is carried completely to the center of the part being pressed, thoroughly working the entire section. The size of the forging is no longer a limitation in press-forging work, since large presses up to capacities approaching 18,000 tons are now available. Figure 9 shows a typical hydraulic-type press used in this work having a capacity of 500 tons.

For small press forgings, closed-impression dies are used, and only

Courtesy Watson Stillman Company.

Fig. 9. 500-ton Forge Press with Rapid Advance and Return Feature.

one stroke of the ram is normally required to perform the forging operation. A close-up view of the bolster plate, dies, and forgings produced in such a press is shown in Figure 10. The work of pressing the conical-shaped blank (left) in the 1300-ton press is accomplished in two operations. The preliminary operation, performed in the dies to the left, compresses the slug (right) and roughly

Courtesy The Ajax Manufacturing Company.

FIG. 10.　Pressing Cone Forgings for Oil-Well Drilling Head.

forms it to shape (center), so that there is a minimum of flow and abrasion to the finishing dies. Presses of this type are now widely used in the forming of nonferrous metals.

In the forging press a greater proportion of the total work put into the machine is transmitted to the metal than in a drop-hammer press. Much of the impact of the drop hammer is absorbed by the machine and foundation. Furthermore, press reduction of metal is faster and the cost of operation is consequently lower. Press forgings are more accurate than drop forgings, since less draft is required; however, many parts of irregular and complicated shapes can be more economically forged by drop forging.

Machine or upset forging. Upset forging entails gripping a bar of uniform section in dies and applying pressure on the heated end, causing it to be upset or formed to shape. A large machine of this type is shown in Figure 11. Here rear-axle drive shafts with flanged ends are being forged from round stock. Machines of this type are an

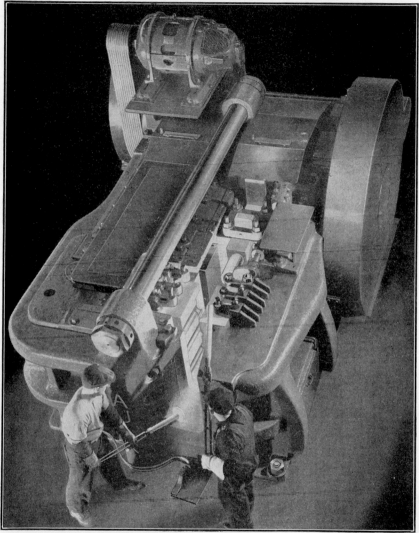

Courtesy The Ajax Manufacturing Company.

Fɪɢ. 11. Five-Inch Upset Forging Machine in Operation—Forging Flanged Rear-Axle Drive Shafts.

outgrowth of smaller machines designed for heading bolts and making nuts.

Dies for these machines consist of two gripper dies, grooved to hold the stock during the various forging operations, and a header or punch assembly. A die for forging a socket wrench in four operations is shown in Figure 12. Such dies are not limited to upsetting operations but may also be used for piercing, punching, trimming, extrusion, or bending. Parts forged by this process include axle shafts, pinions, axle housings, valve stems, engine cylinders, worm gears, and numerous other parts requiring upset ends.

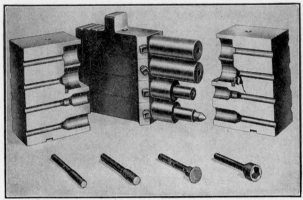

Courtesy The Ajax Manufacturing Company.

FIG. 12. Dies for Upset Forging of Socket Wrench Consisting of Two Gripper Dies and One Punch Assembly.

Forging rolls. Forging rolls are being used in a wide variety of reduced, straight, and taper operations. A typical machine of this type producing automobile rear-axle drive shafts is shown in Figure 13. The rolls in this machine are semicylindrical in cross section and are grooved according to the type of forging or shaping to be done. When the rolls are in open position, the operator places the heated bar between them, retaining it with tongs. As the rolls revolve, the bar is gripped in the roll grooves and pushed toward the operator. This operation is repeated several times, using other grooves, until the part is completely forged to shape. Gages and guiding grooves assist the operator in accurately placing the stock between the rolls. In this manner axles, gear-shift levers, blanks for eyebolts, and connecting rods, brake levers, aluminum propeller blanks, and leaf springs are forged.

In the rolling of wheels, metal tires, and similar items a roll mill of somewhat different construction is used. Figure 14 shows how a rough forged blank is converted into a finished wheel by the rolling action of the various rolls about the circumference of the wheel. As the wheel rotates, the diameter is gradually increased while the

Courtesy The Ajax Manufacturing Company.

FIG. 13. Forging Rolls Producing Automobile Rear-Axle Drive Shafts.

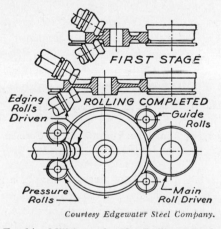

Courtesy Edgewater Steel Company.

FIG. 14. Mill Setup for Hot-Rolling Wheels.

plate and rim are reduced in section.　When the wheel is rolled to
its final diameter, it is then transferred to a press and given a dishing
or coning operation.

Pipe welding.　Pipe and tubular products may be produced by
either welding or seamless processes.　The butt-welding process uses
heated strips of steel, known as *skelp,* the edges of which are first

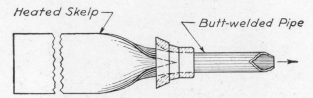

FIG. 15.　Producing Butt-Welded Pipe by Drawing Skelp through a Welding Bell.

beveled slightly so they will meet when formed to a circular shape.
In the intermittent process, one end of the skelp is trimmed to a
V shape to permit it to enter the welding bell shown in Figure 15.
When the skelp is brought up to welding heat, the end is gripped by
tongs which engage a draw chain.　As the tube is pulled through the

Courtesy Bethlehem Steel Company.

FIG. 16.　Skelp Emerging from Furnace at Right Is Formed into Continuous
Butt-Weld Pipe.

welding bell, skelp is formed to a circular shape, and the edges are
welded together.　A final operation passes the pipe between sizing
and finishing rolls to give it correct size and to remove all scale.

Continuous butt welding of pipe is accomplished by supplying the
skelp in coils and providing means for flash-welding the coil ends

together to form a continuous strip. As the skelp enters the furnace, flames impinge on the edges of the strip to bring them to welding temperatures. Leaving the furnace, the skelp enters a series of horizontal and vertical rollers, shown in Figure 16, which form it into pipe. An enlarged view of the rollers, showing how the pipe is

Courtesy Bethlehem Steel Company.

FIG. 17. Skelp Being Formed into Continuous Butt-Weld Pipe.

formed and sized, is shown in Figure 17. As the pipe leaves the rollers, it is sawed into lengths which are finally processed by descaling and finishing operations. Pipe is made in this fashion in sizes up to 3 inches in diameter.

Electric butt welding of pipe necessitates cold forming of the steel plate to shape, prior to the welding operation. The circular form is developed by passing the plate through a continuous set of rolls which progressively change its shape. This method, known as roll forming, is discussed in the next chapter. The welding unit, placed at the end of the roll-forming machine, consists of three centering and pressure rolls to hold the formed shape in position and two electrode rolls which supply current to generate the heat. Immediately after the pipe passes the welding unit, the extruded flash metal is removed from both inside and outside of the pipe. Sizing and finishing rolls then complete the operation by giving the pipe accurate size and concentricity. This process is adapted to the manufacture of pipe up to 16-inch diameter with wall thickness varying from $\frac{1}{8}$ inch to $\frac{1}{2}$ inch in thickness. Pipes of larger diameter are usually fabricated by fusion welding or by hammer welding, the latter being essentially a forge-welding process.

In the lap welding of pipe, the edges of the skelp are beveled as it emerges from the furnace.   The skelp then is drawn through a forming die, or between rolls, to give it cylindrical shape, with the edges overlapping.   After being reheated, the bent skelp is passed between two grooved rolls as shown in Figure 18.   Between the rolls is a fixed mandrel of a size to fit the inside diameter of the pipe, the edges being lap-welded together by pressure between the rolls and the mandrel. Lap weld is made in sizes ranging from 2 to 16 inches in diameter.

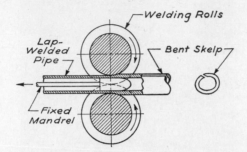

FIG. 18.   Method of Producing Lap-Welded Pipe from Bent Skelp.

Piercing.   To produce seamless tubing, cylindrical billets of steel are passed between two conical-shaped rolls operating in the same direction.   Between these rolls is a fixed point or mandrel which assists in the piercing and controls the size of the hole as the billet is forced over it.

The entire operation of making seamless tubing in both the conventional and the continuous processes is shown in Figure 19.   In the conventional process the solid billet is first center-punched and then brought to forging heat in a furnace before being pierced.   The billet is then pushed into the two piercing rolls which impart to it both rotation and axial advance.   The alternate squeezing and bulging of the billet open up a seam in its center, the size and shape of which are controlled by the piercing mandrel.   As the thick-walled tube emerges from the piercing mill, it next passes between grooved rolls over a plug held by a mandrel and is converted into a longer tube with specified wall thickness.   While still at working temperatures, the tube passes through the reeling machine which further straightens and sizes it and, in addition, gives the walls a smooth surface.   Final sizing and finishing are accomplished in the same manner as for welded pipe.

This procedure applies to seamless tubes up to 6 inches in diameter. Larger tubes up to 14 inches in diameter are given a second operation on piercing rolls. To produce sizes up to 24 inches in diameter, reheated double-pierced tubes are processed on a rotary rolling mill as shown in Figure 20 and are finally completed by reelers and sizing rolls, as described in the single-piercing process.

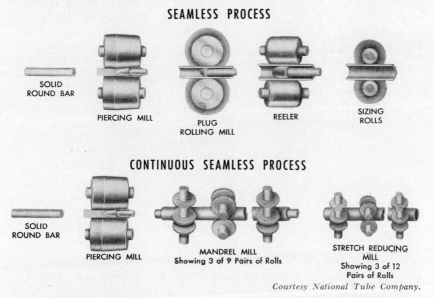

SEAMLESS PROCESS

SOLID ROUND BAR

PIERCING MILL

PLUG ROLLING MILL

REELER

SIZING ROLLS

CONTINUOUS SEAMLESS PROCESS

SOLID ROUND BAR

PIERCING MILL

MANDREL MILL
Showing 3 of 9 Pairs of Rolls

STRETCH REDUCING MILL
Showing 3 of 12 Pairs of Rolls

Courtesy National Tube Company.

Fig. 19. Principal Steps in the Manufacture of Seamless Tubing.

In the continuous method a 5½-inch round bar is pierced as before and is then conveyed to the 9-stand mandrel mill where a cylindrical bar or mandrel is inserted into it. These rolls reduce the tube diameter and wall thickness. The mandrel is then removed, the tube reheated, and the tube then enters the 12-stand stretch reducing mill. This mill reduces not only the wall thickness of the hot tube but also the tube diameter. Each successive roll is speeded up so as to produce a tension sufficient to stretch the tube between stands. The maximum delivery of this mill is 1300 feet per minute for pipe around 2 inches in diameter.

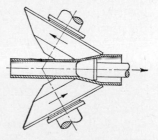

Rotary Rolling Mill
Courtesy National Tube Company.

Fig. 20. Rotary Seamless Process for Large Tubing.

Drawing or cupping. Some thick-walled tubes or cylinders are produced by drawing circular heated plates through a die, as illustrated diagrammatically in Figure 21. The entire procedure is made up of several drawing operations, between each two of which the cup-shaped cylinder must be reheated to provide the necessary plasticity for working. After about two drawing operations, the formed cup is pushed through a horizontal drawbench consisting of several dies of successively decreasing diameter, mounted in one frame. The hydraulically operated punch forces the heated cylinder through the full length of the draw-

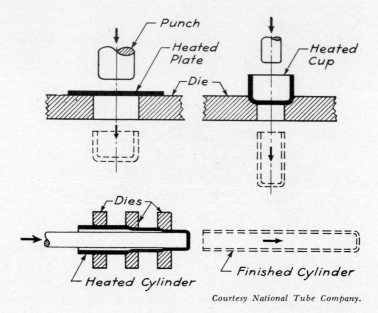

FIG. 21.   Drawing Thick-Walled Cylinders from Heated Plates.

bench. For long thin-walled cylinders or tubes, repeated heating and drawing may be necessary. If the final product is to be a tube, the closed end is cut off and the balance is sent through finishing and sizing rolls, similar to those used in the piercing process. To produce closed-end cylinders, similar to those for storing oxygen, the open end is swaged to form a neck.

Extrusion

Any plastic material can be extruded to uniform cross-sectional shape by the aid of pressure. The principle of *extrusion,* similar to the simple act of squirting toothpaste from a tube, has long been utilized in processes ranging all the way from the production of brick, hollow tile, and soil pipe, to the manufacture of macaroni. Some metals, notably lead, tin, and aluminum, may be extruded cold, whereas others require the application of heat to render them plastic or semisolid before extrusion. In the actual operation of extrusion the processes differ slightly, depending on the metal and application, but in brief they consist of forcing metal (confined to a pressure chamber) out through specially formed dies. Rods, tubes, molding trim, structural shapes, brass cartridges, and lead-covered cable are typical products of metal extrusion.

The coating of wire cable with lead sheathing, as illustrated in Figure 22, is an important example of hot extrusion. Molten lead is

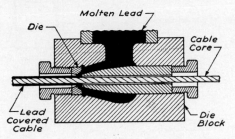

FIG. 22. Method of Extruding Lead Sheathing on Wire Cable.

poured into the cylinder above the die and allowed to solidify under slight pressure of the cylinder plunger. When the correct extruding temperature is reached (around 500 F), the plunger, actuated by hydraulic means, forces the lead in two streams around the cable, which weld together underneath. The lead is forced through the die, forming a uniform lead coating which grips the cable sufficiently to draw it through the die block. At the end of the stroke the plunger rises, more lead is added, and the cycle is repeated.

An interesting example of *extrusion by impact* is in the manufacture of collapsible tubes for shaving cream, toothpaste, and paint pigments. These extremely thin tubes are pressed out from slugs, as illustrated in the upper half of Figure 23. The punch strikes a single blow of considerable force, causing the metal to squirt up around the punch.

The outside diameter of the tube is the same as the diameter of the die, and the thickness is controlled by the clearance between the punch and die. The tube shown in the figure has a flat end, but any desired shape can be made by properly forming the die cavity and the end of the punch. On the upstroke, the tube is blown from the ram with compressed air. The entire operation is automatic, with a production rate of 35 to 40 tubes per minute. The tubes are then inspected, trimmed, enameled, and printed. Zinc, lead, tin, and aluminum alloys are worked in this fashion.

In the lower half of the figure is illustrated a variation of what is known as the *Hooker* process for extruding small tubes or cartridge cases. Small slugs or blanks are used as in the impact-extrusion

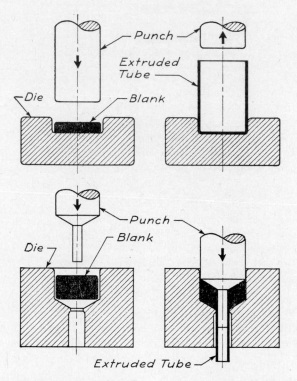

Fig. 23.   Methods of Cold-Impact Extrusion of Soft Metals.

process, but in this case the metal is extruded downward through the die opening. The size and shape of the extruded tube are controlled by the space between the punch end and die cavity wall. Copper tubes having wall thicknesses of 0.004 to 0.010 inch can be produced in lengths of about 12 inches.

For the extrusion of large rods, tubes, and special shapes, high-capacity hydraulic presses have been developed similar to the one shown in Figure 24. Although some nonferrous alloys can be extruded cold, most metals are heated to facilitate the operation. For steel tubing extrusion, a round billet is used which is first heated up to about 2400 F and then placed in the machine. A mandrel is advanced and pushed through the ingot as shown in the line diagram. The press stem then advances and extrudes the metal through the die at

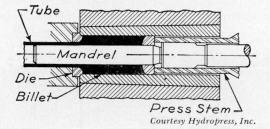

Courtesy Hydropress, Inc.

Fɪɢ. 24. Extruding a Large Tube from a Heated Billet.

the other end of the billet container. The entire operation must be rapid to prevent the outer surface of billet from cooling. Speeds up to 120 inches per second have been used in making steel tubes.

Review Questions

1. Distinguish between hot- and cold-working of steel.
2. List the various methods of mechanically hot-working metals.
3. What defects are found in ingots, and how are they eliminated?
4. Describe each of the following shapes used in connection with the rolling of steel: Ingot, bloom, slab, and billet.
5. What is the usual temperature range for hot-working steel?
6. Show by sketch the various roll arrangements used in rolling mills.
7. Describe the process of drop forging.
8. What is a board hammer, and how does it operate?
9. What advantages does press forging have over drop forging?
10. List the various methods used in producing pipe and tubular products.
11. What type of work is done by upset forging?
12. Describe the process of producing lap-welded pipe.
13. Describe the continuous method of making seamless tubing.
14. Show by sketch how wire is coated with lead.
15. How are collapsible tubes produced?
16. Describe the Hooker process of extrusion.
17. How is steel improved by hot working?

References

Bᴏʟᴢ, R. W., *Production Processes*, Vol. 1, Penton Publishing Company, 1949.

Cᴀᴍᴘ, J. M., and C. B. Fʀᴀɴᴄɪs, *The Making, Shaping and Treating of Steel*, 5th edition, Carnegie-Illinois Steel Corporation.

Fʀɪᴇᴅᴍᴀɴ, J. H., "Hot Press and Upset Forgings," *Transactions ASM*, Vol. 25, March 1937.

Fɪsʜᴇʀ, D. A., *Steel Making in America*, United States Steel Corporation, 1949.

Impact Die Forging, Chambersburg Engineering Company, 1944.

KOENIG, PHIL, "Impact Extrusion and Cold Pressing of Airplane Parts," *Transactions SAE,* Vol. 51, November 1943.

Metals Handbook, 1948 edition, American Society for Metals.

Metal Quality, Drop Forging Association, 1949.

NANJOKS, W., and D. C. FABEL, *Forging Handbook,* American Society for Metals, 1939.

PEARSON, C. E., and R. GENDERS, *The Extrusion of Metals,* John Wiley & Sons, 1944.

Pipes and Tubes in the Making, National Tube Company, 1945.

TEICHERT, E. J., *The Manufacture and Fabrication of Steel,* Vol. 2, McGraw-Hill Book Company, 1944.

CHAPTER
9

COLD FORMING OF METALS
MISCELLANEOUS PROCESSES

Many of the same operations used in hot working may also be used in cold working, but the effect on the crystalline structure of the metal is different. Hot work, performed on the metal in a plastic state, actually refines the grain structure, whereas cold work merely distorts it and does little toward reducing its size. Cold working is normally done at room temperature; however, for steel, temperatures up to the critical range may be included.

Many products are cold-finished after hot rolling to make them commercially fit for their intended use. For example, hot-rolled strips and sheets are soft, have surface imperfections, and lack dimensional accuracy and certain desired physical properties. In the cold-rolling operation there is a slight reduction in size which permits accurate dimensional controls. A smooth surface is obtained, and both hardness and strength are increased. In general, the same results are obtained in the cold rolling of shafting, wire drawing, or other forms of cold work. Brittleness results if the metal is overworked, and an annealing operation is then necessary before further work can be done.

Cold-Working Processes

Press working may or may not accomplish the results just described. Operations involving bending, drawing, and squeezing metal result in grain distortion and changes in physical properties, whereas shearing or cutting operations change only form and size. The following classification lists the various methods of mechanically cold-working metals, including press operations.

COLD-WORKING OPERATIONS—METAL AT NEAR ROOM TEMPERATURE

1. Drawing
   (a) Blanks.
   (b) Tubes.
   (c) Embossing.
   (d) Wire.
   (e) Metal spinning.
   (f) Stretch forming.

215

2. Squeezing

  (*a*) Coining.

  (*b*) Cold rolling.

  (*c*) Sizing.

  (*d*) Swaging or cold forging.

  (*e*) Thread rolling and knurling.*

  (*f*) Riveting.

  (*g*) Staking.

3. Bending

  (*a*) Angle bending.

  (*b*) Roll forming.

  (*c*) Plate bending.

  (*d*) Curling.

  (*e*) Seaming.

* See Chapter 14.

† See Chapter 8.

4. Shearing

  (*a*) Blanking.

  (*b*) Punching.

  (*c*) Cutting off.

  (*d*) Trimming.

  (*e*) Perforating.

  (*f*) Notching.

  (*g*) Slotting.

  (*h*) Sprue cutting.

5. Extruding †

  (*a*) Cold.

  (*b*) Impact.

6. Shot peening.

7. Hobbing.

Tube drawing. Tubing which requires dimensional accuracy, smooth surface, and improved physical properties is finished by a cold-drawing operation. This method also produces tubes having

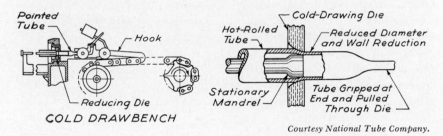

Courtesy National Tube Company.

Fig. 1. Process of Cold-Drawing Tubing.

smaller diameters or thinner walls than can be obtained by hot rolling. Special shapes and rounds up to 12 inches in diameter can be produced by this process.

Hot-rolled tubing must first be treated by pickling and washing to remove all scale and then covered with a suitable lubricant. The drawing is done in a *drawbench,* shown diagrammatically in Figure 1. One end of the tube is reduced in diameter by a swaging operation to permit it to enter the die, and it is then gripped by tongs fastened to the chain of the drawbench. In this operation the tube is drawn through a die smaller than the outside diameter of the tube, the inside surface and diameter being controlled by a fixed mandrel over which the tube is drawn. This mandrel may be omitted for small sizes or for larger sizes if the accuracy of the inside diameter is not important. Drawbenches require a pulling power ranging from 50,000 to 300,000 pounds and may have a total length of 100 feet.

The operation of drawing a tube is very severe: the metal is stressed above its elastic limit to permit plastic flow through the die. The maximum reduction for one pass is around 40%. This operation increases the hardness of the tube so much that, if several reductions are desired, the material must be annealed after each pass.

Wire drawing. Wire is drawn by pulling a rod through several dies of decreasing diameter, as illustrated in Figure 2, until the final diameter is obtained. Rods from the mill, first cleaned in acid baths to remove scale and rust, are coated in various ways to prevent oxidation and to facilitate being drawn through the die. The dies are usually made of carbide materials, although diamonds may be used for small diameters.

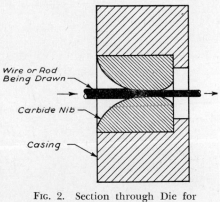

Both single-draft or continuous-drawing processes may be used. In the first method a coil is placed on a reel or frame and the end of the rod pointed so that it will enter the die. The end is grasped by tongs on a drawbench and pulled through to such length as may be wound around a drawing block or reel.

Fig. 2. Section through Die for Drawing Wire.

From there on, the rotation of the draw block pulls the wire through the die and forms it into a coil. These operations are repeated with smaller dies and blocks until the wire is drawn to its final size.

In continuous drawing, as shown in Figure 3, the wire is fed through several dies and draw blocks arranged in series. This permits drawing the maximum amount in one operation before annealing is necessary. The number of dies in the series will depend on the kind of metal or alloy being processed and may vary from 4 to 12 successive drafts.

Metal spinning. *Metal spinning* is the operation of shaping thin metal by pressing it against a form while it is rotating. The nature of the process limits it to symmetrical articles of circular cross section. This type of work is done on a speed lathe similar to the one shown in Figure 4. A spinning lathe is like the ordinary wood lathe except that, in place of the usual tailstock, it is provided with some means of holding the work against the form.   The forms are usually turned from hard wood and attached to the face plate of the lathe, although smooth steel chucks are recommended for production jobs.   This type

Courtesy Wickwire Spencer Steel Company.

FIG. 3.   View of Vaughn Continuous Wire Drawing Machine Used to Reduce Round Stock to Around 0.072 Inch in Six Drafts.   Dies Are All Tungsten Carbide and Are Water-Cooled.   Roll Wire Pointer Is at Right Center.

of chuck will not develop interior imperfection and is more economical where surface finish is to be considered.

Practically all parts are formed by the aid of blunt hand tools which press the metal against the form.   The cross slide has a hand or compound tool rest in the front for supporting the hand tools and some means for supporting a trimming cutter or forming roll in the rear. Parts may be formed either from flat disks of metal or from blanks that have previously been drawn in a press. The latter method is used as a finishing operation for many deep-drawn articles. Most

Courtesy Phoenix Products Company.

Fig. 4. Spinning 16-Gage Steel into 30-Inch-Diameter Hemisphere.

spinning work is done on the outside diameter as shown in the figure, although inside work is also possible.

Bulging work on metal pitchers, vases, and similar parts is done by having a small roller, supported from the compound rest, operate on the inside and press the metal out against a form roller. Figure 5 shows a cutaway view of a part being spun over an off-center chuck or roll. In an operation such as this one, the part must first be drawn, and possibly given a bulging operation beforehand, as spinning cannot be done near the bottom. Contact of the spinning tools can only take place next to the chuck.

Lubricants such as soap, beeswax, white lead, and linseed oil are used to reduce the tool friction. Of these, ordinary laundry soap proves very satisfactory, particularly for aluminum spinning. Since metal spinning is a cold-working operation, there is a limit to the amount of drawing or working the metal will stand, and one or more annealing operations may be necessary. Spinning lends itself to short-run production jobs, although it has many applications in continuous

Courtesy Aluminum Corporation of America.

FIG. 5. Metal Spinning over an Off-Center Roll.

production work. It is frequently used in the making of bells on musical instruments, light fixtures, reflectors, kitchenware, and large processing kettles.

Swaging and cold forging. These terms refer to methods of cold working by pressure or impact which causes the metal to flow to some desired shape. *Swaging* is usually thought of as a means of reducing the ends of bars or tubes by rotating dies which open and close on the work, as illustrated in Figure 6. The rotating dies are rapidly opened and closed, and the end of the rod is tapered or reduced in size by a combination of pressure and impact. The swaging action, being rather severe, hardens the metal and necessitates an annealing operation if much reduction is desired.

Cold forging of heads on bolts, rivets, and other similar parts is done in cold-header machines. Since the product of the cold-header is made from unheated material, the equipment must be able to with-

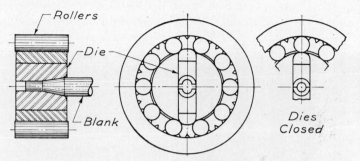

FIG. 6. Illustrating the Operation of Dies in a Swaging Machine.

stand the high pressures that are developed; furthermore, there must be accuracy of alignment of the upsetting tool with the dies so that the work turned out will be accurate and free from defects. A solid die machine of this type is illustrated in Figure 7. The rod is fed by

Courtesy The National Machinery Company.
FIG. 7. Solid Die Cold-Header.

straightening rolls up to a stop and is then cut off and moved into the header die. The heading operation may be either single or double, and upon completion the part is ejected from the dies.

Bolt-making machines are also available which completely finish the bolt before it leaves the machine. In this machine the operations (shown in Figure 8) consist of cutting off an oversize blank, extruding the shank, heading, trimming, pointing, and roll threading. All operations are carried on simultaneously, and outputs range from 50 to 110 pieces per minute.

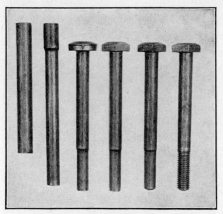

Courtesy The National Machinery Company.

Fɪɢ. 8.   Sequence of Operations in Making a Bolt in Boltmaker Machine.

Nails, rivets, and small bolts are made from coiled wire and forged cold, whereas large bolts require the end of the rod to be heated before the heading operation.

Coining and embossing.   The operation of *coining,* shown in Figure 9, is performed in dies which confine the metal and restrict its flow in a lateral direction.   Shallow configurations on the surfaces of flat objects, such as coins, are produced in this manner. Special-type presses developing high pressures are required in this operation, and, because of this, its use is limited to fairly soft alloys.

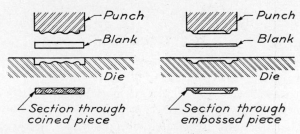

Fɪɢ. 9.   Illustrating the Difference between the Processes of Coining and Embossing.

Embossing is more of a drawing or stretching operation and does not require the high pressures necessary for coining.   The punch is usually relieved so that it touches only that part of the blank that is being embossed.   The mating die conforms to the same configuration as the punch so there is very little metal squeezing in the operation and practically no change in the thickness of the metal.

Riveting and staking.   Both these processes are used to fasten parts together, as illustrated in Figure 10.   In the usual *riveting* operation, a solid rivet is placed through holes made in the parts to be fastened together, and the end is pressed to shape by a punch. Hollow rivets may have the ends secured by curling them over the edges of the plate.

Staking is a similar operation in that the metal of one part is upset in such a fashion as to cause it to fit tightly against the other part. A staking punch may have one or more projections on it as shown in the figure, or it may be in the form of a ring with sharp chisel-like edges. Both operations can be performed on small presses as not much pressure is required.

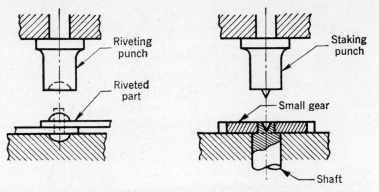

Fig. 10.   Riveting and Staking Processes Used for Fastening Parts Together.

Roll forming.   Cold-roll-forming machines are constructed with a series of mating rolls which progressively form strip metal as it is fed continuously through the machine at speeds ranging from 50 to 300 feet per minute. The number of roll stations depends on the intricacy of the part being formed; for a simple channel four pairs may be used, whereas for more complicated forms several times that number may be required. In addition to the mating horizontal rolls, these machines are frequently equipped with guide rolls mounted vertically to assist in the forming operation and straightening rolls to true up the product as it emerges from the last forming pass.

An example of this method of forming is shown in Figure 11 where tubular sections are being produced by five pairs of rolls. In this case the tubular section enters a resistance welder after being formed and is continuously welded as it passes through the machine. After this operation the flash is removed and the completed tube straightened.

This process is economical for large-quantity production of a uniformly true product. Only bending takes place in the forming, and the metal thickness is uniform throughout. The product may be cut to any length desired, and, with the proper attachments, the formed product may be coiled into shape as is done in the manufacture of bicycle rims. Figure 12 shows a typical variety of shapes that have been roll-formed by this process.

Plate bending. Another method of bending metal plates and strips into cylindrical shapes is by means of a roll-bending machine as

Courtesy The Yoder Company.

FIG. 11*A*. Cold-Roll Tube-Forming Machine. Strip Enters Machine from Coil (not Shown) and Is Bent to Tubular Shape by 5 Pairs of Rolls before Entering Welder Shown in Fig. 11 *B*.

illustrated in Figure 13. This machine is made up of three rolls of the same diameter, two of them being held in a fixed position and one adjustable. As a metal plate enters and goes through the rolls, its final diameter is determined by the position of the adjustable roll; the closer it is moved to the other rolls, the smaller will be the diameter. Machines of this type are made in capacities ranging from those that form small gage thicknesses to others that form heavy plates up to 1¼ inch in thickness.

Seaming. In the manufacture of metal drums, pails, cans, and numerous other products made of light-gage metal, several types of seams are used. The most common of these are shown in Figure 14. The *lock seam* used on longitudinal seams is adapted for joints that do not have to be absolutely tight. After the container is formed, the edges are folded and pressed together. The *compound seam,* sometimes called the Gordon or box seam, is much stronger and tighter than the lock seam and is suitable for holding fine materials. Both these joints may be formed and closed on either hand- or power-seaming presses.

Courtesy The Yoder Company.

FIG. 11*B*. Disk Electrodes in Contact with Tube Being Welded while Edges Are Being Pressed Together by Vertically Mounted Squeeze Rolls.

Bottom seams, which are somewhat similar to the longitudinal seams, are made in either *flat* or *recessed styles.* Flat-bottom recessing is limited to one end of a container, as the container must be open to make the joint. Double seaming with recessed bottoms can be done on both ends of a container. Edge flanging, curling, and flattening, the operations necessary to make a recessed double seam, are shown in the figure.

Double-seaming machines may be hand-operated, semiautomatic, or automatic. Semiautomatic machines must be loaded and unloaded by the operator, but the operation of the machine is automatic. In automatic machines the cans are brought to the machine by conveyor, and ends are supplied by magazine feed. The cans are fed from the conveyor to a star wheel, which transfers them to an automatic delivery turret.   The delivery turret feeds them into position with the seaming heads, and the closing seam is made.

Shot peening.   This method of cold working has recently been developed to improve the fatigue resistance of the metal by setting up compressive stresses in its surface.   This is done by blasting or hurling a rain of small shot at high velocity against the surface to be peened.

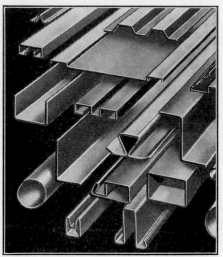

Courtesy The Yoder Company.

FIG. 12.   Small Assortment of Shapes Cold-Roll-Formed from Coiled Strip.

As the shot strikes, small indentations are produced, causing a slight plastic flow of the surface metal to a depth of a few thousandths of an inch.   This stretching of the outer fibers is resisted by those underneath, which tend to return them to their original length, thus producing an outer layer having a compressive stress while those below are in tension.   In addition, the surface is slightly hardened and strengthened by the cold-working operation.   Since fatigue failures result from tension stresses, having the surface in compression greatly offsets any tendency toward such a failure.

Shot peening is done by air blast or by some mechanical means. Figure 15 shows the unit from a machine that utilizes centrifugal force for hurling shot upon the work at a high velocity.   This unit is similar to the one used in the machine shown in Figure 17, Chapter 4, for cleaning castings.   Shot enters the funnel at *A,* which feeds it to the rotating wheel at *G.*   The wheel then discharges the shot at a high velocity by its rotation.   The surface obtained by this action is shown in Figure 16.   The surface roughness or finish can be varied according to the size of shot used.   Stress concentrations due to the roughened

Courtesy Aluminum Corporation of America.

Fig. 13.   Plate Bending Rolls.

surface are offset for the reason that the indentions are close together and no sharp notches exist at the bottom of the pits.*   Intense peening is not to be desired, for it may cause weakening of the steel.

This process adds increased resistance to fatigue failures of working parts and can be used either on parts of irregular shape or on local areas that may be subject to stress concentrations.   Surface hardness and strength are also increased, and, in some cases, the process is used

* H. F. Moore, *Shot Peening and the Fatigue of Metals,* American Foundry Equipment Company, 1944.

to produce a suitable commercial surface finish. However, it is not effective for parts subjected to reversing stresses, nor is its effect appreciable on heavy sections.

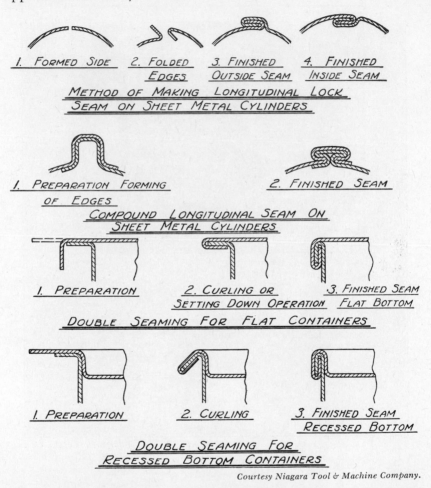

Courtesy Niagara Tool & Machine Company.

Fig. 14. Typical Seams Used in Manufacture of Light-Gage Metal Containers.

Hobbing. Mold cavities, such as shown in Figure 17, may be produced by forcing a hardened steel form or *hob* into soft steel. The hob, machined to the exact form of the piece to be molded, is heat-treated to obtain the necessary hardness and strength to withstand the tremendous pressures involved in the process. Pressing the hob into the blank requires much care, and frequently several alternate pressings and annealing are necessary before the job is complete. During the hobbing operation the flow of metal in the blank is restrained from any appreciable lateral movement by a heavy retainer ring placed

Courtesy American Foundry Equipment Company.

FIG. 15. Unit from Wheelapeening Machine Utilizing Centrifugal Force for Hurling Shot upon Work of High Velocity.

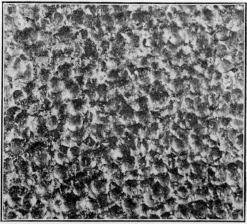

Courtesy American Foundry Equipment Company.

FIG. 16. Surface of SAE 1030 Shot-Peened Steel. Magnification ×7.

around it. The actual pressing is done in hydraulic presses having capacities ranging from 250 to 8000 tons.

The advantage of the process is that multiple cavities may be economically produced which are identical. The surfaces of the cavities have a highly polished finish and no machine work is necessary

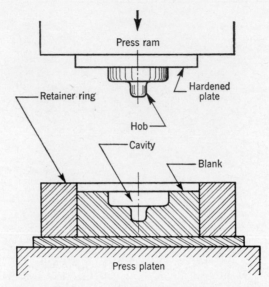

FIG. 17.   Die Hobbing—Producing Mold Cavities by Pressing Hob into Soft Steel.

other than to remove surplus metal from the top and sides of the blank. This process is used a great deal in producing molds for the plastic and die casting industries.

Review Questions

1. Why is shafting usually cold-rolled?
2. Describe the operation of wire drawing.
3. For what type of work is metal spinning used?
4. What is meant by swaging and how is it done?
5. Describe the process of putting heads on small bolts and rivets.
6. How does coining differ from embossing?
7. Distinguish between riveting and staking.
8. For what type of work is roll forming used?
9. Describe the operation of a plate-bending machine.
10. For what purposes is shot peening used?
11. How is die hobbing done?
12. Describe how the fatigue resistance of metal can be improved by cold working.

References

CAMPBELL, J. S., JR., *Casting and Forging Processes in Manufacturing*, McGraw-Hill Book Company, 1950.

KENT's *Mechanical Engineers' Handbook*, 12th edition, John Wiley & Sons, 1950.

Shot Peening, American Wheelabrator & Equipment Company, 1947.

Tool Engineers Handbook, American Society of Tool Engineers, McGraw-Hill Book Company, 1949.

TURNBULL, D. C., "Fatigue Life of Stressed Parts Increased by Shot Peening," *American Machinist*, August 31, 1941.

CHAPTER
10

COLD FORMING OF METALS
PRESS WORK

The machine used for most cold-working operations is known **as** a *press.* It consists of a machine frame supporting a bed and a ram, a source of power, and a mechanism to cause the ram to move in line with and at right angles to the bed.   The illustrations in this chapter show numerous typical designs of press equipment.

A press in itself is not sufficient as a production machine but must be equipped with tools commonly called *dies* and *punches,* designed for certain specific operations.   Although some presses are better adapted for certain types of work than others, most of the forming, punching, and shearing operations can be performed on any standard press if the proper dies and punches are used.   This versatility makes it possible to use the same press for many different jobs and operations, which is a desirable feature for short-run production.

Presses are capable of rapid production, since the actual time of operation is only the time necessary for one stroke of the ram plus the time necessary to feed the stock.   Accordingly, production costs may be kept very low.   Any product that can be fabricated from thin metal and does not require extreme accuracy in dimensional tolerances can be economically made on this type of machine.   Its special adaptation to mass-production methods is evidenced by its wide application in the manufacture of automotive and aircraft parts, hardware specialties, toys, and kitchen appliances.

Types of Presses

A classification of press machines is difficult to make, as most presses are capable of varied types of work.   Hence, it is not entirely correct to call one press a *bending press,* another an *embossing press,* and still another a *blanking press,* since all three types of operations can be done on one machine.   However, some presses, especially designed for one type of operation, may be known by the operation name, as for example, a *punch press,* or a *coining press.* The simplest classification would be according to source of power—either manually operated or power-operated. Many manually operated machines are used for thin sheet-metal work, particularly in jobbing work, but most production machines are power-operated. Other ways of grouping presses would be according to number of rams or method of operating the rams. Most manufacturers name them according to the general design of the frame, although in many cases they are designated according to the power-transmitting arrangement or the main purpose for which the press will be used. If this method of classification is used, most presses can be listed under the following headings:

TYPES OF PRESSES

A. According to design of frame

1. Bench.	3. Gap.	6. Horn.
2. Inclinable.	4. Arch.	7. Pillar.
	5. Straight side.	

B. According to method of applying power to ram

1. Crank.	4. Power screw.	7. Hydraulic.
2. Cam.	5. Rack and pinion.	8. Toggle.
3. Eccentric.	6. Knuckle joint.	9. Pneumatic.

C. According to purpose of press

1. Squaring shears.	6. Seaming.	10. Transfer.
2. Circle shears.	7. Straightening.	11. Knibbler.
3. Brake.	8. Forcing.	12. Stretching.
4. Punching.	9. Coining.	13. Turret.
5. Extruding.		14. Forging.

In the selection of the type of press to use for a given job, a number of factors must be considered. Among these are the kind of operation to be performed, size of the part being worked upon, power required, and speed of operation. For most punching, blanking, and trimming operations, crank or eccentric-type presses are generally used. In these presses the energy of the flywheel may be transmitted to the main shaft either directly or through a gear train. For coining, squeezing, or forging operations, the knuckle-joint press is ideally suited. It has a short stroke and is capable of exerting a tremendous force. Presses for drawing operations normally operate at slower speeds than for operations such as blanking, and hydraulically operated presses are especially desirable for this work. The standard practice is not to exceed 65 feet per minute when working mild steel; however, aluminum and other nonferrous metals may be worked at speeds up to 125 and 150 feet per minute. Hydraulic presses may also be used for forging, straightening, sizing, and similar operations.

Inclined press. In Figure 1 is shown a single-action, single-crank, permanently inclined high-speed press having a capacity of 56 tons.

Courtesy Verson Allsteel Press Company.

FIG. 1.   Single-Action, Single-Crank, Permanently Inclined High-Speed Press.

The equipment on the right side of the press consists of a single-roll feed with a five-roll stock straightener and oiler. The fact that the frame of the machine is inclined is of value in discharging the work or scrap from the press. With the table in an inclined position parts can slide by gravity into a tote box, or material may be fed by chute into the dies. Most inclinable presses, however, are adjustable and may be varied from the vertical to a rather steep angle position. For diversified press work this arrangement is to be preferred as many jobs are best done with the press in a vertical position—this is particularly true if the parts are discharged through the die.

Inclinable presses are often preferred in the production of small parts involving bending, punching, shearing, and similar operations.

Arch press. The arch-type press shown in Figure 2 is named from the peculiar shape of its frame. The lower part of the frame near the bed is wide to permit the working of large-area sheet metal; the upper part is narrow. The crankshafts are small in relation to the area of the slide and press bed, as these presses are not designed for heavy work. The press in the figure is shown set up for a blanking operation on light-gage metal, which is typical of the work this press is designed to do. It is also used for stamping, bending, and trimming in the manufacture of large-sized paint cans and numerous other tin products. Other applications are the blanking and forming of shovels, the embossing of letters on metal panels, and the manufacture of kitchenware.

Gap press. Gap or C-frame presses are so named because of the open throat arrangement of the press frame. This design provides excellent clearance about the dies and permits the press to be used for long or wide parts. The usual stamping operations may be performed on a gap press, and frequently the inclinable feature is used with this type frame.

Courtesy E. W. Bliss Company.

Fig. 2. Blanking Operation on an Arch Press.

Straight-side press. As the capacity of a press is increased, it becomes necessary to increase the strength and rigidity of the frame. Straight-side presses accomplish this as loads imposed on the dies are taken up in a vertical direction by the heavy side frames and there is little tendency for punch and die alignment to be affected by the strain.

Presses of this type are made with many variations in means of supplying power and the method of operation. For the smaller presses a single crank or eccentric usually furnishes the power, but, as the size of the work increases, additional cranks are necessary to distribute the load on the slide uniformly. A straight-side, double-crank press, equipped with roller feed for moving stock across dies in a perforating operation, is shown in Figure 3. This press is a single-acting press; that is, there is only one driven ram used in the press operation.

Courtesy Niagara Machine & Tool Works.

FIG. 3. Straight-Side Double-Crank Press.

Double-acting presses, used a great deal for drawing operations, have an outer ram which precedes the punch and clamps the blank before the drawing operation. The outer ram is usually driven by a special link motion or cams, whereas the inner ram carrying the punch is crank-driven. Drawing operations may also be performed on a single-acting press by clamping the blank with a holding ring backed up with air cushions below the bolster plate.

Figure 4 is a view of a large straight-side toggle press drawing steel tops for automobiles. Pressure is applied on the slide in four places, which is a distinct advantage in large-area presses, as such construction prevents tilting of the slide with unbalanced loads. This press is a double-acting toggle press, with built-in air-cushion drawing attachments.

The *toggle* mechanism in this machine is for the purpose of controlling the motion of the blank holder.   "A toggle mechanism may

Courtesy E. W. Bliss Company.

FIG. 4.   Double-Action Toggle Press Forming Steel Tops for Automobiles.

be described as a grouping of cranks, levers, and slides with the necessary connecting links, so arranged that the train of movement may contain several dead-center positions at approximately the same time. If the motion is so controlled that the several points pass through dead center a little way and back through it again in returning, the effective dwell period may be extended within certain limits."* The dwell period means an interval of time during which there is no motion of the blank holder. This is necessary for blank holding on

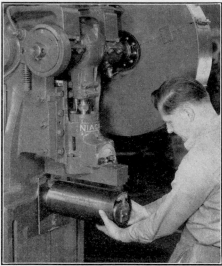

Courtesy Niagara Machine & Tool Works.

FIG. 5. Horn Press Equipped for Side-Seaming Operation.

drawing operations, and it is frequently advisable to have a slight dwell on the punch to allow the metal to adjust itself properly under pressure.

Straight-side presses are used on both mechanical and hydraulic presses. Typical operations performed by this type of press include work on heavy-gage metal, forging, coining, and deep drawing.

Horn press. Horn presses are provided with a heavy shaft in place of the usual bed, or, if a bed is included, provision is made to swing it to one side when the horn is used. Figure 5 shows a horn press set up for a side-seaming operation. This press is used a great deal for work on cylindrical objects involving seaming, flanging edges, punching, riveting, and embossing.

Press brake. A press brake, arranged for corrugating light-gage metal, is shown in Figure 6B, and Figure 6A above illustrates die setups for the progressive forming of a large bead on the edge of a long plate of steel. This figure illustrates the adaptability of this machine for

* E. V. Crane, *Plastic Working of Metals*, John Wiley & Sons, p. 302.

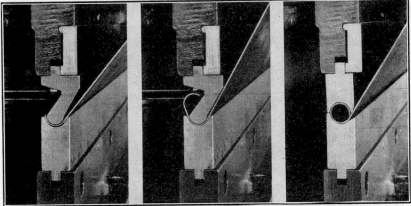

FIG. 6A. Progressive Forming of Bead on Press Brake.

FIG. 6B. Corrugating Light-Gage Metal with Press Brake.

processing large sheets of relatively thin metal. Aside from the usual brake or forming operations, a press of this type may be used for corrugating, seaming, embossing, trimming, and multiple punching. These presses are made in lengths ranging from 4 to 20 feet, with metal thickness ranging from light gage to 5/8 inch.

The pressure capacity of a press brake required for a given material is determined by the length of work it will take, the thickness of the metal, and the radius of the bend. The minimum inside radius of a bend is usually limited to a radius equal to the thickness of the

Courtesy The Cincinnati Shaper Company.

FIG. 7.   Metal Shear—Capacity 1/4 Inch × 10 Feet.

material; however, the thickness rating of a press can be increased slightly if a larger radius is used. For bending operations the required pressure varies directly as the tensile strength of the material. Press brakes have short strokes and are generally equipped with an eccentric-type drive mechanism.

Squaring shears. This machine is used entirely for shearing sheets of steel and is made in both manual and power-operated sizes. Figure 7 shows a large shear capable of shearing sheets up to a width of 10 feet. Hydraulic hold-down plungers are provided every 12 inches to prevent any movement of the sheet during the cutting operation. In operation the sheet is advanced on the bed so that the line of cut is under the shear. When the foot treadle is depressed, the hold-down plungers come down, and the shearing blade cuts progressively across the sheet.

Turret press. The principal features of the press shown in Figure 8 are the upper and lower turrets designed for carrying the different-size punches and dies. The two turrets are geared together and, when operating, are securely locked in position for exact alignment. The table shown in front of the machine with its cross slide offers an accurate and convenient means of locating the sheet under the punching

Courtesy Wiedemann Machine Company.

FIG. 8. Turret Punch Press in Operation.

station. When a number of identical parts are to be made, a fixed template is prepared and, if the template is followed with the movable stylus, all holes are accurately positioned. The large hand wheel just below the table is used for rotating the turret. Other machines of this general type have gaging tables which accurately position the work under the turret by turning two hand wheels in front of the operator.

These punches are designed to handle short-run production and jobbing work in an efficient manner. Aside from ordinary metal punching, these machines can also be set up for slotting, embossing, notching, and louver operations.

Power screw or percussion press. Figure 9 shows a percussion press adapted for applications where a hard end pressure is required. The friction drive accelerates the flywheel gradually on the down stroke, and all its energy is utilized as it comes to a stop striking the work. Regulation of the blow is obtained by raising or lowering the position of the die. If the die is raised, the flywheel is stopped at a higher point and has less force, since its speed is less. For a given setting the

Courtesy Zeh & Hahnemann Company.

Fig. 9. Percussion Power Press.

blows are the same, and overloading is impossible. Since all the force of the blow is absorbed in the frame of the machine, expensive foundations are unnecessary.

Small machines of this type are used for striking medals and signet rings, stamping and embossing jewelry, and similar applications. Larger machines can be used for cold-stamping and pressing small metal parts as well as for hot pressing brass and other forgeable metals.

The largest of these machines, exerting 50,000 foot-pounds per stroke, can be used to replace drop-forging operations.

The hot pressing of brass (60% copper and 40% zinc) has proved very satisfactory with this type of press.

Knuckle-joint press. Presses designed for coining, sizing, and heavy embossing must be quite massive to withstand the large concentrated loads imposed upon them. The press shown in Figure 10 is designed for this purpose and is equipped with a *knuckle-joint mechanism* for actuating the slide. The upper link or knuckle of this point is hinged at the upper part of the frame at one end and fastened to a wrist pin at the other. The lower link also is attached to the same wrist pin and the other end to the slide. A third link is fastened to the ends of the wrist pin and acts in a horizontal direction to move the joint. As the two knuckle links are brought into a straight-line position, tremendous force is exerted by the slide. The press shown in the figure has a capacity of 150 tons.

This type of press has always been widely used in the striking of coins. According to tests made at the Philadelphia

Courtesy E. W. Bliss Company.

Fig. 10. Knuckle-Joint Press.

United States Mint, a pressure of 98 tons is required to bring out clear impressions on silver half dollars made in a closed die.

Aside from striking coins, many other parts, such as medals, key blanks, car tokens, license plates, watch cases and silverware, are cold-pressed in this type of machine. Sizing, cold heading, straightening, heavy stamping, and similar operations can also be performed on this machine. As the stroke of this type of press is short and slow, it is not adapted to some of the usual press operations.

Hydraulic press. Hydraulic presses have longer strokes than mechanical presses and develop full tonnage throughout the entire stroke.   However, the capacity of these presses is readily adjustable, and only a fraction of the tonnage may be used if desired.   Also the length of the strokes may be adjusted to whatever is needed.   The presses are especially adapted to deep-drawing operations because of their slow uniform motion.   They are also used for numerous other

Courtesy Watson Stillman Company.

Fig. 11.   800-Ton Double-Action Drawing and Forming Hydraulic Press.

press operations requiring heavy tonnage such as briquetting powdered metals, extruding, laminating, plastic molding, and press forging. They are not recommended for heavy blanking and punching operations as the break-through shock is detrimental to the press. Maintenance is higher than for mechanical presses even though the operation of the press is much slower.

The 800-ton press shown in Figure 11 is a self-contained unit with all pumping equipment mounted on top of the press.   It is of the four-column-type construction and is adapted for drawing and forming operations.

Fig. 12. Special Presses Form a Tube out of Flat Steel in Three Operations.

Press for forming pipe. The three special hydraulic presses in Figure 12 progressively form 40-foot skelp into large tubes up to 26 inches in diameter. The skelp is formed to a U shape in the first press and to a near tubular section in the second and closed to a tubular form in the third. The joint is closed by flash welding, after

Courtesy Verson Allsteel Press Company.

FIG. 13. Loading End of 10-Station Transfer Press Producing 6-Inch and 8-Inch Trim Rings and Drip Pans for Electric Ranges.

which the flash is removed, the ends are faced, and the pipe is sized, straightened, and tested. Other methods of forming pipe are discussed in the previous chapter.

Transfer press. Presses of this type are fully automatic and capable of performing consecutive operations simultaneously. Figure 13 shows the loading end of a 250-ton, 10-station press for producing circular parts for electric ranges. In this case round blanks are loaded in the stack feeder, but roll or other type feeders may be used if desired. In operation the stock is moved from one station to the next by a mechanism synchronized with the motion of the slide. Each die is a separate unit and is provided with a punch which may be independently adjusted from the main slide.

The economic use of transfer presses is dependent upon quantity production, as their usual production rate is 500 to 1500 parts per hour. Typical products made by this equipment include headlight bodies, brake-drum shells, ice-cube trays, refrigerator doors, and stove parts.

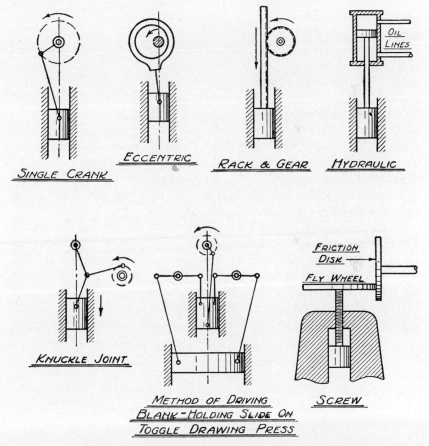

FIG. 14.   Various Drive Mechanisms Used on Presses.

Drive Mechanism Used on Presses

Figure 14 shows most of the drive mechanisms used in presses for transmitting power to the slide. The type of mechanism used in a given press is determined largely by the kind of work that is to be done.

The most common drive is the *single crank,* which gives a movement to the slide approaching simple harmonic motion. On a down stroke the slide is accelerated, reaching its maximum velocity at midstroke, and is then decelerated. Most press operations occur near the middle of the stroke, at maximum slide velocity. The *eccentric drive* gives a motion like that of a crank and is often used where a shorter stroke is desired. Some proponents of this drive claim for it greater rigidity and less tendency for deflection than a crank drive might have. *Cams* are used where some special movement is desired, such as a dwell at the bottom of the stroke. This drive has some similarity to the eccentric drive, except that roll followers are used to transmit the motion to the slide.

Rack and gear presses are used only where a very long stroke is desired. The movement of the slide is much slower than in crank presses, and uniform motion is attained. Such presses are provided with stops to control the stroke length and may be equipped with some quick-return feature to raise the slide back to starting position. The common arbor press is a familiar example of this type.

Hydraulic drive is used in many presses for a wide variety of work. It is especially adapted to large pressures and slow speeds in forming, pressing, and drawing operations.

In the *screw* drive, the slide is accelerated by means of the friction disk engaging the flywheel, and, as the flywheel moves down, greater speed is applied to it. From beginning to end of the stroke, the slide motion is an accelerated one. At the bottom of the stroke the entire amount of stored energy is absorbed by the work. The action resembles that of a drop hammer, but it is slower and there is less impact.

Several link mechanisms are used in press drives, either because of the type of motion they have or because of the mechanical advantage they develop. The *knuckle joint* is very commonly used, because it has a high mechanical advantage near the bottom of the stroke when the two links approach a straight line. Because of the high load capacity of this mechanism, it is used for coining and sizing operations. The drive may be eccentric or hydraulic in place of the crank shown in the figure. *Toggle mechanisms,* used primarily as a means of holding the blank on a drawing operation, are made in a variety of designs. The auxiliary slide in the figure is actuated by a crank, but eccentrics or cams may likewise be used. The principal aim of this mechanism is to obtain a motion having a suitable dwell so that the blank may be held effectively.

Feed Mechanisms

Safety is a paramount consideration in press operation, and every precaution must be taken to protect the operator. Wherever possible, material should be fed to the dies by some means that eliminates any chance of the operator having his hands near the dies. In long-run production jobs such features can be economically worked out in various ways. Feeding devices are best applied to small- and medium-sized presses and have the advantage of rapid uniform machine feeding in addition to the safety features.

Courtesy F. J. Littell Machine Company.

Fig. 15. Littell 12-Station Dial Feed.

One of the most common types of feeding mechanisms is the double-roll feed, as shown on the presses in Figures 1 and 3. The operation of the rolls is controlled by an eccentric on the crankshaft through a linkage to a ratchet wheel. Each time the ram moves up, the rolls turn and feed the proper amount of material for the next stroke. By providing the machine with a variable eccentric, the amount of stock fed through the rolls can easily be varied.   The rolls are relieved before the stroke to permit proper alignment of the stock.   For heavy material, straightening rolls can be used which also act as feeding rolls.

Another type of feeding device is the dial-station feed shown in Figure 15.   This method is designed to take care of single parts previously blanked or formed in some other press.   Again the indexing is controlled by an eccentric on the crankshaft through a suitable link mechanism to the dial.   Each time a stroke is made, the dial indexes one station.   All feeding by the operator takes place at the front of the machine away from the dies.

Light parts can be stacked in a magazine and successfully placed in position by a suction device.   A blank is lifted off the top of the stack by suction fingers and placed against a stop gage on the die. Magazine feeds may also be used with a reciprocating mechanism which feeds blanks from the bottom of the stack.   Gravity feed is sometimes used on inclined presses, the blank sliding into a recess at the top of the die.

Punches and Dies

The tools used in most presses come under the general heading of punches and dies.   The *punch* refers to that part of the assembly which is attached to the ram of the press and is forced into the die cavity; the *die* is usually stationary and rests on the press bed.   It has an opening to receive the punch, and the two must be in perfect alignment for proper operation.   Punches and dies are not interchangeable, but must work together as a unit.   A single press may do a large variety of operations, depending on the type of dies used.

Dies may be classified according to either the way they operate or the type of work they can do.   A simple classification including most dies is as follows:

TYPES OF DIES

A. According to method of operation or construction

1. Simple.	4. Transfer.
2. Compound.	5. Hydraulic.
3. Progressive.	6. Rubber.

B. According to type of work performed

1. Bending—angle bending, curling, folding, and seaming.
2. Drawing—forming tubes, cupping, bulging, embossing, and reducing.
3. Squeezing—coining, sizing, flattening, swaging, cold forging, riveting, upsetting, hot pressing, and extruding.
4. Shearing—blanking, trimming, cutting off, punching, perforating, notching, slitting, and shaving.

A simple blanking punch and die are shown in Figure 16. The parts that do the cutting are made of tool steel and are built in as inserts. The punch is made up of a holder having a shank and the tool-steel punch. The shank of the punch fits into the press slide or a punch plate attached to the slide. The die is supported on a cast-steel die shoe which, in turn, is fastened to the bolster plate on the press bed. The die shown in the figure is designed for blanking disks from strip metal. Steel is fed in the opening at one end of the die up

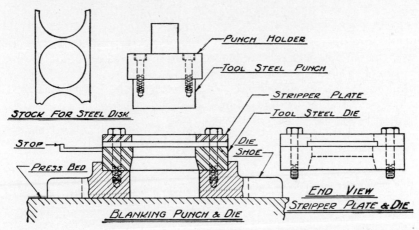

FIG. 16. Blanking Punch and Die.

to a stop provided at the other end. The steel plate over the stock is called a stripper plate, since it holds the blanked strip in place as the punch moves up to its starting position. Blanks which have been sheared by the punch drop through it to a container underneath the press.

The clearance between punch and die will vary according to the type of material being processed. It is expressed in percentage of stock thickness and ranges from 5 to 12%.* The smaller percentages are for small work and soft materials; larger jobs using a fairly hard steel require more clearance.

A typical forming die, designed to bend a flat strip of steel to a U shape, is shown in Figure 17. The punch holder is made large and is provided with accurate holes to fit with the guide rods set in the die shoe. As the punch descends and forms the piece, the knockout plate is pressed down, compressing the spring at the bottom of the press. When the punch moves up, the plate forces the work out of

* F. A. Stanley, *Punches and Dies*, McGraw-Hill Book Company.

the die with the aid of the spring. Such an arrangement is necessary in most forming operations, as the formed metal presses against the walls of the die, making its removal difficult. Parts that tend to stick to the punch are removed by a knockout pin which is engaged on the up stroke.

Compound dies are those that combine two or more operations at one station such as the punch and die illustrated in Figure 18. In

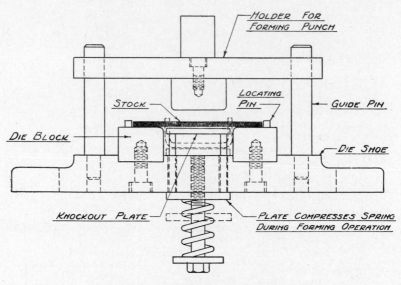

FIG. 17. Forming Punch and Die.

this case strip stock is progressively moved through the die, and, each time the press slide descends, two holes are punched, and the piece is blanked. When the operations are not similar, as in the case of a blanking and forming operation, dies of this type are frequently known as combination dies.

A *progressive* die set is one that performs two or more operations simultaneously but at different stations. A punch and die set of this type is shown in Figure 19. As the strip enters the die, the small square hole is first punched. The stock is then advanced to the next station where it is properly positioned by the pilot as the blanking punch descends to complete the part. This general type of design is simpler than the construction necessary for compound dies as the respective operations are not crowded together. Regardless of the number of operations to be performed, the finished part is not separated from the strip block until the last operation. A progressive die set which performs 15 operations on a can opener, completing one at each stroke, is shown in Figure 20. Production is rapid with this type of die, but close tolerances are difficult to maintain.

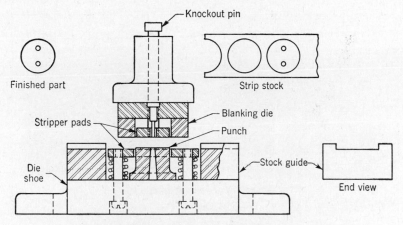

FIG. 18. Compound Punch and Die.

Misalignment of punch and die causes excessive pressures, shearing or chipping of die edges, or actual breaking of the tools. Such action may occur through shifting, even though the setup is originally

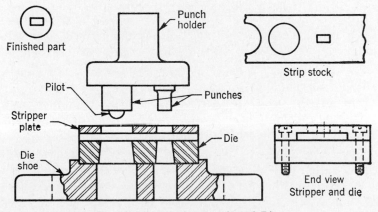

FIG. 19. Progressive Punch and Die.

correct. To prevent such occurrences, proper alignment is insured by providing guide rods at two or four corners of the die which fit into holes provided in the punch holder. Such dies are known as *pillar dies*. This arrangement of having the punch and die always held in proper alignment greatly facilitates the setting up of the tools. A similar arrangement, known as a *subpress die* (occasionally used on small work), employs a punch and die mounted in a small

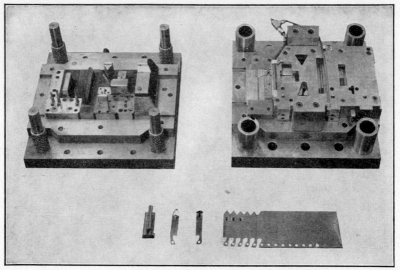

FIG. 20. Progressive Die Set Which Performs 15 Operations on Can Openers and Completes One at Each Stroke.

frame so that accurate alignment is always maintained. Pressure is applied by a plunger which extends out of the top of the assembly.

Special Forming Processes

Guerin process. This process greatly reduces the cost of dies in the blanking and forming of thin sheet required for aircraft manufacture. In place of expensive steel-mating dies, it employs a single die of low-cost material and a thick pad of rubber which adapts itself to the die while under pressure. Sheet metal placed between the resilient pad and the die can be cut readily or formed to the desired shape.

Rubber has proved satisfactory in this work because of its similarity to a fluid when properly restrained. Thick pads are mounted on the moving platen of the press and held in a container which extends about 1 inch past the pad. On the bed of the press is mounted a pressing block which fits into the container recess and upon which are mounted the cutting and forming dies. As the platen moves down and the rubber is confined, the force of the ram is exerted evenly in all directions, resulting in the sheet metal being pressed against the die block as illustrated in Figure 21. Cutting die blocks are merely steel templates of the required parts and need not be over ⅜ inch thick. Forming dies may be made of Masonite, wood, aluminum, and magnesium, as well as of steel.

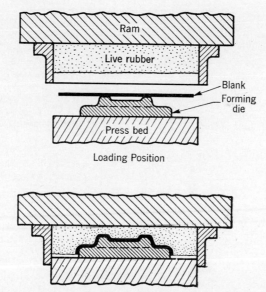

Loading Position

Forming Complete

Fig. 21. Method for Forming Sheet Metal Using Single Die and Rubber Pad.

This process is limited in the cutting of soft aluminum to sheet thickness up to 0.051 inch. For bending and forming, the usual limit is around ³⁄₁₆ inch thick. Thin gages of stainless steel may also be fabricated, and magnesium alloys may be hot-formed. In the latter application heater plates are mounted on the loading table, and the form blocks are maintained at the correct temperature.

The advantages of this process include simplicity of tooling, low tooling cost, use of gang setups, minimum material waste, uniform pressure on the metal, and adaptability to various press operations.

Marform process.* This process is somewhat similar to the one just described and represents a further development in forming technique which permits the deep drawing and forming of irregularly shaped parts without certain defects heretofore present in these

* Developed by the Glenn L. Martin Company.

operations. A confined rubber pad is used on the movable platen
of the press, and a stationary punch is located below, as shown in
Figure 22. In the operation shown, a metal cup is in the process of
being formed. At the start of the operation, a flat piece of metal is
placed on the blank holder plate which is then flush with the top of

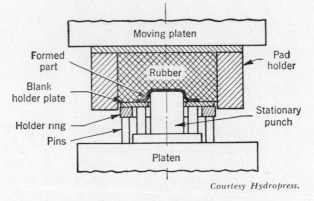

Courtesy Hydropress.

Fɪɢ. 22. Arrangement of the Marform Components in a Forming Operation.

the punch. As the movable platen descends, the rubber pad contacts
the blank and clamps it securely against both the top of punch and
surrounding plate. As the downward movement continues, the blank
is formed over the end of the punch, and at the same time sufficient
pressure is exerted over the unformed portion so that no wrinkling of
the metal occurs. In this respect the process is superior to the Guerin
process, as in the latter the pressure on the blank at the start of the
draw does not build up to the point where wrinkles are prevented.
During the drawing operation, the downward movement of the blank
holding plate is opposed by pressure pins which are hydraulically
operated and can be controlled to exert any pressure desired. Any
tendency for tearing around the top of the drawn piece is materially
decreased as the rubber locks the drawn metal against the punch as
the operation continues.

A complete Marform unit is mounted in the four-column hydraulic
press shown in Figure 23. This unit may be removed if it is desired
to use the press for other operations. Advantages claimed for this
process are deeper draws than are possible in one operation by other
methods, low tooling costs, no damage to surface finish, and the possibility of forming tapered and other difficult shapes economically.
Shearing is also possible by providing undercuts in the punch or blank

holder plate. In the forming of aluminum, sheets ranging from 0.010 to 0.675 inch thickness have been processed.

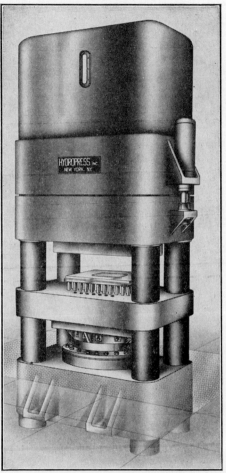

Courtesy Hydropress.

Fig. 23. Hydraulic Four-Column Press Arranged for Marforming.

Hydrodynamic process.* This process is designed for shallow forming and embossing operations of thin metal by hydraulic means. The die arrangement used in the process is shown in Figure 24, and, when in actual operation, it is mounted on a hydraulic press, the

* Covered by U. S. Patents 2,066,085, 2,399,775, and 2,156,889.

pressure-pad holder and forming die being attached, respectively, to the lower and upper platens. The cycle of operation consists of laying a blank upon the pressure pad, closing the dies, and turning on the high-pressure water. A uniform fluid pressure. (acting as the punch)

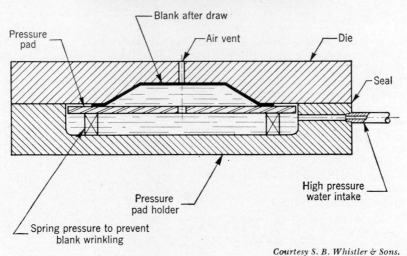

Fig. 24. Dies Used in Hydrodynamic Process for Forming Tapered Part Shown Above.

is exerted on the entire blank area, and there are no localized strains involved. Many odd-shaped and tapered pieces can be readily formed to shape in one operation by this process, as illustrated by the tapered part shown in the figure.

Review Questions

1. List the various operations that can be done with press equipment.
2. What advantages does an inclined press have over one with a rigid frame?
3. Describe an arch press, and state the type of work for which it is designed.
4. How does a double-acting press operate, and for what type of work is it used?
5. What type of work is a press brake used for?
6. Describe the operation of a screw or percussion press.
7. Show by sketches how a knuckle-joint mechanism operates. On what type of press is it used?

8. For what type of press work do you recommend the use of hydraulically operated presses?

9. What is a transfer press, and for what type of work is it used?

10. List and describe briefly five types of press drives.

11. Distinguish between the Guerin and Marform processes.

12. Describe the hydrodynamic process of forming.

13. What is a compound die?

14. Illustrate the use of a progressive die by some part that can be made in this manner.

15. What type of press do you recommend for each of the following jobs: Forming steel tops for automobiles, stamping coins, making corrugated iron siding, forming stiffening ribs for airplane wings, and drawing brake drums for automobile wheels?

References

BROOTZKOOS, S. D., *The Selection of Presses*, Dryden Press, 1941.

CAMP, J. M., and C. B. FRANCIS, *The Making, Shaping and Treating of Steel*, 5th edition, Carnegie-Illinois Steel Corporation.

CHARNOCK, G. F., and F. W. PARTINGTON, *Mechanical Technology*, 2d edition, Constable & Company, London, 1934.

CORY, C. R., *Die Design Manual*, Parts I and II, General Motors Corporation, 1939.

CRANE, E. V., *Plastic Working of Metals and Nonmetallic Materials in Presses*, 3d edition, John Wiley & Sons, 1944.

HINMAN, C. W., *Die Engineering Layouts and Formulas*, McGraw-Hill Book Company, 1943.

HINMAN, C. W., *Press Working of Metals*, McGraw-Hill Book Company, 1941.

JEVONS, J. D., and W. W. SWIFT, *The Metallurgy of Deep Drawing and Pressing*, John Wiley & Sons, 1942.

SCHULZE, R. B., "Deep and Tapered Stampings Without Wrinkles," *Metal Progress*, June 1950.

STANLEY, F. A., *Punches and Dies*, McGraw-Hill Book Company, 1937.

Tool Engineers Handbook, American Society of Tool Engineers, McGraw-Hill Book Company, 1949.

CHAPTER

II

POWDER METALLURGY

Powder metallurgy is the art of producing commercial products from metallic powders by pressure. Heat may or may not be used in the process; if it is, the temperature is kept below the melting point of the powder. The application of heat during the process or subsequently is known as *sintering* and results in bonding the fine particles together, thus improving the strength and other properties of the finished product. Sintering is also defined as "the process by which solid bodies are bonded by atomic forces."[*] Products made by powder metallurgy are frequently alloyed or contain nonmetallic constituents. Such combinations may be made to improve the bonding qualities of the particles, but more frequently the purpose is to improve certain properties or characteristics of the final product. For example, cobalt or other metals are necessary in the bonding of tungsten carbide particles, whereas graphite is added with bearing-metal powders to improve the lubricating qualities of the finished bearing. Electric contacts are alloyed, because, in addition to having good heat and electric conductivity, they must also be wear-resistant and somewhat refractory.

To be economical, powder-metal parts must be produced in large quantities. Metal is higher in cost in powder form than in solid form, and the process requires expensive dies and machines. This higher cost is often justified by the unusual properties obtained. Some products cannot be made by any other process; others made by this process compete favorably with their counterparts made by other methods, because the close tolerances maintained in this process eliminate the necessity of any further processing.

Important Characteristics of Metal Powders

Since the particle size, shape, and size distribution of metal powders have definite effects on the characteristics and physical properties of

[*] P. E. Wretblad and J. Wulff, "Sintering," *Powder Metallurgy*, American Society for Metals, 1942, p. 36.

the compacted product, powders are produced according to certain specifications. The points covered in specifications are structure or shape, fineness, particle-size distribution, flowability, chemical properties, compressibility, apparent specific gravity, and sintering properties.

The *shape* of a powder particle, depending largely on how it was produced, may be spherical, ragged, dendritic, flat, angular, or otherwise. Although the shape is important, the manufacturer is limited in his selection by the method through which a given metal can be produced. *Fineness* may be determined by passing the powder through a standard sieve or by microscopic measurement. Standard sieves ranging from 100 to 325 mesh are used for checking sizes and also for determining particle-size distribution within that range. *Particle-size distribution* is also important, since it has considerable influence in determining the flowability and apparent density, as well as the final porosity, of the product. Once it is established for a product, it cannot be varied appreciably without affecting the size of the compact. *Flowability* is that characteristic of a powder which permits it to flow readily and conform to the mold cavity. It can be described as the rate of flow through a definite orifice. *Chemical* properties have to do with the purity of the powder, amount of oxides permitted, and the percentage of other elements allowed. Clean surfaces on particles are essential for attaining desired mechanical properties. *Compressibility* of powders, which varies considerably, is influenced by the particle-size distribution and shape. Dependent on this characteristic is the green strength of the powders which must be sufficient to hold the pressed forms together in the manufacturing operations. Compressibility may be expressed as a ratio of the volume of initial powder to the volume of the compressed piece. The *apparent density* or specific gravity of a powder may be expressed in grams per cubic centimeter. As the apparent density decreases, it is necessary to use more powder to produce a part. It should therefore be kept constant so that the same amount of powder can be fed into the die each time. *Sintering* ability should be good and should not require too narrow a temperature range. Procedures for testing most of the above characteristics may be found in ASTM and Metal Powder Association Standards.

Methods of Producing Powders

Although all metals can be produced in the powder form, only a few find wide application in the manufacture of pressed-metal parts. Some lack the desired characteristics or properties described above which are necessary for economical production. The two principal types in use are the iron- and copper-base powders. Both lend themselves well to this process and are produced in a wide variety of alloys. While bronze is used in porous bearings, brass and iron are more often used in small machine parts. Other powders of steel, nickel silver, tungsten, and aluminum alloys have a limited but important application in the field of powder metallurgy.

Metal powders, because of their individual physical and chemical characteristics, cannot all be manufactured the same way. The procedures vary widely, as do the sizes and structures of the particles obtained from the various processes. Machining results in coarse particles and is used principally for producing magnesium powders. Milling processes, utilizing various types of crushers, rotary mills, and stamping mills, break down the metals by crushing and impact. Brittle materials may be reduced to irregular shapes of almost any fineness by this method; however, the process is also used in pigment manufacture for ductile materials. With ductile materials, flake particles are obtained, an oil being used in the process to keep them from sticking together. *Shotting* is the operation of pouring molten metal through a sieve or orifice and cooling by dropping into water. Spherical or pear-shaped particles are obtained by this process. Most metals can be shotted, but the size of the particles is too large in many instances. *Atomization,* or the operation of metal spraying, is an excellent means of producing powders from many of the low-temperature metals such as lead, aluminum, zinc, and tin. The particles are irregular in shape and are produced over quite a range of size distribution. A few metals can be converted into small particles by rapidly stirring the metal while it is cooling. This process, known as *granulation,* depends on the formation of oxides on the individual particles during the stirring operation. *Electrolytic deposition* is a common means for processing copper, iron, tantalum, silver, and several other metals. The characteristic structure obtained by this method is dendritic, and the apparent density is low. Reducing metal oxides in powder form by contact with a reducing gas at temperatures below the melting point is an economical method for some metals. Tungsten, iron, molybdenum, nickel, and cobalt are all produced commercially by this process.

Various other methods involving precipitation, condensation, and other chemical processes have been developed for producing powdered metals. These methods as well as some of those previously mentioned are not widely used but prove satisfactory for some metals. Production cost for metal powders should gradually be reduced, as further research develops the processes and the demand for powder-compacted products increases.

Pressing to Shape

Powder for a given product must be carefully selected to insure economical production and to obtain the desired properties in the final compact. If only one powder is to be used in the product, no additional processing or blending will be necessary before pressing, unless the particle-size distribution is not correct. In some cases various sizes of powder particles are mixed together to change such characteristics as flowability or density; but most powder is produced with sufficient particle-size variation to make mixing unnecessary. Mixing or blending becomes necessary in production when the powders are alloyed or when nonmetallic particles are added. Any mixing or processing of the powder must be done under conditions that will not permit oxidation or defects to develop.

Practically all powders have lubricants added in the blending operation to reduce die wall friction and to aid in the ejection. Although these lubricants add to the porosity, they permit a greatly increased production rate and are necessary in presses using automatic powder feed. Lubricants used include stearic acid, lithium stearate, and powdered graphite. If hand feeds are used, the lubricant may be omitted in the powder and the die cavity coated manually.

Powders are pressed to shape in steel dies under pressures ranging from a few thousand to 200,000 pounds per square inch. Because the soft particles can be pressed or keyed together quite readily, powders that are plastic do not require so high a pressure as the harder powders to obtain adequate density. Quite obviously, the density and hardness increase with the pressure; but in every case there is an optimum pressure above which little advantage in improved properties can be obtained. Furthermore, owing to the necessity for strong dies and large capacity presses, production costs increase with high pressures.

Many of the commercial presses developed for other materials are adaptable for use in powder metallurgy. Though mechanically operated presses are generally used because of their high rate of production, hydraulic presses may be employed if the part is large and high pressures are required. Two types are common: the single-punch press and the high-speed rotary multiple-punch press. Both types of presses are designed so that their operation from the filling of the cavity with powder to the ejection of the finished compact can be either continuous or a single cycle. Rotary table presses have a high rate of production, as they are equipped with a series of die cavities, each provided with top and bottom punches. In the course of production the table indexes around, and the operations of filling, pressing, and ejecting the product are accomplished at the various stations. Presses of this type are designed with 6 to 35 stations, and production rates up to 1000 compacts per minute can be obtained in some cases.

A large machine, combining both mechanical and hydraulic means of operation, is shown in Figure 1. The upper punch is controlled

Courtesy Kux Machine Company.

FIG. 1. Rotary Press for Compressing Powdered Metals into Solid Form.

by a toggle mechanism and the lower by hydraulic means which provides pressures up to 150 tons. This machine is automatic in its operation and is capable of 15 strokes a minute. Compacts up to 6 inches in diameter can be made, and the maximum depth of fill is 6 inches.

In Figure 2 is shown a press setup for compacting small pinions from metal powders. Many products similar to this are entirely completed by the pressing operation and require no further processing other than sintering. The sintering operation increases the strength and improves the crystalline structure. Another method used is to combine the pressing and heating operations. Although this procedure has certain advantages in improved properties, it is more difficult to accomplish.

Courtesy Moraine Products Division of General Motors Corporation.

FIG. 2.   Pressing Small Pinions from Powdered Metal.

Sintering

The operation of heating a "green compact" to an elevated temperature is known as *sintering*.   As previously stated, it is the process by
which solid bodies are bonded by atomic forces.   Baeza* states that by
the application of heat the particles are pressed into more intimate
contact, and the effectiveness of surface-tension reactions is increased.
Plasticity is increased, and there is a possibility that better mechanical
interlocking is produced by building a fluid network.   Also, any inter-
fering gas phase present is removed by the heat.   The temperatures
used in sintering are usually well below the melting point of the principal powder constituent but may vary over a wide range up to a temper-

* W. J. Baeza, *A Course in Powder Metallurgy*, Reinhold Publishing Company.

ature just below the melting point. Tests have proved that there is usually an optimum sintering temperature for a given set of conditions, with nothing to be gained by going above this temperature. Aside from the temperature, other factors in sintering are time and atmosphere. The time element varies with different metals, but in most cases the effect of the heating is complete in a very short time, and there is no economy in prolonging the operation. Atmosphere is nearly always

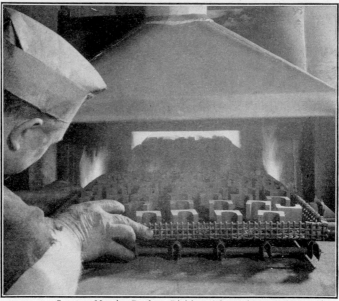

Courtesy Moraine Products Division of General Motors Corporation.

Fig. 3. Textile-Machine Bearings Entering a Sintering Furnace.

important, as the product, being made up of small particles, has a large surface area exposed. The problem is to provide a suitable atmosphere of some reducing gas or nitrogen to prevent the formation of undesirable oxide films during the process. Textile-machine bearings entering a sintering furnace are shown in Figure 3. In the fabricating of powder-metal parts, dimensional accuracy should be maintained so that no subsequent machining is necessary. There is always some dimensional change in the operation of sintering; it may be either a growth or a shrinkage.* What happens depends on the shape and particle-size variation of the powder, the powder composition, sintering procedure, and briquetting pressure. Accurate size is main-

* R. P. Koehring, "Sintering Atmospheres for Production Purposes," *Powder Metallurgy*, American Society for Metals, 1942.

tained by compensating for the change in making the green compact and then maintaining uniform conditions.

Hot Pressing

Considerable effort has been made to combine the operation of pressing and sintering. Such combination, of course, has obvious advantages. Experiments with several metals have demonstrated that this method can produce compacted products with improved strength and hardness over the usual methods of production. Factors to overcome for successful operation are atmospheric control, method of applying heat, and suitable dies to resist high-temperature wear and creep.

Sizing and Finishing Operations

Products requiring close tolerances may necessitate a final coining or sizing operation. Coining is usually a cold-working operation. In addition to providing close dimensional tolerance, it gives the product necessary strength and density.

All pressed-metal products may be heat-treated although the results obtained do not conform in all cases to those obtained with solid metals. Best results are obtained with dense structures. Porosity influences the rate of heat flow through the part and permits internal contamination if certain salts are used in the process.

Recent developments in plating permit the electroplating of parts with usual plating metals. Again it is important to have considerable density in the structure for best results. Other finishes used on powder-metal parts include enameling, staining, lacquering, and phosphate coatings.

Advantages and Limitations

The use of powder metallurgy is rapidly increasing today, and many products are being made better and more cheaply than by other manufacturing methods. Some of the advantages obtained by this process are as follows:[*][†]

1. Many products such as sintered carbides and porous bearings cannot be produced by any other method or process. This applies also to a number of products from alloys containing both metallic and non-metallic powders. It is also possible to mold layers of different metal powders to form bimetallic products.

[*] E. Schumacher and A. G. Souden, "Powder Metallurgy," *Metals & Alloys*, November 1944.

[†] P. Schwarzkopf and C. G. Goetzel, "Processing Trends in Powder Metallurgy," *Iron Age*, September 19, 1940.

2. It is possible to produce parts with controlled porosity, such, for example, as is found in self-lubricating bearings made from nonferrous powders and graphite.

3. Large-scale production of many small parts can compete favorably with machined parts because of the close tolerances and surface finish that are obtained.   On parts up to 2 inches in diameter, tolerances of ± 0.001 inch or less can be maintained.

4. Products of extreme purity can be made, as it is possible to obtain powders in a very pure state.   In the operation of pressing there is little chance for impurities to enter.

5. The process is economical in material, since there are no losses of material in the fabrication, and in most cases the dimensional accuracy is so close that no material allowance is needed for machinery.

6. Labor cost is low: skilled mechanics are not required to operate presses or other necessary equipment.

7. A wide range of physical properties is possible with any given material.   These can be controlled by varying the die pressure, particle size, or sintering temperature, or by introducing alloying elements.

Powder metallurgy has certain limitations which will restrict its use, particularly with those products that can be made economically by other manufacturing processes.   In addition there are certain other limitations such as pertain to the mechanical equipment, the thermal characteristics of the powder, safety, and design.   Some of these limitations are as follows:

1. Metal powders are expensive and in some cases difficult to store without some deterioration.   Prices of powders should gradually decrease as the demand increases and the methods of production improve.

2. Equipment costs are high.   Presses with capacities up to 60 tons per square inch are required for certain products.   Dies operating in these presses must be accurately machined and capable of withstanding high pressures and temperatures.   Sintering furnaces present problems of temperature and atmospheric control.   These facts preclude the use of this process for short-run jobs.

3. The size of powder-fabricated parts is controlled by the capacity of the presses available and also by the compression ratio of the various powders.   Compression ratios of different powders vary considerably. A compression ratio of 4–1 means the mold depths must be four times the finished compact.   Since pressure is not distributed uniformly in a powder as it is in a liquid, the final product is not so likely to be

uniform in density. This will affect the shape and dimensional accuracy when a sintering operation is necessary.

4. Intricate designs in products are difficult to attain, since there is no flow of the metal particles during compacting. Abrupt changes in thickness must be avoided; and it is not possible to mold undercuts, internal threads, and grooves. Uniform density is difficult to attain in long pieces.

5. Some thermal difficulties appear in sintering operations, particularly with the low-melting powders such as tin, lead, zinc, and cadmium. Most oxides of these metals cannot be reduced at temperatures below the melting point of the metal; hence, if such oxides exist, they will have detrimental effects on the sintering process and result in an inferior product.

6. Some powders in a finely divided state present explosion and fire hazards, and precaution must be taken to keep dust out of the air. Such metal powders include aluminum, magnesium, zirconium, and titanium.

7. A completely dense product is not possible if the sintering operation is carried out. However, porosity can be reduced materially if the heating accompanies the pressing operation.

Metal-Powder Products*

Many metals are now available for use in powder-metal parts, and the number of products made by this process is steadily increasing. A representative selection of machine parts made from a wide variety of metal powders is shown in Figure 4. It is interesting to note the intricate shape and design of the parts, most of which are made complete without the necessity of machining. Some of the prominent powder-metal products are as follows.

Cemented carbides. Tungsten carbide particles are mixed with a cobalt binder, pressed to shape, and then sintered at a temperature above the melting point of the matrix metal. The metal cobalt binds the carbide particles together and gives strength and toughness to the final product. Cemented carbides are used for cutting tools, dies, and various wear-resistant applications.

Motor brushes. Brushes for motors are made by mixing copper with graphite in sufficient quantities to give the compact adequate mechanical strength. Tin or lead may also be added in small quantities to improve wear resistance.

* H. E. Hall, "Development in Metal Powders and Products," *Powder Metallurgy*, American Society for Metals, 1942.

Porous bearings. Most bearings are made from copper, tin, and graphite powders, although other metal combinations also are used. After sintering, the bearings are sized and then impregnated with oil by a vacuum treatment. Porosity in the bearings can be controlled readily and may run as high as 40% of the volume.

Courtesy Chrysler Corporation—Amplex Divisions.

Fig. 4. Machine Parts Made from a Wide Variety of Metal Powders.

Metallic filters. Porous metal filters having greater strength and shock resistance than ceramic filters are made with porosities up to 80%. Bronze and nickel are common metals used for this purpose.

Gears and pump rotors. Gears and pump rotors are made from powdered iron mixed with sufficient graphite to give the product the desired carbon content. Parts are produced with close dimensional accuracy requiring a minimum of machining. A porosity of around 20% is obtained in the process; and after the sintering operation the pores are impregnated with oil to promote quiet operation. The physical properties of iron-powder parts are close to those of ordinary gray cast iron.

Magnets. Excellent small magnets can be produced from iron, aluminum, nickel, and cobalt when combined in powder form. Alnico magnets made principally from iron and aluminum powders are superior to those cast. A finer-grain structure is obtained, there are no internal defects, and the magnets are produced with close dimensional tolerances.

Contact parts. Electric-contact parts lend themselves well to powder-metallurgy fabrication, since it is possible to combine several metal powders and still maintain some of the principal characteristics of each. Contact parts must be wear-resistant and somewhat refractory and at the same time must have good electrical conductivity. Many combinations such as tungsten–copper, tungsten–cobalt, tungsten–silver, silver–molybdenum, and copper–nickel–tungsten have been developed for electrical applications.

Numerous other parts including clutch faces, tungsten filaments, diamond cutting wheels, brake bands, laminated metals, and welding rod are produced by powder metallurgy. There are many other uses for powdered metals which are not pressed to shape, as, for example, the use of paint pigments and other protective coatings. Aluminum powder is used in Thermit welding; and, in the field of pyrotechnics and explosives, powdered aluminum and magnesium are both prominent. The addition of powdered metals to plastics increases their strength and contributes other metallic properties.

Review Questions

1. What is powder metallurgy?
2. What is meant by sintering, and how is it accomplished?
3. What characteristics should be included in specifying a metal powder?
4. Why is particle-size distribution important in a given product?
5. What determines the compressibility of a powder, and how is it expressed?
6. What two powders have greatest use in compressed-powder products?
7. Name and describe five methods of producing powders.
8. What is the purpose of adding certain lubricants to the powder before processing?
9. Describe the usual steps in producing a metal-powder part.
10. What types of presses are generally used in this work?
11. What are the various factors that must be considered in the operation of sintering?
12. Why not hot-press all products and eliminate the sintering operation?
13. What types of finish may be used on powder-metal parts?
14. What are the advantages claimed for powder-metal parts?
15. List the limitations of this manufacturing process.

16. Name three products made by powder metallurgy that cannot be made by other processes.

17. What advantages do bearings made by this process have over cast bearings?

18. What uses are found for metal powders that are not compressed to a solid form?

References

BAEZA, W. J., *A Course in Powder Metallurgy,* Reinhold Publishing Company, 1943.

BALKE, C. C., "Powder Metallurgy—Some Theoretical Aspects," *Iron Age,* April 17, 1941.

CLAUSER, H. R., "Structural Parts from Metal Powders," *Materials & Methods,* September 1949.

GOETZEL, C. G., "Sintered, Forged, and Rolled Iron Powders," *Iron Age,* October 1, 1942.

LENEL, F. V., "Powder Metallurgy," *Mechanical Engineering,* July 1943.

Powder Metallurgy Today, F. S. Stokes Company, 1949.

SCHUMACHER, E. E., and A. G. SOUDEN, "Some Aspects of Powder Metallurgy," *Bell System Technical Journal,* Vol. XXIII, October 1944.

SCHWARZKOPF, P., and C. G. GOETZEL, "Processing Trends in Powder Metallurgy," *Iron Age,* September 19, 1940.

SKAUPY, F., *Principles of Powder Metallurgy,* Philosophical Library, 1944.

VICTOR, M. T., and C. A. SORG, "Design of Powder Metallurgy Parts," *Metals & Alloys,* March 1944.

WULFF, J., *Powder Metallurgy,* American Society for Metals, 1942.

CHAPTER

12

PLASTIC MOLDING

In general, the term "plastic" is applied to all materials capable of being molded or modeled. Modern usage of this word has changed its meaning to include a large group of synthetic organic materials that become plastic by the use of heat and are capable of being formed to shape under pressure. Cellulose derivatives, natural and synthetic resins, and protein matter constitute the principal materials from which the plastics are made. These plastic materials lend themselves to a variety of methods of manufacture including molding, casting, extruding, and the production of various coatings and laminates.

Plastic molding as a large-scale manufacturing process is of comparatively recent date. The discovery of ebonite or hard rubber by Charles Goodyear in 1839 and the development of Celluloid by Hyatt about 1869 marked the beginning of plastic products. It was not until 1909, however, that one of the most important materials, phenol formaldehyde resin, was developed by Dr. L. H. Baekeland and his associates. Since then numerous other synthetic materials which vary widely in physical properties have been developed.

Products made from plastic materials can be produced rapidly with close-dimensional tolerance and excellent surface finish. In many cases they have replaced metals where lightness in weight, corrosion resistance, and dielectric strength are to be considered. Another important characteristic of these products is that they may be made either transparent or in colors. There are about 45 different kinds of plastics in commercial production today offering a wide variety of physical properties which are continually being improved. Surface hardness and ability to resist high temperatures have been the most difficult to improve.

Plastic Materials

Plastic materials may be broadly classified in two groups: *thermosetting* and *thermoplastic*. Thermosetting compounds are formed to shape under heat and pressure, resulting in a product that is permanently hard. The heat first softens the material, but, as additional heat and pressure are applied, the plastic is hardened by a chemical change known as *polymerization.** A group of parts molded from thermosetting resins is shown in Figure 1. Thermoplastic materials

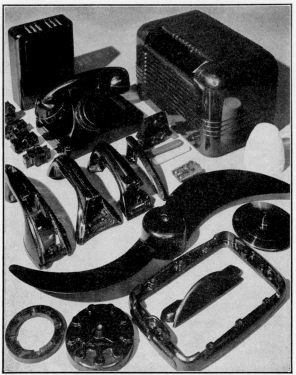

Courtesy The Hydraulic Press Manufacturing Company.

FIG. 1. A Group of Parts Molded from Thermosetting Resins. A Majority of These Parts Were Compression-Molded.

undergo no chemical change in molding and do not become hard with the application of pressure and heat. They remain soft at elevated temperatures until they are hardened by cooling and may be remelted repeatedly by successive applications of heat. The melting of paraffin is a good analogy of this process.

In actual production these molding compounds or resins are frequently mixed with other materials to provide special properties or to decrease the cost. Fillers of wood, flour, cotton, rag fibers, asbestos,

* Polymerization is a chemical process resulting in the formation of a new compound whose molecular weight is a multiple of that of the original substance.

powdered metals, graphite, and other materials are used for this purpose. The selection of the filler is based on the properties wanted in the final products. In addition to fillers, dyes may be added to give color to the product. Plasticizers or solvents are used with some compounds to soften them or to improve their flowability in the mold. Finally, lubricants may be added to improve the molding characteristics of the compound. These materials are mixed with the granulated resins before molding.

Some of the common plastic compounds are as follows.

Phenol formaldehyde. This compound, originally developed by Dr. Baekeland, is one of the principal thermosetting plastics used in industry today. The synthetic resin made by the reaction of phenols with formaldehyde forms a hard high-strength durable material which is capable of being molded under a wide variety of conditions. This material has high heat and water resistance, and may be produced in a wide range of colors. It is used in the manufacture of coating materials, laminated products, grinding wheels, and metal and glass bonding agents, and may be cast into many useful items. Products made from this material include molded cases, appliance plugs, bottle caps, knobs, dials, knife handles, radio cabinets, and numerous electrical parts.

Urea formaldehyde. This plastic component, also thermosetting, may be obtained in the form of molding powder or in solution for laminating and similar treatments. Also it has wide use as an adhesive, possessing good bonding qualities and strength as well as being resistant to water. In its manufacture, the chemical combination of urea with formaldehyde forms a colorless resin especially adapted to light-colored articles which resist ultraviolet light and remain colorless for a long period of time. These products also have a hard surface and high dielectric strength, are light in weight, and may be produced in all colors. Typical applications are tableware, light fixtures, buttons, instrument dials, veneer bonds, and clock cases. An interesting use of urea resins is for a binder for sand cores in the casting of light metals.

Phenol furfural. Furfural is obtained by processing waste farm products as corncobs and hulls from rice and cottonseeds with certain acids. The thermosetting resin obtained flows readily at low molding temperatures and cures rapidly when the proper temperature is reached. Products of furfural are dark in color and water-resistant, have excellent electrical qualities, and can be fabricated by most processes. Commercial products of this material are used as instrument housings, brake linings, electrical parts, binder for abrasive wheels, and varnish for impregnating laminates.

Melamine. Melamine resins, principally melamine formaldehyde, are a comparatively recent addition to the plastic family. The compound melamine, made from carbon, nitrogen, and hydrogen, produces an excellent shock- and heat-resisting product. It is a thermosetting plastic and is adapted to processing by either compression or transfer molding. Being arc-resistant and having high dielectric strength, it is highly useful for electrical parts such as telephone sets, circuit breakers, and terminal blocks. Other uses include laminated products, tableware, and enamel.

Cellulose derivatives. Cellulose derivatives are thermoplastic and are widely used in the United States because of the availability of cellulose material in cotton and wood.

Cellulose nitrate, the first to be used, is highly inflammable, but has the advantage of being extremely tough, water-resistant, and clear in color. It is used in fountain pens, ping pong balls, jewelry, handles for tooth brushes, and fish lures.

Cellulose acetate is a more stable compound, having considerable mechanical strength and ability to be fabricated into sheets or molded by injection, compression, and extrusion. Display packaging, toys, knobs, flashlight cases, bristle coating for paint brushes, radio panels, and extruded strips are successfully made of this compound.

Cellulose acetate–butyrate molding compound is similar to cellulose acetate, and both are produced in all colors and by the same processes. In general, cellulose acetate–butyrate is recognized for its low moisture absorption, toughness, dimensional stability under various atmospheric conditions, and ability to be continuously extruded. Typical butyrate products include steering wheels, football helmets, goggle frames, trays, belts, furniture trim, insulation foil, and extruded tubing for gas and water.

Ethyl cellulose, one of the newer cellulose plastics, is the lightest of the cellulose derivatives. In addition to its use as a base for coating materials, it is also employed extensively in the various molding processes because of its stability and resistance to alkalies. Other outstanding properties are its surface hardness, good electrical properties, and mechanical strength. Typical applications include containers, drill jigs and forming dies, trim moldings, heads for golf clubs, and flexible coatings. It may also be produced in thin sheets or extruded shapes.

Cellophane (regenerated cellulose) is produced in thin sheets by an extruding process and is useful for packaging materials since it provides a protective coating against moisture and other contaminating influences. Because of its durability, pleasing appearance, and fire resistance, this material is also being used for curtains and draperies.

Polystyrene. Polystyrene is a thermoplastic material especially adapted for injection molding and extrusion, although some other methods of processing can be used. Some of its outstanding characteristics are low specific gravity (1.07), availability in colors from clear to opaque, resistance to water and most chemicals, dimensional stability, and insulating ability. Electrical insulation has been one of its major applications to date as it is an excellent rubber substitute for insulation purposes. In addition, styrene resins are molded into such products as battery boxes, dishes, radio parts, lenses, and wall tile.

Polyethylene. Polyethylene products are flexible at both room and low temperatures, waterproof, unaffected by most chemicals, and capable of being heat-sealed, and can be produced in a variety of colors. Polyethylene is one of the lighter plastics and in solid form can float on water. Although one of the newer plastics, it has many applications including such products as ice-cube trays, developing trays, fabrics, film for packaging, collapsible nursing bottles, coaxial cable, and insulating parts for high-frequency fields. Polyethylene products may be made by molding or blow molding, or extruded into sheets and monofilaments.

Vinyl resins. A number of vinyl resins commercially available include copolymers of vinyl chloride and vinyl acetate, polyvinyl butyrals, polyvinyl chloride, polyvinyl alcohol, and polyvinyl acetate. All are thermoplastic materials capable of being processed by compression, injection, or extrusion into a wide variety of products. The *copolymers* of *vinyl chloride* and *vinyl acetate* are obtained with a wide range of properties by varying the ratio of the two resins. They are especially suitable for surface coatings and for both flexible and rigid sheeting. In addition, they are extruded and molded into many products, a special grade being used in the manufacture of fibers that have chemical resistance and considerable strength. *Polyvinyl butyral,* used for interlayers in safety glass, raincoats, sealing fuel tanks, and flexible molded products, is a clear tough resin. It has resistance to moisture, great adhesiveness, and stability toward light and heat. *Polyvinyl chloride* resin has a high degree of resistance to many solvents and will not support combustion. It has found wide industrial use in resilient rubberlike products. *Polyvinyl alcohol* products are durable and have excellent resistance to oils and chemicals. Products fabricated from this material include extruded tubing, molded trim, seals, gaskets, binders, and abrasive-resistant linings. *Polyvinyl acetate* is used as an adhesive for bonding many materials and as a base for various coatings, lacquers, ink, and plastic wood.

Acrylic resins.   This resin is of special value because of its excellent light-transmitting power, ease of fabrication, and resistance to moisture. The acrylic resin most commonly used is *methyl methacrylate,* but it is better known by the commercial names Lucite (du Pont) and Plexiglas (Rohm & Haas).   It is a thermosetting material and can be fabricated by casting, extruding, molding, and stretch forming.   Typical applications include airplane windows, shower doors, gage covers, toilet articles, transparent models, and covers where visibility of operation is desirable.

In addition to the materials previously listed, many other synthetic and natural resins, protein substances, and other materials are used in the manufacture of plastics.   *Nylon* monofilaments are used for hosiery, parachute shroud line, glider tow ropes, and brush bristles. Examples of molded and extruded products of nylon are bearings, tumblers, kitchen accessories, luggage, tubes, and furniture trim.   The *shellac* resins are used as coating material, binder for abrasive wheels, phonograph records, and insulators.   A variety of cold-molding compounds consisting of materials such as asbestos fibers with bituminous, cement, or shellac binders are made into such products as knobs, handles, connector plugs, and arc shields.   Casein and protein plastics, of all colors and nonflammable, are made into buttons, novelties, sheets, and tubing.

Synthetic rubber.   Attempts to synthesize natural rubber have been made for many years.   The fact that many highly industrialized nations had no source of raw rubber under their control was a contributing factor in developing research along this channel.   Recent research has produced many synthetic materials possessing some of the characteristics of rubber, but out of this group there are five that have had commercial acceptance as synthetic rubbers.*   They are Thiokol, GR-M or Neoprene, GR-S or Buna S, GR-A or Buna N, GR-I or butyl.   Of this group GR-S is produced in the largest quantity and is particularly adapted for tire use.   It is very similar to natural rubber and can be substituted in most instances.   It is a copolymer of butadiene and styrene and can be cured to any degree of hardness desired.   The strength of GR-S is improved by adding carbon black, and for tire use is frequently compounded with natural rubber.   The butadiene–acrylonitrile copolymers (known as GR-A, Buna N, or nitrile rubbers), employed principally because of their resistance to oils, find use in such products as oil hose, gaskets, and diaphragms.   They also serve to some extent as a blending material with phenolics and vinyl plastics.

* A. Black, "Recent Developments in Engineering Materials," *Mechanical Engineering*, April 1945.

The organic polysulfides, known as Thiokols, are very resistant to gasoline, oils, and paints, as well as to sunlight, and are used in the manufacture of hose, shoe heels and soles, coated fabrics, and insulation coatings. Resilient solid objects can be molded in conventional machines used for other plastics.

Courtesy E. I. duPont de Nemours.

Fig. 2.   Neoprene Being Dumped from a Polymerization Kettle.

The chloroprene polymer, known as Neoprene or GR-M, is produced from the basic raw materials: coal, limestone, water, and salt. Calcium carbide, a product of coal and limestone, when added to water, forms acetylene gas (C_2H_2). This gas, in combination with hydrogen chloride, forms chloroprene which is changed to Neoprene by polymerization. Figure 2 shows a batch of Neoprene being dumped from a polymerization kettle and illustrates the rubberlike consistency of this material. Neoprene has good resistance to oils, heat, and sunlight, and is used for such articles as conveyor belts, shoe soles, protective clothing, insulation, hose, printing rolls, and tires and tubes, and as a bonding material for abrasive wheels. It has a wider application than other synthetic rubbers and can replace natural rubber in any of its present uses. Butyl or GR-L, an isobutylene copolymer, has many of the properties and characteristics of natural rubber. Because of its strength, resistance to abrasion, and low permeability to gases, it is used most in the manufacture of inner tubes. Other uses include steam hose, conveyor belting for heated materials, and tank linings.

Courtesy General Electric Company.

FIG. 3. Close-up View of Rotary Preforming Press Used in Making Disk Pellets of Various Molding Compounds.

Methods of Processing

Plastic materials differ greatly from each other and lend themselves to such processing methods as compression molding, transfer molding, injection molding, jet molding, casting, extrusion, blowing, and laminating. Each material is best adapted to some one of the methods, although many can be fabricated by several. In most processes the molding material is in powder or granular form, although for some there is a preliminary operation of *preforming* the material before use.

Preforming. This operation consists of compressing a powder into small pellets of a size and shape that conforms to a known mold cavity.

All preforms are of the same density and weight, and the operation avoids waste of material in loading molds and, in general, speeds up production by rapid-mold loadings. Also, there is no possibility of overloading the molds. In the preforming operation the thermosetting powder is cold-molded, and no curing takes place. Preforms are used only in compression- and transfer-molding processes.

A rotary preforming press used in making disk pellets of various molding compounds is shown in Figure 3. The powder is fed by gravity from the hopper into the mold cells, and any excess powder

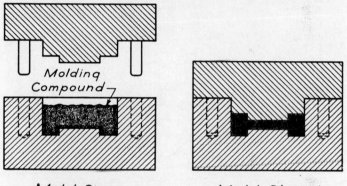

FIG. 4. Diagrammatic View of Compression-Molding Process.

is scraped off. The amount of material fed into each cell is controlled by regulating the lower punch. As the table revolves, pressure is applied uniformly on both sides, compressing the powder charge, and at the end of the cycle the tablet is ejected. In some cases tablets of more than one size are made at the same time, the only objection to this procedure being that there is some difficulty encountered in sorting the tablets.

Reciprocating machines, having only a single set of dies, are also used for a wide variety of preforming operations. The dies can be changed quickly, but the output is much lower than that of the rotary machines. When preforms are used in multiple-cavity molds, they are first transferred to a loading tray. The tray locates them accurately with reference to the mold cavities in the machine, and all preforms are molded simultaneously.

Compression molding. Compression molding is illustrated in Figure 4. A given amount of material is placed into a heated metallic mold, and, as the mold closes, pressure is applied, causing the softened material to flow and conform to the shape of the mold. The material can be used either in a granulated state or preformed into a tablet. Pressures used in compression molding vary from 100 to 8000 pounds per square inch, depending on the material used and size of the product. The temperature range is 250 to 400 F. Heat is very important

Courtesy F. J. Stokes Machine Company.

FIG. 5. Automatic Compression-Molding Press.

for thermosetting resins, as it is required first to plasticize and then to polymerize or make them hard. Uniform heating of the powder is desirable, but not always easy to attain, because of the poor heat conductivity of the material.

Some thermoplastic materials are processed by compression, but the cycle of rapid heating and cooling of the mold adds to the difficulty in using such material. Unless the mold is sufficiently cooled before ejection, distortion of the piece is apt to result.

A large variety of hydraulic presses, ranging from hand-operated to completely automatic, are available for compression molding. The function of the press is to apply the necessary pressure and at the same time sufficient heat to plasticize properly and cure the plastic materials.

Heat may be transferred from heated platens or applied directly to the metal mold. It is supplied by steam, heated liquids, electrical resistance, or ultrahigh-frequency electric currents.

The simplest type of press is the hand-operated one. Separate molds are used, which are loaded and unloaded outside the press, and the only function of the press is to supply the necessary pressure for the operation. Other presses, also manually controlled, have the molds permanently mounted on the press and consequently can use much larger molds. Semiautomatic presses are those that operate automatically for one cycle only. This type eliminates variations due to the personal element, as the operator need only load and unload the machine. Completely automatic presses, similar to the one shown in Figure 5, are those that operate continuously for a long period of time. All operations such as measuring and feeding the raw material are automatically controlled and accurately timed so as to maintain uniform molding conditions. Presses of this type are rapid in operation and require a minimum of attention.

Transfer molding. In the process of transfer molding, the thermosetting powder or preforms are placed, not into the mold cavities, but into a pressure chamber above them, as illustrated in Figure 6. They are then plasticized by heat

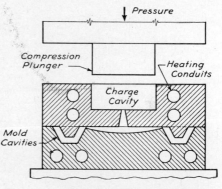

Fig. 6.   Arrangement for Transfer Molding.

and pressure and injected into the mold cavities as a hot liquid where the material is cured and becomes hard. This process is especially desirable for producing parts requiring small metal inserts, since the hot plastic material enters the mold gradually and without great pressure. Intricate parts and those having large variation in section thickness can also be produced to advantage by this method. The process differs from the injection molding of thermoplastic materials in that the mold is kept heated at all times and parts are ejected without cooling. In some equipment provision is made to use high-frequency electric current as a means of heating the preformed tablets.

A self-contained transfer-molding press for plastics is shown in Figure 7. The mold is closed and clamped by the upward-acting press platen. A center opening in the upper grid or bolster permits the operator to drop the molding material into the transfer chamber or well, where the material is plasticized. A downward-acting plunger forces the liquid molding material into the mold where it is cured under heat and pressure. This press can be used universally for regular transfer molding, conventional compression molding, or molding that requires the addition of a high-frequency unit for plasticizing the molding material.

Courtesy F. J. Stokes Machine Company.

FIG. 7. Hydraulic Press for Transfer or Compression Molding.

Injection molding. A typical injection-molding machine of average capacity is shown in Figure 8. The operation of this type of machine is very similar to that of a plunger-type die-casting machine. Molding material is fed by gravity from a hopper and a metering device (see insert in figure) to a circular heating chamber, where it is compressed, softened, and finally injected into the closed mold under considerable pressure. The finished product is hardened in the mold by the cooling effect of water circulated through conduits in the mold. After the injection plunger retracts, the mold is opened and the product ejected.

The heating-chamber construction of all injection machines is about the same. It is cylindrical in shape with a torpedolike spreader in the center so that the incoming material is kept in a thin enough layer to be uniformly and rapidly heated. The heating chamber temperature

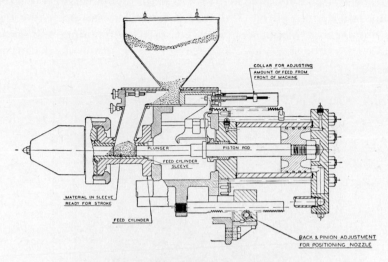

UNIT BEFORE INJECTION STROKE

Heating Cylinder and Injection End of Machine.

Courtesy Reed Prentice Corporation.

Plastic Injection-Molding Machine—8-Ounce Capacity.

FIG. 8.

ranges from 250 to 500 F, depending on the kind of material being charged and the size of the mold. Heat is furnished by a series of electrical-resistance coils. These chambers must be of substantial construction, as injection pressures may reach as high as 30,000 pounds per square inch.

Injection machines are built in the following three general styles: of horizontal construction, as shown in Figure 8; with the heating and injection unit in a vertical position, as illustrated in Figure 9; and a

Courtesy Lester Engineering Company.

FIG. 9. An Automatic Injection-Molding Machine, 22-Ounce Capacity, Having the Heating-Cylinder Assembly in a Vertical Position.

completely vertical unit such as a compression-type machine, with the molds held in a horizontal position. The machine shown in Figure 9, with the injection unit in a vertical position, has certain desirable construction features by which the feeding of the material into and through the heating chamber is facilitated. The entire heating-chamber unit can be swung away from the mold for purposes of cleaning, repair, and change of nozzles. This 22-ounce machine with a maximum output of around four shots per minute is especially adapted for the manufacture of steering wheels and other large parts. Although the capacities of injection machines vary from 2 ounces to 8 pounds, the custom production of small-parts machines of from 8- to 16-ounce capacity is most popular.

Thermoplastic materials are generally used in injection molding, as they are especially suited for rapid production. Compared to compression molding, this process is much faster, since the mold does not have to be alternately heated and cooled. The mold is maintained at

Courtesy Nalle Plastics.

FIG. 10. Mold for Making Berry Baskets in an Injection-Molding Machine.

a constant temperature, usually 165 to 200 F, by circulating water; and a production cycle of two to six shots per minute is possible. Mold costs are lower, as fewer cavities are necessary to maintain equivalent production by injection molding. Articles of difficult shapes and of thin walls are successfully produced, as illustrated in Figure 10. Metal inserts, such as bearings, contacts, or screws, can be applied in the mold and cast integrally with the product. Material loss in the process is low, as sprues and gates can be re-used.

Thermosetting materials can be injection-molded by a process known as *jet molding*. With a few minor changes, nearly any standard thermoplastic injection-molding machine can be converted to a jet-molding machine. The torpedo spreader in the heater is removed, and the main heating of the resin materials is concentrated at the nozzle passage to the sprue. As soon as the mold is filled, the nozzle area is

cooled by circulating water, and the pressure in the chamber is released.   No further chemical changes of the material take place until
the cycle is repeated.

Extruding. Thermoplastic materials, such as the cellulose derivatives, vinyl resins, polystyrene, polyethylene, and nylon, may be extruded through dies into simple shapes of any desired length.
Thermosetting compounds are not well adapted to this process because
of the rapidity with which they harden but are used to a limited extent
in the production of thick-walled tubes.   A schematic diagram of a
typical extruding press is shown in Figure 11.   Granulated or pow-

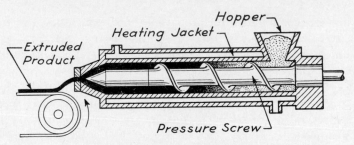

Fig. 11.   Schematic Diagram of Typical Plastic Extrusion Press.

dered material is fed into the hopper and then forced through a heated
chamber by a spiral screw.   In the chamber the material becomes a
thick viscous mass, in which form it is forced through the die.   As it
leaves the die, it is cooled by air or water and gradually hardens as it
rests on the conveyor.   Long tubes, rods, molding sections, and many
special sections are readily produced in this manner.   Because they can
be bent or curved to various shapes after extrusion by immersion in
hot water, such products as conduits for electric conductors and for
handling chemicals are made by this process.   Much insulation is now
extruded directly on wire—such insulation is economical to produce
and has excellent physical properties.   Filaments for plastic fabrics and
sheeting for curtains and packaging purposes are both becoming important products of this process.

Casting. Thermosetting materials used for casting include the
phenolics, the polyesters, and the allyl resins, the last being especially
useful for optical lenses and other applications requiring excellent
clarity.   These resins have a wider use in casting than the thermoplastics, as they have greater fluidity in pouring.   Ethyl cellulose and
cellulose acetate butyrate, both thermoplastics, are used where impact
strength and rigidity are desired.   These materials find use as drop-

hammer and stretch dies. Acrylics are used in the casting of transparent articles and flat sheets.

Plastics are cast when the number of parts desired is not sufficient to justify the making of expensive dies. Frequently open molds of lead are formed by dipping a steel mandrel of desired shape into molten lead and stripping the shell from the sides of the mandrel after it solidifies. Cores of lead, plaster, or rubber may be introduced if desired. Hollow castings are also produced by the slush-casting method. Solid objects may be made from molds of plaster, glass, wood, or metal. In cases where parts have numerous undercuts, the molds are made of synthetic rubber.

Casting is recommended for preparing short rods, tubes, and various shapes that are to be used in subsequent machining operations or carving. Machined surfaces have a dull white appearance which may be removed by tumbling with wood blocks and abrasive particles or by buffing. Costume jewelry and novelties are cast because of the pleasing color combination that can be obtained and the fact that frequent style changes do not justify the preparation of expensive die equipment. Other examples of cast products are knobs, clock and instrument cases, handles, drilling jigs, and punches and dies for sheet-metal fabrication in the airplane industry.

Laminated plastics. Laminated plastics consist of sheets of paper, fabric, asbestos, wood, or similar materials which are first impregnated or coated with resin and then combined under heat and pressure to form commercial materials. These materials are hard, strong, impact-resisting, and unaffected by heat or water, and have desirable properties for numerous electrical applications. The final product may consist of either a few sheets or over a hundred, depending on the thickness and properties desired. Although most laminated stock is made in sheet form, rods and tubes as well as special shapes are available. The material has good machining characteristics which permit its fabrication into gears, handles, bushings, furniture, and many other articles.

In the manufacture of laminated products, the resinoid material is dissolved by a solvent to convert it into a liquid varnish. Rolls of paper or fabric are then passed through a bath for impregnation. This is a continuous operation, and, as the sheet leaves the resinoid bath, it goes through a drier, which evaporates the solvent, leaving a fairly stiff sheet impregnated with the plastic material. To facilitate lamination, the sheets are then cut into convenient sizes and stacked together in numbers sufficient to make up the desired thickness of the final sheet. Each group is assembled between polished metal plates at top and bottom and is then stacked in a hydraulic press, as shown in Figure 12. Under the action of heat and pressure, a hard rigid plate having desirable properties for many industrial applications, is obtained. Tubes are made by machine-winding strips of the prepared

Courtesy Bakelite Corporation.

Fig. 12. Sheets Impregnated with Phenolic Varnish Being Placed between Heated Platens of Hydraulic Press.

stock around a steel mandrel. The tubes are cured by being placed in a circulating-hot-air oven or are subjected to both heat and pressure in a tube mold. Properties of laminates depend largely on the sheet material or filler used. Paper-base materials are used often in electrical products because of their excellent characteristics and their ability to be held to close tolerances.* Fabric-base materials are stronger and

* According to NEMA (National Electrical Manufacturers Association) there are 12 grades of laminates which are standard for most applications. Six grades have paper base, four have fillers of cotton fabric, one has an asbestos paper filler, and one uses asbestos fibers.

tougher and, hence, better for stressed parts. Gears made of a canvas base are quiet in operation and have proved very satisfactory. Asbestos and fiber-glass cloth are recommended for heat-resisting and low water-absorption uses. Thin sheets of wood are now being laminated to produce a light material equal in strength to some metals and resistant to moisture. These sheets, produced with a smooth surface, can be formed into panels without expensive machining operations. Safety glass is, in effect, a laminated-plastic product, since thermoplastic layers are used between the glass sheets to make it nonshattering. In addition, many other materials, including rubber, metal, rayon, and spun glass, are used in the manufacture of laminated products.

Blowing or vacuum forming. Many plastic materials can be formed into thin hollow shapes by air-pressure differentials when the sheet material is heated and in a soft pliable condition. To accomplish this, the sheet is clamped to the top surface of a vacuum or pressure con-

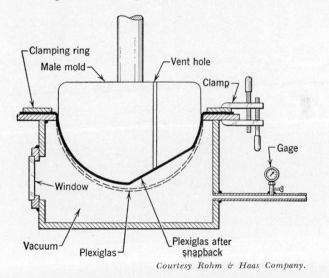

Courtesy Rohm & Haas Company.

Fig. 13. Vacuum Snapback Forming of Heated Thermoplastic Sheets.

tainer and drawn or blown into a form approximating a section of a sphere. No dies are required, and upon cooling it retains its formed shape.

A somewhat similar process known as vacuum snapback forming is illustrated in Figure 13. After the heated sheet is clamped, a vacuum is created in the chamber, which causes the sheet to be drawn down as shown by the dotted lines. The male mold is then introduced into the formed sheet, and the vacuum is gradually reduced, causing the sheet to snap back against the mold form. By having ample draft, so that the mold can be withdrawn when the sheet is cooled, surface defects are eliminated. In Figure 14 is shown a setup where sheets are formed to shape by air pressure and actually blown into the mold. This process is used where more complicated shapes are desired and possible surface defects are not objectionable. However, by using special synthetic greases on the mold, the tendency for marks to show

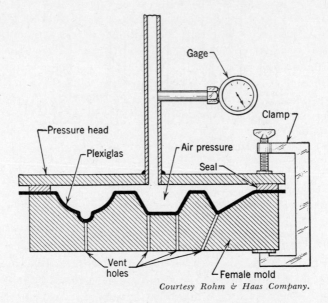

Courtesy Rohm & Haas Company.

Fig. 14. Forming Heated Thermoplastic Sheets by Blowing into a Mold.

on the formed part is materially decreased. Similar results may be obtained by vacuum drawing, but there are more apt to be surface defects from air bubbles in the grease.

Certain plastics can be formed into bottles and containers in a fashion similar to the methods used in blowing glass bottles. In this operation a tube or parison of thermoplastic material is either injected or extruded into an open mold, as shown in Figure 15. With the tube still in contact with the extruding nozzle, the mold closes and air pressure from an outlet within the nozzle expands the plastic against the walls of the mold. The extrusion is then cut from the nozzle, and the mold indexes to the next position. Here a blow head descends on the mold and holds the blown container under pressure until it is removed. It is ejected from the mold by an air jet and cooled to room temperature by a water spray. Articles made by blowing include

Christmas tree ornaments, atomizer bulbs, cosmetic containers, bottles, floats, and certain synthetic-rubber articles as hot-water bottles. Polyethylene, cellulose nitrate, and the acrylics are among those plastics that can be formed by blowing techniques.

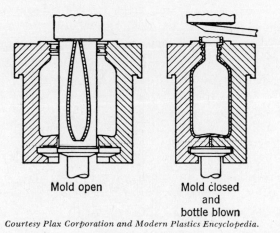

Mold open   Mold closed
and
bottle blown

Courtesy Plax Corporation and Modern Plastics Encyclopedia.

FIG. 15. Blow-Molding a Thermoplastic Bottle Using an Extruded Parison.

Molds for Plastics

Molds for both the compression and injection processes are made of steel and are heat-treated. The production of these molds demands the same type of machine work and the usual precision required for dies used in pressure casting. There are, however, some differences in construction because of varying characteristics in the materials being processed. Ample draft and fillets should be provided to facilitate removing the article from the mold. Ejector pins are usually provided for this purpose and should be located at points where the pin marks are not noticeable. Like metals, plastic materials shrink on cooling, and some allowance must be provided. Shrinkage varies according to the type of material and method of processing but is usually 0.003 to 0.009 inch per inch.

Compression molds are made in *hand* and *semiautomatic* types. Each type might be further subdivided into *positive, semipositive,* and *flash* designs. The hand molds are charged and unloaded on a bench. Heating and cooling are accomplished by plates on the presses which are provided with the necessary circulating facilities. The semiautomatic molds are fastened rigidly to the presses and are heated or cooled by adjacent plates. Work is ejected automatically from the molds as they open. Both these types are made in either single- or multiple-cavity molds.

Further classification of hand and positive molds may refer to the method of confining the plastic material in the mold. A positive mold is one that entirely confines the material in the mold. An example of this is a cylinder with a close-fitting plate at the bottom and a plunger which enters the cylinder to compress the powder. The thickness of the part being molded is controlled by the amount of powder charged. Molds of this type are commonly used in mounting metallurgical specimens. Semipositive molds are designed so that there is some provision for overflow. A landed mold of this type, shown in Figure 16, permits the escape of some material, but, owing to the telescoping feature, has some of the characteristics of a positive mold. This type of mold is very successful and is used more than either the positive or flash types. Ejector pins are brought into play as the mold opens to force the molded parts from the mold. The flash-type mold has no telescoping action whatsoever, and the material is not confined until the end of the stroke. As a result there is a slight fin, a few thousandths of an inch thick, around the lands of the mold where the closing is made.

Since most compression molding is done with thermosetting materials, alternate heating and cooling of the mold is not required. The molding temperature for these plastics is obtained from gas, steam, electricity, or heated liquids. Heat not only softens the plastic material so that it can be shaped to the mold, but also causes the chemical change which hardens it.

Injection molds are made in two pieces, one half being fastened to the fixed platen and the other half to the movable platen. Contact between the halves is made on accurately ground surfaces or lands surrounding the mold cavities. Neither half telescopes with the other, as is the case with many of the compression molds. The cavities should be centrally located with reference to the sprue hole in the fixed half so as to obtain an even distribution of material and pressure in the mold. For locating purposes, guide pins are used which are similar to those employed on metal-press dies. These pins are fastened in the fixed half of the mold and enter hardened bushings in the movable part of the mold.

Mold cavities can extend into both halves of the mold. It is best, however, to have the outside of the molded part in the fixed half, providing the shape is suitable for this arrangement. In the cooling process the plastic material tends to shrink away from the cavity walls and is withdrawn from this half as the mold opens. It is retained on the cores of the movable half until the ejector mechanism operates.

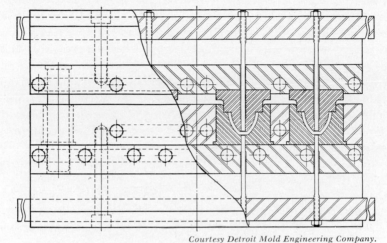

Courtesy Detroit Mold Engineering Company.

Fig. 16. Multicavity Compression Mold.

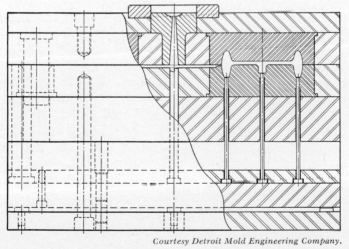

Courtesy Detroit Mold Engineering Company.

Fig. 17. Injection Mold.

Injection molds have cooling channels in both halves to permit maintaining a uniform temperature for chilling the molded part, since most materials fabricated by this process are thermoplastic. The material is forced into the mold from the heater cylinder under pressure ranging from 2 to 20 tons per square inch and ejected from the mold at a temperature of approximately 125 F. Ejection of the parts occurs as the mold opens and is accomplished by either ejector pins or stripper plates.

An illustration of a typical injection-mold design is shown in Figure 17. This is a multicavity mold with half the cavity extending into each plate. As the mold opens, the sprue is pulled, and the ejector pins then push the molded parts free from the cavity.

Any cores required in injection molding are placed on the movable half of the mold. The normal shrinkage of the molded part tends to cling to the cores, causing it to withdraw freely from the stationary half as the mold opens. Vents, to permit the escape of entrapped air, are extremely small and are located in such a way as to permit all air to escape quickly.

Review Questions

1. List the principal materials used in the manufacture of plastic articles.
2. Distinguish between thermosetting and thermoplastic materials.
3. Name the various methods used in forming plastic materials.
4. Describe the process of injection molding.
5. What is meant by polymerization?
6. Which resin is widely used in the manufacture of flexible products?
7. What resin is used for making transparent products?
8. How does synthetic rubber differ from natural rubber?
9. What are the basic raw materials used in making Neoprene?
10. What is the purpose of preforming molding powder?
11. Describe the process of compression molding.
12. What advantages does transfer molding have over compression molding?
13. What type of plastic material is generally used in injection molding? Why?
14. What plastic products are formed by the extruding process?
15. What kind of molds are used in plastic casting?
16. List the various materials that are laminated with plastics.
17. Describe the vacuum snapback method of forming.
18. How are plastic bottles made?
19. What is the difference between positive- and flash-type molds?
20. How are molds for plastics vented?

References

AKIN, R. B., "Vinyl Resins in War and Peace," *Chemical Industries*, April and May 1943.

ASTM Standards on Plastics, American Society for Testing Materials, 1943.

Bakelite Molding Plastics, Bakelite Corporation, 1940.

BELL, L. M. T., *The Making and Moulding of Plastics*, Chemical Publishing Company.

DEARLE, D. A., *Plastic Molding*, Chemical Publishing Company, 1941.

DELMONTE, J., *Plastics in Engineering*, Penton Publishing Company, 1940.

DuBois, J. H., *Plastics*, American Technical Society, 1945.

FLYNN, H. L., "How to Work With Plastics," *American Machinist*, April 11, 1946.

LEHMANN, GEORGE P., "Proper Molds for Plastics," *American Machinist*, June 25, 1941.

LOUGEE, E. F., *Plastics from Farm and Forest*, Plastic Institute, Chicago, 1943.

Plastics Catalog, Plastic Catalogue Corporation, 1950.

SASSO, J., *Plastics for Industrial Use*, McGraw-Hill Book Company, 1942.

SIMONDS, H. R., and C. ELLIS, *Handbook of Plastics*, D. Van Nostrand Company, 1943.

SIMONDS, H. T., *Industrial Plastics*, 3d edition, Pitman Publishing Company, 1945.

Tenite Injection Molding, 3d edition, Tennessee Eastman Company, 1949.

Tenite Extrusion, Tennessee Eastman Company, 1950.

THAYER, G. B., *Plastic Mold Designing*, American Industrial Publisher, 1941.

INSPECTION—MEASURING INSTRUMENTS AND GAGES

Mass production requires that all parts be made according to rigid specifications and working drawings. No matter how carefully these drawings and specifications are prepared, they lose their value unless they are adhered to by the production department. It is the function of inspectors to see that the standards established by the engineering department are maintained in the shop.

Inspection

Inspection departments in companies demanding close quality control of their product are separate from the production department. Since it is the aim of the production department to produce goods as fast as possible, there is some tendency to lower quality standards if maintaining quality means lowering the output. For this reason it is advisable to place the inspection department in a position on the organization chart that will insure it sufficient authority to act independently and for the best interest of quality control. Frequently it is directly responsible to the engineering department, since it is from this department that the drawings originate.

The inspector occupies a very important place in an organization. He should have personal qualities that warrant placing him in an authoritative position: Ability, tact, impartiality, and thoroughness are all essential qualities for an inspector. To understand the problems of the operator, he must have a knowledge of materials, manufacturing processes, and tools. His acceptance or rejection of work must be based entirely on merit and on established specifications. He must avoid arbitrary methods of inspection at all times.

The amount of inspection given to the product will vary according to the nature of the product, the degree of accuracy required, and the type of equipment used. When greater accuracy is demanded in the product, more inspection is necessary. A watch factory may use one inspector for seven to ten workmen, whereas a foundry requires only one inspector for 30 to 40 workmen. After being set up, certain types of machines, particularly presses for blanking, punching, and forming, require very little attention from the inspector. In such cases the tools and first parts produced are carefully inspected at the start, and, from then on, periodic inspection (aside from the attention given the machines by the operator) is sufficient. Automatic screw machines and other similar automatic equipment can be handled in the same way. Once the machine is set up, the change in the product due to wear of the tools is so slight that the periodic inspection given by a roving inspector is sufficient.

A system of inspection known as *sampling* is used on most bulk materials such as coal, batch materials, and foundry sand. It is used also in the dimensional inspection given parts in machine shops. If a proper sample can be determined readily, this method offers a means of reducing inspection costs. The frequency or method of sampling must be such that there is no possibility of producing a large number of defective parts before an error is discovered.

Many parts that require accurate machine work should be given 100% inspection to eliminate any possibility of performing expensive operations on defective parts. Crankshafts, bearing races, and gears are typical parts that should be treated in this manner. In many cases 100% inspection is necessary at several points in the manufacturing cycle as well as at completion. In any event, a final inspection should always be given before assembly operations.

Types of Fits

The term "interchangeable manufacture" implies that the parts which go into the assembly of the machine can be selected at random from a large number of parts. In such a system of manufacture, selective fitting is unnecessary except possibly for special close-working parts. To make this possible, manufacturing methods must be standardized and limits of accuracy specified on details. Extreme accuracy is not always necessary or desirable, since manufacturing costs increase greatly as working limits become closer. In many cases, on modern production machines, it is possible to maintain a limit of accuracy in excess of that required by the part with no added expense; however, no part should be made with any greater degree of accuracy than is required by its use in a given mechanism or machine. A balance must be established between cost of manufacture and ease of assembly.

The fact that there is a need for various types of fits in manufacturing work is clearly evident.   A given industry may require only a few; others will maintain that a large number is necessary.   In general, there are but three types of fits: a *clearance fit*, a *tight fit*, and an *interference fit*.   It is quite obvious that these three conditions will not satisfy all needs, as the amount of clearance or interference of the mating parts is also an important factor.   Hence, it becomes necessary to subdivide these classifications further to include those fits most commonly used in manufacturing work.   Any such classification or standard will probably not satisfy all manufacturers, but it should include the general needs of all industry.*

According to the American Standards Association, fits are classified as follows:

Loose fit.   This fit provides for a large allowance giving considerable freedom and is used where accuracy is not essential.

Free fit.   For running fits with speeds of 600 rpm or over, and journal pressures of 600 pounds per square inch or over.   Closer allowance than for a loose fit.

Medium fit.   Used for parts revolving easily.   For speeds under 600 rpm and with journal pressures less than 600 pounds per square inch. This is also applied to sliding parts and is the largest allowance for freedom consistent with accuracy.

Snug fit.   This calls for zero allowance and is the closest fit that can be assembled by hand without appreciable pressure.   It will not rotate easily, and no shake is permissible.   A snug fit is not intended to move freely under a load.

Wringing fit.   This is a metal-to-metal contact with no negative allowance.   It allows for no movement and is assembled with slight pressure.   Wringing fits are not usually interchangeable.

Tight fit.   This is a wringing fit with slight negative allowance. This fit is for parts permanently assembled or subject to pressure.   It is much used in ordnance work.

Medium-force fit.   For permanently assembled parts, but subject to disassembly without severe pressure.   The fit is the tightest possible for cast iron or parts where internal stress will be detrimental.

Heavy-force fit.   Used for steel holes where the metal can be highly stressed without exceeding its elastic limit.   Parts united by force fit form one unit without other means of holding.

Shrink fit.   This is the heavy-force fit applied to larger parts where a force fit is impractical, such as for locomotive wheel tires.   A definite

* John Gaillard, *Tolerances for Cylindrical Fits*, American Standards Association.

negative allowance is given, and the outer part is expanded by heat before assembly.*

Tolerance and Allowance

In dimensioning a drawing, the figures placed in the dimension lines represent *nominal sizes*. Nominal sizes are only approximate; they do not represent any degree of accuracy unless it is so stated by the designer. To specify a degree of accuracy, it is necessary to add *tolerance* figures to the dimension. Tolerance is the amount of variation permitted in the part or the total variation allowed in a

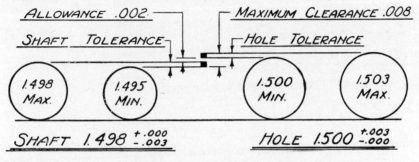

Fig. 1. Loose or Clearance Fit.

given dimension. A shaft might have a nominal size of 2½ inches, but for practical reasons this figure could not be maintained in manufacture without great cost. Hence, a certain tolerance would be added, and, if a variation of ±0.003 inch could be permitted, the dimension would be stated 2.500 ± 0.003. Where dimensions are given close tolerances, the reason is that the part must fit properly with some other part. Both must be given tolerances in keeping with the type of fit and allowance desired.

Allowance, which is sometimes confused with tolerance, has an altogether different meaning. It is the minimum clearance space intended between mating parts and represents the condition of tightest permissible fit. Figures 1 and 2 illustrate exaggerated conditions for clearance and interference fits. The tolerances for shaft and hole are indicated by the black bars. In the figure showing a clearance fit, the allowance is the difference between the largest shaft size and the smallest hole size indicated as 0.002 inch. This value represents the minimum allowable clearance space, and 0.008 inch represents the

* American Standard B4a—1925, *Tolerances, Allowances, and Gages for Metal Fits.*

maximum. All shafts and mating parts have tolerances, which, if maintained, will give clearances between these two extremes. Figure 2, representing an interference fit, has tolerances limiting the interference to values between 0.001 and 0.005 inch. In both cases there is

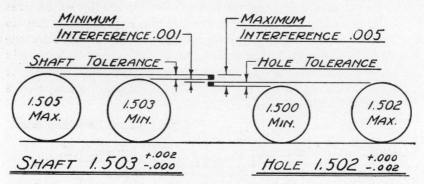

FIG. 2.   Tight or Interference Fit.

probably one clearance or interference value that is best, but for manufacturing reasons a variation is necessary. To obtain the best value, selective or assembly fitting would have to be resorted to.

Tolerances may be either *unilateral* or *bilateral*. Unilateral tolerance means that any variation is made in only one direction from the

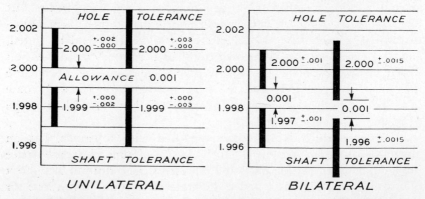

FIG. 3.   Illustrating the Application of Unilateral and Bilateral Tolerances.

nominal or basic dimension. Referring again to Figure 1, we see that the hole is dimensioned $1.500 \, ^{+0.003}_{-0.000}$, which represents a unilateral tolerance. If the dimensions were given as 1.500 ± 0.003, the tolerance would be bilateral; that is, it would vary both over and under the nominal dimension. The majority of manufacturing concerns in the United States use the unilateral system. The reason for this can be determined by reference to Figure 3 which illustrates the use of both types of tolerance. The unilateral system permits changing the tolerance and still retaining the same allowance or type of fit. With the bilateral system this is not possible without also changing the nominal size dimension of one or both of the two mating parts. In mass production, where mating parts must be interchangeable, unilateral tolerances should always be used.

MEASURING INSTRUMENTS

Standard of Measurement

The standard of measurement in the United States is the *meter*. This standard, adopted by Congress in 1866, has reference to the international meter at the International Bureau of Weights and Measures at Sèvres, France. Our legal *yard* is defined as $3600/3937$ of the length of the meter at a temperature of 68 F, from which 1 meter is equal to 39.37 inches. The British standard yard is slightly different, 1 meter being equal to 39.370113 inches. An inch under this system is equal to about 25.39998 mm, whereas the United States inch is equal to about 25.40005 mm. Although this difference does not seem to be of any great importance in ordinary shopwork, it is noticeable in accurate measurements. In 1933 these values were changed in both countries to permit the use of a uniform ratio: 1 inch equals 25.4 mm.* This change makes it possible to convert readily from one system to the other and eliminates any possible confusion.

The standard of angular measurement is the *degree* which is obtained by dividing a circle into 360 parts. A degree is further divided into 60 minutes, and each minute is divided into 60 seconds. This standard of measurement is universal.

Classification of Measuring Instruments

A measuring instrument is any device that may be used to obtain a dimensional or angular measurement. Some instruments, such as a steel rule, may be read directly; others, like the caliper, are used for transferring or comparing dimensions. Also, various principles are employed in obtaining measurements. A micrometer, for example, utilizes a different principle from a steel rule or a vernier caliper. Here are a number of the common measuring instruments listed according to use:

* American Standard B48.1–1933, *Inch-Millimeter Conversion for Industrial Use*, and British Standard BS350–1930, *Conversion Tables*.

1. **Linear measurement**
   (a) Steel rule.
   (b) Micrometer.
   (c) Vernier caliper.
   (d) Depth gage.
   (e) Vernier height gage.
   (f) Calipers.
   (g) Dividers.
   (h) Telescopic gages.
   (i) Combination square.
   (j) Measuring machine:
      (1) Mechanical.
      (2) Optical.

2. **Angular measurement**
   (a) Adjustable bevel.
   (b) Bevel protractor.
   (c) Sine bar.
   (d) Square.
   (e) Angle gage blocks.
   (f) Dividing head.

3. **Plane-surface measurement**
   (a) Level.
   (b) Straight edge.
   (c) Surface gage.
   (d) Profilometer.
   (e) Optical flat.

Linear Measuring Instruments

Rule. The most common measuring device in the shop is the steel *rule*—made of tempered steel, carefully ground, and accurately graduated on both sides. Usually one side is graduated in eighths and sixteenths and the other in thirty-seconds and sixty-fourths, although

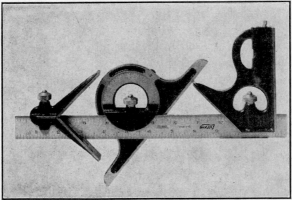

Courtesy The Lufkin Rule Company.

FIG. 4. Combination Set Including Square, Center Head, Protractor, and Scale.

numerous other graduations in both metric and English systems are used. This tool is very satisfactory for rough machine work, layout work, checking dimensions, and many other shop applications. Mechanics with considerable skill and experience can attain a high degree of accuracy in measuring with a rule and calipers.

Combination set. A combination set (see Figure 4) consists of a steel rule or blade on which is mounted a *square head,* a *center head,* and a *bevel protractor*. Although a set includes all three accessories, only one is used at a time. With the square head mounted on the blade, it serves as both try and miter squares; and it can be adjusted to be used as a marking gage. Placing it on the end converts the tool into a height gage. The head alone may be used as a level. When the center head is mounted on the blade, centers of all cylindrical work can be determined. The bevel protractor, used in connection with the blade, permits the measurement, layout, and checking of angles.

Depth gage. As shown in Figure 5, narrow steel scales are frequently mounted in a head which has a straight edge at right angles to the scale. This forms a depth gage, with a scale that can be adjusted and clamped so as to extend a given amount below the straight edge. Similar gages are made with micrometer adjustments.

Caliper. The caliper is used for approximate measurements, both external and internal. It does not measure direct, but must be set to size, with a steel rule or some form of gage being used. Most shop calipers, known as *spring calipers,* consist of two legs with a flat spring head plus a nut and screw to hold them in position. Some calipers are provided with a "quick nut" for making rapid adjustments. On release of the pressure, this nut slides freely along the screw, but with the slightest leg pressure it grips the threads of the screw firmly. *Hermaphrodite* calipers are used principally for locating centers and layout work.

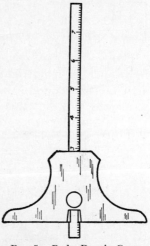

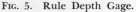

FIG. 5. Rule Depth Gage.

They have one leg similar to the leg on an outside caliper while the other is a straight point. In layout work the curved leg rests against the edge of the work while the other leg is used as a scriber.

Divider. A divider is similar in construction to a caliper except that both legs are straight with sharp hardened points at the end. This tool is used for transferring dimensions, scribing circles, and general layout work.

Micrometer caliper. The *micrometer* is used for quick, accurate measurements to the thousandth part of an inch. This tool illustrates the use of an accurate screw thread as a means of obtaining a measurement. The screw is attached to a spindle and is turned by movement of a thimble at the end. The barrel, which is attached to the frame, acts as a nut to engage the screw threads, which are very accurately made with a pitch of 40 threads per inch. Each revolution of the thimble advances the screw $\frac{1}{40}$ of an inch, or 0.025 inch. The outside of the barrel is graduated in 40 divisions, and any movement of the thimble down the barrel can be read next to its beveled end. When the spindle is in contact with the anvil on a 1-inch micrometer, the zero readings on barrel and thimble should coincide.

The scale on the barrel and thimble edge can best be understood by reference to the enlarged view of Figure 6. On the beveled edge

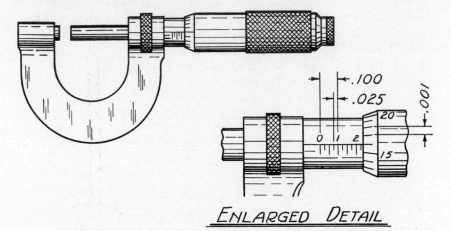

FIG. 6. Micrometer with Enlarged View Showing Graduations.

of the thimble are 25 divisions, each division representing 0.001 inch. To read the micrometer, the division on the thimble coinciding with the line on the barrel is added to the number of exposed divisions on the barrel converted into thousandths. Thus, the reading shown in Figure 6 is made up of 0.200 plus 0.025 on the barrel, or 0.225 inch, to which is added 0.016 on the thimble to give a total reading of 0.241 inch.

Since a micrometer reads only over a 1-inch range, in order to cover a wide range of dimensions several micrometers are necessary. The micrometer principle of measurement is also applied to inside measurements and depth reading, and to the measurements of screw threads.

For accurate shop measurements to 0.0001 inch a supermicrometer as shown in Figure 7 may be used. This machine is set to correct size by precision-gage blocks, and readings may be made directly from the dial on the headstock. Constant pressure is maintained on all objects being measured. Standard measuring machines are similar in appearance but may be read to an accuracy of 0.00001 inch. Direct readings are obtained by electrolimit pressure control on the tailstock.

Courtesy Pratt & Whitney—Division Niles-Bement-Pond Company.

FIG. 7. Supermicrometer for Accurate Measurements up to 0.0001 Inch.

Vernier calipers. In Figure 8 is a *vernier caliper* which may be used for taking both inside and outside measurements over a wide range of dimensions. It consists of a main scale graduated in inches and an

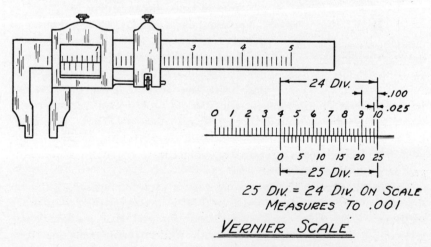

FIG. 8. Vernier Caliper and Enlarged View Showing Scale.

auxiliary scale having 25 divisions. Each inch on the main scale is divided into tenths and each tenth into four divisions, so that in all there are 40 divisions (each 0.025 inch) to the inch. The 25 divisions on the auxiliary or sliding scale correspond to the length of 24 divisions on the main scale and are equal to $^{24}\!/_{40}$ of an inch. One division would be equal to $\frac{1}{25}$ times $^{24}\!/_{40}$, or $^{24}\!/_{1000}$ inch, which is $\frac{1}{1000}$ inch less than a division on the main scale. Hence, if the two scales were on zero readings, the first two lines would be 0.001 inch apart, the tenth lines 0.010 inch apart, and so on.

In actual use, the reading on the main scale is first observed and converted into thousandths, and to this figure is added the reading on the vernier. The vernier reading is obtained by noting which line coincides with a line on the main scale. If it is the 15th line, then 0.015 inch is added to the main scale. These scales are shown in some detail in the enlarged view of the vernier scale. As shown, the vernier reads exactly 0.400 inch.

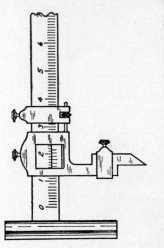

FIG. 9.   Vernier Height Gage.

Outside measurements are taken with the work between the jaws; inside measurements with the work over the ends of the two jaws. This method of measurement is not so rapid as a micrometer but has the advantage of having a wider range with equal accuracy. It also has some use on protractors for angular measurement.

Vernier height gage. An application of the vernier scale to a *height gage* is shown in Figure 9. This tool differs from a vernier caliper in that it rests on a heavy base and has a beveled pointer on the movable jaw. In using this instrument the work is placed on a surface plate, and distances are measured above this reference elevation. The reading of the scale is identical with that of a vernier caliper. This measuring tool is used principally for accurate height measurements and scribing lines in layout work.

Telescopic gage. The *telescopic gage* is used for measuring the inside size of slots or holes. This method is much quicker than other methods. The gage consists of a handle and two plungers, one telescoping into the other and both under spring tension. The plungers may be locked in any position by the knurled screw at the end of the handle. In using the telescopic gage, the plungers are first compressed and locked in position. Next, the plunger end is inserted into the hole and the screw released, allowing the plungers to expand to the hole size. Finally, the plungers are locked in place and removed, after which the over-all length of the plungers is measured with an outside micrometer.

Toolmakers' microscope. Because of their extreme accuracy and their ability to measure parts without pressure or contact, numerous optical instruments have been devised for inspecting and measuring.

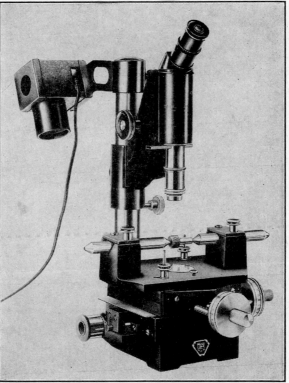

Courtesy Bausch & Lomb Optical Company.

FIG. 10.   Toolmakers' Microscope with Lead Measuring Attachment in Position.

A typical microscope for toolroom work is shown in Figure 10. An object viewed is greatly enlarged, and the image is not reversed as in the ordinary microscope. To be measured, a part is first clamped in proper position on the cross-slide stage. The microscope is focused and the part to be measured brought under the crossline seen in the microscope. The micrometer screw is then turned until the other extremity is under the crossline, the dimension being obtained from the difference in the two readings. The micrometer screws operate in either direction and read to an accuracy of 0.0001 inch. In the illustration the microscope is shown with a screw-measuring attachment in position for checking the lead of the screw.

Angular Measurements

As previously stated, the basic unit of angular measurement is the *degree*. This unit is defined as the angle formed by two radii subtending an arc $\frac{1}{360}$ of the circumference of a circle. Although degrees may be further subdivided by fractions, the usual smaller subdivisions are minutes and seconds. Common angular measuring instruments read the degrees directly from a circular scale scribed on the dial or circumference. There are also devices that require the aid of other measuring instruments and calculations to obtain the result. Some few, such as the ordinary square, measure only a single angle and are not adjustable. Fixed instruments of this type are more correctly classified as gages.

Bevel protractor. The plain or universal *bevel protractor* measures directly in degrees and is adapted to all classes of work where angles

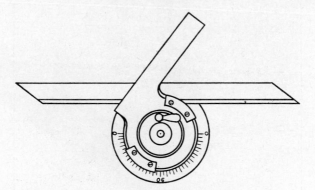

Fig. 11.   Vernier Bevel Protractor.

are to be laid out or established. The universal protractor, shown in Figure 11, is graduated in degrees and, in addition, is provided with a vernier scale for fine measurements. Most such protractors read to 5 minutes or $\frac{1}{12}$ of a degree.

Adjustable bevel. An instrument known as an *adjustable bevel* or a bevel gage is widely used for checking or transferring angles. This tool consists of two blades, which can be set and locked in relation to each other. No direct reading is obtained, and the angle must be set or checked from some other angular measuring device.

Sine bar. A *sine* bar is a simple device used either for accurately measuring angles or for locating work to a given angle. Mounted on the center line are two buttons of the same diameter and at a known distance apart, the distance on most sine bars being either 5 or 10 inches. For purposes of accurate measurement the bar must be used in connection with a true surface.

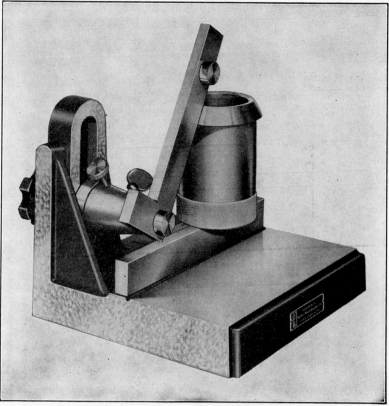

FIG. 12. Checking the Angle of a Tapered Surface with Sine-Bar Fixture.

The operation of the sine bar is based on the trigonometric relationship that the sine of an angle is equal to the opposite side divided by the hypotenuse. Hence, if the hypotenuse is known, the angle may be determined by measuring the height of the opposite side, dividing it by the known figure, and referring to trigonometric tables. Measurement of the unknown side is accomplished with either a height gage or by means of precision blocks.

Figure 12 shows the setup for checking the included angle of a taper plug gage, using a 10-inch sine bar. The 10-inch dimension is the center distance between the two buttons shown on the side of the bar. The difference in elevation of the two buttons represents a value ten times the sine of the included angle. Using a five-place trigonometric table, we may obtain the angle in degrees and minutes without further calculation.

When work is set up to be machined at a given angle, the operation is reversed. The bar is then set at the proper angle, which in turn acts as a gage to position the work correctly. Various designs of the sine bar have been worked out, but the method of measuring the angle is the same in all cases.

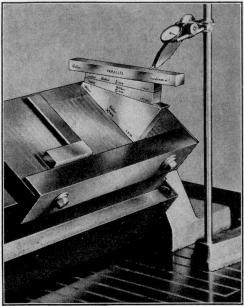

Courtesy Webber Gage Company.

FIG. 13. Angle Gage Block Used to Set Universal Magnetic Chuck to a Precise Desired Angle.

Angle gage blocks. A quick and convenient means of measuring angles is by means of angle gage blocks made with the usual accuracy of standard gage blocks. A set of 16 angle blocks will permit the measuring of some 356,400 angles in steps of one second. In Figure 13 is shown a revolving magnetic chuck being set to an angle of 38 degrees. Three blocks are assembled with a parallel, and an indicator is used to tell if the setting is correct. Such an operation can be quickly performed and does not require the calculations necessary when a sine bar is used.

Dividing heads. Index or *dividing heads* were originally developed for use on milling machines, but their use has been extended to inspection work for checking angles about a common center. The head is made up of a worm and worm-gear set having a ratio of 40 to 1. Hence, one turn of the crank will turn the spindle $\frac{1}{40}$ of a revolution or 9 degrees. By using index plates with the head, we may obtain any desired angle with great accuracy. The operation of this device is discussed in the chapter on milling machines, Chapter 19. For inspectional work it is used in connection with a surface plate for checking parts already machined.

Surface Measurements

Surface checking instruments are for the purpose of obtaining some measure of the accuracy of a surface or the condition of a finish. Much of this type of work is done on a flat accurately machined casting known as a *surface plate*. It is the base upon which parts are laid out and checked with the aid of other measuring tools. These plates are very carefully made and should be accurate to within 0.001 inch from the mean plane, any place on the surface. Small plates, known as *toolmakers' flats*, are lapped to a much greater degree of accuracy. Their field of application is limited to small parts, and in most cases they are used with precision gage blocks.

Straightedge. This tool is a bar of steel having either one or two straight edges. It is used for the inspection of surfaces for straightness, checking flat surfaces before straightening, and for accurately scribing straight lines. The ordinary shape is rectangular, but for accurate work one edge is beveled or formed into a knife edge. When one is working to a close tolerance, a feeler gage should be used to check the surface variations.

Courtesy The Lufkin Rule Company.

Fig. 14. Surface Gage.

Surface gage. The *surface gage*, shown in Figure 14, is used to check the accuracy or parallelism of surfaces and, in addition, finds much use in transferring measurements by scribing them on a vertical surface. When in use, it is set in approximate position and locked. Fine adjustment of the spindle can be made by turning the knurled nut which controls the rocking bracket. When used with the scriber, it is a line-measuring or locating instrument. If the scriber is replaced by a dial indicator, it then becomes a precision instrument for checking surfaces.

Optical flat. Measurements to the millionth part of an inch are made by interferometry, the science of measuring with light waves. Measurement by this principle is made with a small instrument known

Courtesy The DoALL Company.

FIG. 15. Examining the Surface Condition of a Rejected Comparator Anvil.

as an *optical flat*. Optical flats are usually made from natural quartz because of its hardness, low coefficient of expansion, and resistance to corrosion. They are flat lenses having very accurately polished surfaces with light-transmitting quality. The usual optical-flat set consists of two lenses 2 inches in diameter and $\frac{5}{8}$ inch thick, although they may be obtained in various sizes and shapes up to 5 inches. It is not necessary that the two surfaces of a flat be absolutely parallel. A light having a single color (monochromatic light) is used, because it gives interference bands that are complete and dark in color.

One of the common uses for optical flats is the testing of plane surfaces. The optical flat is placed on the flat surface to be tested, and light is reflected both from the optical flat and the surface being tested. The interference between the rays reflected from the bottom of the flat and from the top of the work causes dark bands (Newton's rings) or areas to appear. If the surface is irregular, the appearance is similar to a contour map. The position and number of lines show the location and extent of the irregularities. When bands are straight, evenly spaced, and parallel to the line of contact, the surface is perfectly flat. Since we know the wave length of the light source, any deviation from this pattern indicates an error in the surface, the amount of which can be measured. For ordinary daylight, the difference between bands is 10 millionths of an inch (one-half wave length). Sodium light has a separation in one-half wave length equal to about 12 millionths of an inch. In Figure 15 is shown a 6-inch optical flat

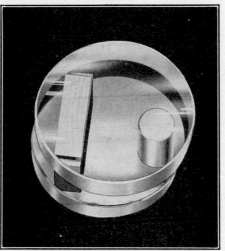

Courtesy Bausch & Lomb Optical Company.

FIG. 16. Optical Flat Showing Newton's Rings.

used in examining the surface condition of a rejected comparator anvil. The center left edge is 174 millionths higher than the lower right corner.

In Figure 16 are shown two optical flats being used in connection with a gage block to check the height of an object. The part and gage block are wrung to the lower flat, and the upper flat is placed securely on the two top surfaces. If the parts are not the same size, the flat will be tilted slightly, and parallel interference lines will appear on the top surface of the gage block. The difference in height can be determined from the position and number of bands that appear. Each band indicates a difference of 12 millionths of an inch. To facilitate calculations the contact lines of the flat on the part and the gage blocks are usually placed apart a distance equal to the width of the gage block.

Surface smoothness. Several devices have been developed that have as their purpose the measurement of surface smoothness. The need for some measure of surface finish for various machine operations is brought about by the necessity for smooth bearing surfaces in high-speed machinery. The unit of measurement in this work is the "micro-inch" (0.000001 inch).

Several methods of smoothness measurement have been established, the simplest being a visual comparison with some established standard. Direct measurement of scratch depth can be made by light interference

Courtesy Physicists Research Company.

FIG. 17. Profilometer Setup for Measuring Smoothness of Production Parts, Using Tracer, Amplimeter, and Reading Recorder.

in a manner similar to that described in the discussion of optical flats. This method requires surfaces having good reflecting qualities. Another optical method employs a microscope which magnifies a shadow cast by the scratches of a surface. Light is directed at an angle to a straight edge, and the shadows from it are projected from the scratches. This method is not suitable for very fine finishes, and its use is further limited in that only a small part of the entire area can be inspected.

The *profilometer* is a direct-reading instrument which measures smoothness by passing a fine tracing point over a surface. The vertical movement of the tracer is magnified electrically so that a readable profile curve can be obtained. Some of the important features of this instrument are that it has variable magnification, is adapted to quick reading of large areas, can be used for both plane and curved surfaces, and is capable of measuring any surface roughness from 3 to 1000 microinches. The unit shown in Figure 17 consists of a tracer, which converts the vertical movements of the tracing point into a small fluctuating voltage; an Amplimeter, which shows the roughness of the work in microinches rms as the tracer moves over the surface; a motor-driven device for operating the tracer; and a recorder for making a record of the roughness. The operation of checking a surface may be done either manually or mechanically.

GAGES

Production work requires speed as well as accuracy in measuring parts. Measuring instruments, such as those just described, can be used for this type of work, but many of them are more elaborate than necessary and require adjustments for each individual reading. Consequently, they are used only on short-run jobs where the expense of fixed gaging equipment is unwarranted. To attain the quick measurements required in production work, a measuring device that has a fixed shape or size is used. It represents a standard with which the manufactured parts are compared. Since its use is limited to one dimension and no adjustments are required, the operation of inspecting a part requires a minimum of time. Much gaging is done by operators in the shop while their equipment is in operation, with no loss of production time.

Classification of Gages

Numerous kinds of gages are used, varying widely in shape and size. Gages are classified, by the Ordnance Department of the Army and many industries as well, as *inspection gages* and *manufacturing gages*. Inspection gages are those used by inspectors in the final acceptance of the product. They are to insure that the product is made in accordance with the tolerance specifications on the working blueprints. Manufacturing or working gages are those used by the machine operators in the actual production of parts. These gages are frequently made to slightly smaller tolerances than the inspection gages, the idea being to keep the size near the center of the limit tolerance. Parts, then, made around limit sizes may still pass the inspector's gage. In addition to these, a third type of gage, known as a *master gage*, is sometimes used. Such a gage is merely a reference gage with which inspection gages are periodically compared. Most industries have abandoned this type of gage and have adopted precision measuring instruments and methods for this purpose. The equipment used consists of such tools as precision-gage blocks, measuring machines, optical flats, microscopes, and projecting equipment.

The following gages represent those most commonly used in production work. The classification is principally according to the shape or purpose for which each is used. A complete classification would require more subdivisions under the various headings.

GAGES

1. Plug.
2. Ring.
3. Snap.
4. Length.
5. Form
   (a) Screw thread.
   (b) Fillet.
   (c) Center.
   (d) Drill point.
   (e) Angle.

   (f) Gear tooth.
   (g) Special contour, etc.
6. Thickness
   (a) Precision gage blocks.
   (b) Feeler.
   (c) Wire, etc.
7. Indicating.
8. Air-operated.
9. Projecting.

Gage materials. The true value of a gage is measured by its accuracy and service life, which, in turn, depend on the workmanship and materials used in its manufacture. Since all gages are continually subject to abrasive wear while in use, the selection of the proper material is of great importance. High-carbon and alloy tool steels have been the principal materials used for many years. These materials can be accurately machined to shape, and they respond readily to heat-treating operations which increase their hardness and abrasive resistance. Objections to steel gages are that they are subject to some distortion because of the heat-treating operation and that their surface hardness is limited.

These objections are largely overcome by the use of chrome plating or cemented carbides as the surface material. Chrome plating permits the use of steels having inert qualities, as wear resistance is obtained by the hard chromium surface. This process also is widely used in the reclaiming of worn gages. Cemented carbides applied on metal shanks by powder-metallurgy technique provide the hardest wearing surface obtainable. Although their cost is several times that of a steel gage, their life is much greater, and the additional cost is more than justified.

Description of Gages

Plug gages. A plain plug gage is an accurate cylinder used as an internal gage for the size control of holes. It is provided with a suitable handle for holding and is made in a variety of styles. These gages may be either single- or double-ended, as shown in Figure 18.

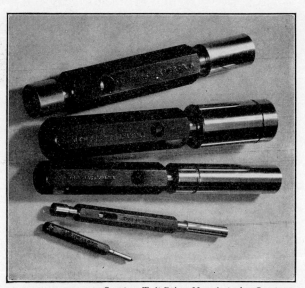

Courtesy Taft Peirce Manufacturing Company.

Fig. 18. Plug-Type "Go—Not-Go" Gages.

Double-ended plain gages have "go" and "not-go" members assembled on opposite ends, whereas progressive gages have both gaging sections combined on one end.

Three separate designs have been recommended for adoption by the American Standards Association.* One is known as the taper-lock design and is the same as those shown in Figure 18. This design applies to all gages from 0.059 inch to and including 1.510 inches. For diameters varying from 1.510 to 8.010 inches the trilock design with reversible gaging members is used. This gage has three wedge-shaped prongs on the handle which are forced into three locking grooves in the gaging cylinder by means of a through screw. The cylinder may be reversed when it becomes worn and thus prolong the life of the gage. Large gages ranging from 8.101 to 12.010 inches are

* Commercial Standard CS8—41, American Gage Design Committee, National Bureau of Standards.

made in the form of a rim with reinforcing web. Holes are drilled
and tapped in the web to receive two ball handles. The annular
design has proved very satisfactory for large gages, as they are light in
weight and easily handled. These same designs are recommended
for thread, taper, and special-form plug gages.

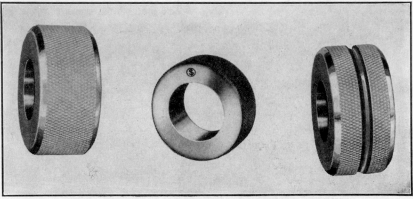

Courtesy Sheffield Gage Corporation.

FIG. 19.   Plain Ring Gages.

Ring gages.   Plain ring gages are also standardized in construction
and general proportion.   The three shown in Figure 19 are typical of
gages up to 1.510 inches.   A plain knurled surface indicates a "go"
gage, whereas a "not-go" gage is identified by an annular groove on

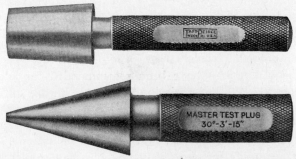

Courtesy Taft Peirce Manufacturing Company.

FIG. 20.   Special Taper Plug Gages.

the periphery.   Above 1.510 inches all gages are flanged to reduce
weight and facilitate handling.   Large gages are provided with ball
handles.   Details of construction, with dimensions of all sizes, have
been worked out by the Standards Committee.

Taper gages. Taper gages are made in both the plug and ring styles and, in general, follow the same standard construction adopted for plain and ring gages. Two taper plug gages are shown in Figure 20. Taper gages are not dimensional gages but rather a means of checking in terms of degrees or inches per foot. Their use in testing is a matter of fitting rather than of measuring. If size is involved, "go" and "not-go" tolerances are indicated on the end of the gage by grooves or by milling off a portion of the gage. This type of gage is widely used in checking the standard tapers and sockets used on tools and production machines.

Spline gages. For inspectional work on splined hubs and shafts, spline gages similar to those shown in Figure 21 are used. These gages are, in effect, special forms of the ordinary plug and ring gages.

Courtesy Sheffield Gage Corporation.

FIG. 21. Spline Plug and Ring Gage.

Standardization of these gages is impractical because of the wide variations in the design of splined parts. Numerous other special shapes are inspected with gages of the same type.

Thread gages. In Figure 22 are shown standard plug and ring gages for inspecting threads. Both these gages are standardized with size variations in the same manner as provided for plain plug and ring gages. Double-ended plug gages have the "go" and "not-go" feature according to the tolerances desired. All ring gages are of the adjustable type, as shown in the figure, with effective means for locking the adjusting screw in position. This feature is desirable, as it is very difficult to measure internal threads accurately in a blank during its manufacture. After completion, they are set to correct size by means of a threaded plug of exact dimensions.

A simple method of approximate checking of the pitch of screws is

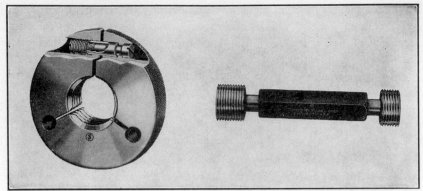

Courtesy Sheffield Gage Corporation.

FIG. 22.   Thread Plug and Ring Gage.

by means of a small screw-pitch gage made up of a consecutive number of blades, each having a profile of one standard pitch thread.

Courtesy Pratt & Whitney
—Division Niles-Bement-Pond Company.

FIG. 23.   Tri-Roll Thread Comparator.

A quick-acting indicating device for checking threads is shown in Figure 23.   Initially the dial is set at zero with a standard threaded plug, and subsequent readings indicate any deviation from the original setting. In operation, the upper roll is raised by depressing a lever, and the work piece is placed between the three rolls. Errors in lead, angle, and pitch diameter are read cumulatively on the dial.

Snap gages. A snap gage, used in the measurement of plain external dimensions, consists of a U-shaped frame having jaws equipped with suitable gaging surfaces. A plain gage has two parallel jaws or anvils

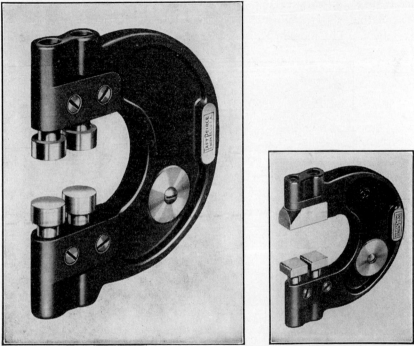

Both Photos Courtesy Taft Peirce Manufacturing Company.

FIG. 24. Adjustable-Type Snap Gage (AGD Model B).

FIG. 25. Snap Gage Equipped with Square Buttons (AGD Model C).

which are made to some standard size and cannot be adjusted. This type of gage is largely being replaced by adjustable gages to provide means of changing tolerance settings or adjusting for wear. Most gages are provided with the "go" and "not-go" feature in a single jaw, and this design is both satisfactory and rapid. A wide variety of snap gages has been developed by various companies, although it is recognized that some disadvantage results from this lack of standardization. Four types, standardized by the American Gage Design Committee, are:

Model A   Employing 4 gaging pins.
Model B   Employing 4 gaging buttons, either square or round.
Model C   Employing 2 gaging buttons, either square or round, and a
           single block anvil.
Model MC   A miniature snap gage with 2 gaging buttons, either square
           or round, and a single block anvil.*

The model-B gage is shown in Figure 24, and the model-C is shown in Figure 25. Model-A gages are similar to the model-B design, except that straight pins are used in place of buttons as the gaging members. The model-MC is similar to the model-C gage, except that

Courtesy Taft Peirce Manufacturing Company.

FIG. 26.   Set of 82 Precision Gage Blocks.

it is in miniature and is used only in gaging diameters up to 0.760 inch.

The general design shown in Figures 24 and 25 has been selected, because it incorporates most of the advantages of all similar gages now in use. It is light in weight, sufficiently rigid, easy to adjust, and provided with suitable locking means, and is designed to permit interchangeability of as many of the parts as possible.

Precision gage blocks. These blocks, of hardened steel, are square or rectangular in shape, having two parallel sides very accurately lapped to some size. Blocks up to one inch are made to size within 5 to 8 millionths of an inch per block and per inch of length on larger blocks.

* Commercial Standard CS8—41.

Laboratory sets may be obtained with a guaranteed accuracy within 2 millionths of an inch per block. The principal uses for these blocks are for reference in setting gages and for accurate measuréments in tool, gage, and die manufacture.

In Figure 26 is shown a set of 81 gage blocks which includes the following:

One ten-thousandth series	0.1001–0.1009 in., inclusive	9 blocks
One thousandth series	0.101 –0.149 in., inclusive	49 blocks
Fifty thousandths series	0.050 –0.950 in., inclusive	19 blocks
Inch series	1.000 –4.000 in., inclusive	4 blocks

With this set it is possible to obtain practically any dimension in increments of 0.0001 inch from 0.100 to over 10 inches by combining blocks of the proper size.

Precision gage blocks are assembled by a wringing process. The blocks must first be thoroughly cleaned. One is placed on the other centrally and oscillated slightly. It is then slid partially out of engagement, and they are wrung together under slight pressure. A slight liquid film between the surfaces of the gages causes them to adhere firmly. Gage blocks put together in this fashion should not be so assembled for more than a few hours.

Many interesting applications of gage blocks can be made with the aid of special holders and base blocks. The holders secure the blocks in one rigid accurate unit as illustrated in Figure 27. This height gage combination can be set by

Courtesy The DoALL Company.

Fig. 27. Height-Gage Combination Using Block and Vernier Gage.

means of a vernier gage block to accuracies of 0.000010 of an inch. When the graduated block is slid to the right one graduation, the height of the vernier gage is increased 10 microinches. Snap gages can also be assembled quickly for accurate inspection on short-run jobs.

Thickness or feeler gage. This gage consists of a number of thin blades which are held together in a thin case. The blades usually vary in thickness from 0.001 to 0.015 inch but may be obtained in any thickness range desired. They are used in checking clearances and for gaging in narrow places.

Dial indicator. A dial indicator is composed of a graduated dial having a hand connected to a test point with suitable means for supporting or clamping it firmly. The dial is graduated in thou-

Courtesy Brown & Sharpe Manufacturing Company.

FIG. 28.   Dial Indicating Gage with Permanent-Magnet Base.

sandths of an inch, the number depending on the accuracy desired. Most indicators have a spindle travel equal to $2\frac{1}{2}$ revolutions of the hand. Between the test point and the hand is interposed an accurate multiplying mechanism which greatly magnifies on the dial any movement of the point. This tool may be considered either a measuring device or a gage. As a measuring device, it is used to measure inaccuracies in alignment, eccentricity, and deviations on surfaces supposed to be parallel. In gaging work, it gives a direct reading of tolerance variations from the exact size.

A dial test indicator equipped with a permanent-magnet base is shown in Figure 28. This base operates in the same fashion as the permanent-magnet chuck described on page 586. With the handle in the base turned to the "on" position, the indicator is held securely on the horizontal, vertical, or overhead flat surface of any machine. Other methods of support are a suitable clamp or a heavy base as used on a surface gage.

Comparator or visual gage. A visual gage giving direct plus or minus readings to close tolerance is shown in Figure 29. This gage

Courtesy Sheffield Gage Corporation.

Fig. 29. Model 5000 Visual Gage.

Courtesy The DoALL Company.

Fig. 30. Checking the Pitch Diameter of a Thread Gage on an Electric Comparator Gage.

employs a feed mechanism in connection with a light beam to obtain high magnification of any movement of the gaging point. The magnification in this instrument is 5000 to 1, and the range on the 5-inch scale is only 0.001 inch. Each graduation on the scale represents 0.000025 inch. This gage is used for checking inspection gages and for toolroom work, as well as for routine production work requiring close size control.

Courtesy Jones & Lamson Machine Company.

Fig. 31.   Pedestal-Type Comparator Showing Threads on Airplane Cylinder Barrels.

An electric comparator having four ranges of magnification is shown in Figure 30. A common model of this type comparator has magnification of 10,000, 5000, 1000, and 500 to one. For the highest magnifica-

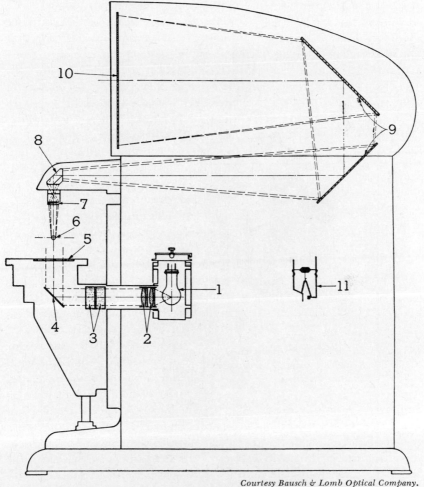

Courtesy Bausch & Lomb Optical Company.

Fig. 32. Path of Light in Bausch and Lomb Contour Measuring Projector.

tion each graduation is 0.000010 of an inch. An electric current is arranged so that a minute motion of the gage spindle produces the height indication on the scale. In the illustration shown a thread gage is being checked for pitch diameter by the three-wire method. The gage is set by means of gage blocks.

Projecting comparators. Projecting comparators are designed on the same principle as the ordinary projection lantern. An image is placed before a light source, and the shadow of the profile is projected on the screen at some enlarged scale. Usual magnifications are ×20 and ×50, although others up to ×100 can be used.

A pedestal-type comparator showing the threads on an airplane cylinder barrel is illustrated in Figure 31. Frequently, in checking threads, a chart showing tolerance variations is prepared on a transparent sheet and placed against the glass screen. This permits the inspector to check the thread for dimensional accuracy as well as for contour and lead. The attachment holding the cylinder is arranged so that it can be moved across the path of the light beam, thus allowing the entire thread to be inspected. Micrometer adjustment to one ten-thousandth of an inch is provided on the work table of some of these machines for accurate checking purposes.

Courtesy Pratt & Whitney
—Division Niles-Bement-Pond Company.

FIG. 33. Multiple-Electric-Contact Gage for Rapid Checking of Several Dimensions Simultaneously.

The path of light in a different type of projector is shown diagrammatically in Figure 32. The object to be inspected is supported at 6 in the figure, and, as the light beam passes by the contour of the object, it enters the projection lens at 7 and is reflected to the screen. Contour inspection is of great value in many tools, dies, gages, and formed products. It is employed in the inspection of many small parts such as needles, saw teeth, threads, forming tools, taps, and gear teeth. Since it checks work to definite tolerances, it can be used for studying wear on tools or distortion caused by heat treatment. Its limitations are based on the size of the object and the number of magnifications desired.

Multiple-electric-contact gages. In quantity production it is frequently desirable to check a number of dimensions simultaneously. This can be done both accurately and rapidly by means of specially constructed contact gages. Each dimension to be checked is provided with pairs of red and green lights which tell the operator whether the dimension is below or above the specified tolerance. Figure 33 shows such a gage made up for simultaneous checking of a number of dimensions. The shell, or part being checked, is within the tolerance if all red and green lights go out. The two master shells at right are for setting the gage to the correct limits for the dimension in question. Multiple-type gages, operating electrically, with air, or mechanically, are widely used for the economical inspection of many parts.

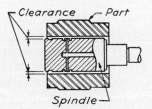

Typical Air Spindle for Internal Checking.

Courtesy Sheffield Gage Corporation.

Dial-Type Precisionaire for Air-Gaging Holes.

FIG. 34.

Air gages. Gaging with the aid of compressed air is accomplished by either measuring the back pressure of the air as it comes out of the gage or metering its flow. A dial-type machine, using the later principle for air-gaging holes, is shown in Figure 34. The air spindle, shown above, has two small diametrically opposed holes through which the air flows. The amount of air flow is controlled by the size of the spaces between the air spindle and the work. This change in flow is registered on the dial which is calibrated to read in fractions of a thousandth of an inch. The relationship between the rate of flow and the size of hole holds true only for small clearances, and the maximum range is around 0.003 inch. High amplification permits reading in fractions of a tenth of a thousandth if very accurate readings are necessary.

Gages of this type can be used for both internal and external checking, and, if desired, multiple checking of several dimensions can be done simultaneously. Advantages claimed for this type of gaging include low wear on gaging spindle, quick indication of true measurement, and little skill required for the operation of the instrument. In addition, air gages will also reveal taper, out-of-round, and tool gouges, which are difficult to detect with the usual plug gage.

Review Questions

1. What is meant by interchangeable manufacture?

2. Distinguish among free fit, snug fit, and shrink fit.

3. Define tolerance. Why is unilateral tolerance usually specified on production drawings?

4. A bearing is dimensioned at 2.750 plus 0.003 minus 0.000. The shaft which runs in the bearing is 2.749 plus 0.0005 minus 0.0015. What is the allowance?

5. What is the standard of length in the United States? What is the standard relationship between inches and millimeters?

6. What is a combination set? State the use of each part.

7. How does a caliper differ from a divider in both construction and use?

8. Show by sketch a micrometer reading for 0.419 inch.

9. Explain the principle used on a vernier caliper.

10. How would you measure the lead of a small screw using a toolmaker's microscope?

11. Explain the use of a telescopic gage in measuring the diameter of a hole.

12. What is the basic unit of angular measurement? List five ways an angle can be measured.

13. A 2-inch gage block is set up under one end of a 5-inch sine bar. What height would have to be used on the other end to check an angle of 15 degrees 30 minutes?

14. Explain the use of a surface plate. How does it differ from a toolmaker's flat?

15. What is an optical flat, and how is it used?

16. If the diameter of a hole is specified as 1.875 plus 0.003 minus 0.001, what should be the diameters of the gaging members of a "go" and "not-go" plug gage?

17. What is the purpose of a projecting comparator? Is it possible to check for dimensional tolerance with this instrument?

18. For what type of work are snap gages used?

19. What use does an inspector make of gage blocks? To what degree of accuracy are they made?

20. Explain how a dial indicator may be used for either measuring or gaging.

21. How does an air gage operate?

References

American Standard B4a—1925, *Tolerances, Allowances, and Gages for Metal Fits*, American Standards Association, 1925.

American Standard B4.1—1947, *Limits and Fits for Engineering and Manufacturing*, American Standards Association, 1947.

COLE, C. B., *Tool Making*, American Technical Society, 1939.

FULLMER, IRVIN H., "Fundamentals of Mechanical Dimensional Control," *Mechanical Engineering*, Vol. 57, no. 12, 1935.

Gages, Pratt & Whitney, no. 11, 1947.

Gages, Jigs, and Fixtures, International Textbook Company, 1936.

KENT's *Mechanical Engineers Handbook*, 12th edition, John Wiley & Sons, 1950.

KURTZ, H. F., "Optical Projection," *Mechanical Engineering*, Vol. 60, no. 6, 1938.

Limits and Fits for Engineering and Manufacturing, (B4.1—1947) American Standards Association, 1947.

MICHELON, L. C., *Industrial Inspection Methods*, Harper & Brothers, 1949.

Precision Products and Services, Sheffield Corporation, 1949.

Production Handbook, Ronald Press Company, 1944.

Quality Control, DoALL Service Company, 1945.

LATHES AND LATHE TOOLS

The *lathe* is a machine that removes material by rotating the work against a cutter. Parts to be machined can be held between centers, attached to a face plate, supported in a jaw chuck, or held in a draw-in chuck or collet. Though this machine is particularly adapted to cylindrical work, it may also be used for many other purposes. Plain surfaces can be obtained by supporting the work on a face plate or in a chuck. Work held in this manner can likewise be centered, drilled, bored, or reamed. In addition, the lathe can be used for cutting threads and turning tapers; with the proper attachment, it can be adapted to simple milling or grinding operations. It is probably the oldest of all the machine tools as well as the most important machine in modern production.

Types of Lathes

It is difficult to make a suitable classification of lathes as there are so many variables in the size, design, method of drive, arrangement of gears, and purpose. In general, the following classification covers most of the lathes used today.

CLASSIFICATION OF LATHES

1. Speed lathe
   (*a*) Wood working.
   (*b*) Centering.
   (*c*) Metal spinning.
   (*d*) Polishing, etc.
2. Engine lathe
   (*a*) Step-cone pulley drive from line shaft.
   (*b*) Step-cone pulley drive from individual motor.
   (*c*) Gear-head drive.
   (*d*) Variable-speed drive.
3. Bench lathe.
4. Toolroom lathe.

5. Special-purpose lathes
   (*a*) Crankshaft.
   (*b*) Car wheel.
   (*c*) Gap.
   (*d*) Multicut.
   (*e*) Duplicating, etc.

Speed lathe. The speed lathe shown in Figure 10 of Chapter 3 is the simplest of all lathes. It consists of a bed, a headstock, a tailstock, and an adjustable slide for supporting the tool. Usually this lathe is driven by a variable-speed motor built into the headstock, although in some cases the drive may be a belt to a step-cone pulley. Because hand tools are used and the cuts are small, these lathes are driven at high speeds. The work is either held between centers or attached to a face plate on the headstock.

This lathe is used principally in the turning of wood for small cabinet work or for patterns, and for the centering of metal cylinders prior to further work on the engine lathe. In the latter operation, the center drill is held in a small chuck fastened to the headstock, and the work is guided to the center drill either by a fixed center rest or a movable center in the tailstock. Metal spinning is done on lathes of this type by rapidly revolving a stamped or deep-drawn piece of thin ductile metal and pressing it against a form by means of blunt hand tools. In all these applications, the work is revolved at high speeds, and hand tools are used.

Engine lathe. The engine lathe derives its name from the early lathes which obtained their power from engines. This lathe differs from a speed lathe in that it has additional features for controlling the spindle speed and for supporting and controlling the feed of the fixed cutting tool. There are several variations in the design of the headstock through which the power is supplied to the machine. Lathes that receive their power from an overhead line shaft are belt-driven and equipped with a step-cone pulley, usually a four-step pulley. This gives a range of four spindle speeds driven directly from the line shaft. In addition, these lathes are equipped with back gears which, when connected with the cone pulley, provide four additional speeds. This type of lathe requires an overhead countershaft carrying a cone pulley which matches the one on the lathe, plus two additional pulleys equipped with clutches to cause forward and reverse rotation of the work.

Another type of engine lathe receives its power from an individual motor mounted either on the side or beneath the lathe. In this case the general design of the headstock is the same, but the power is supplied through a short belt from the motor or from a small cone-pulley countershaft driven by the motor. This machine has the advantage of an individual motor drive. A machine of this type with the principal parts labeled is shown in Figure 1.

A *geared-head lathe* (see Figure 2) varies the spindle speeds by means of a gear transmission. Various speeds are obtained by setting certain

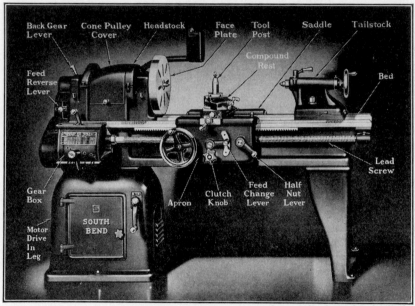

Courtesy South Bend Lathe Works.

Fig. 1.   Engine Lathe.

speed levers in the head. Such lathes are usually driven by a constant-speed motor mounted on the lathe, but in a few cases variable-speed motors are used. This type of lathe has the advantage of a positive drive and has a greater number of spindle speeds available than are usually found on a step-cone-driven lathe. Recently some lathes have been developed with a variable-speed mechanism built into the head-stock, thus permitting close regulation of the spindle rotation.

Bench lathe. The name bench lathe is given to a small lathe that is mounted on a work bench. In design it has the same features as ordinary speed or engine lathes and differs from these lathes only in size and mounting. It is adapted to small work, having a maximum swing capacity of 9 inches at the face plate. Many lathes of this type

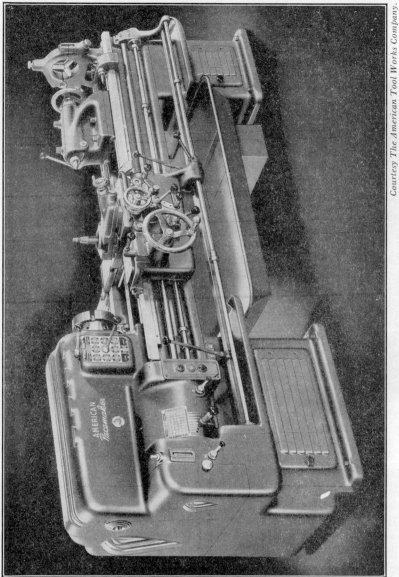

Fig. 2. American Pacemaker Geared-Head Engine Lathe.

are used for precision work on small parts, such as jeweler's lathes. A bench lathe adapted for precision work is shown in Figure 3.

Toolroom lathe. The toolroom lathe, the most modern type of engine lathe, is equipped with all the accessories necessary for accurate tool work. Such lathes (see Figure 4) are usually individually driven geared-head lathes with a considerable range in spindle speeds. They

Courtesy Rivett Lathe & Grinder.

Fig. 3.   Rivett 10-Inch Bench-Type Precision Toolroom Lathe.

are equipped with center steady rest, quick change gears, lead screw, feed rod, taper attachment, thread dial, chuck, indicator, draw-in collet attachment, pump for coolant, and frequently a relieving attachment to control the motion of the tool. In some cases a "live" or antifriction center is used in the tailstock which eliminates any scoring of the center, preserving its accuracy. All toolroom lathes are carefully tested for accuracy and, as the name implies, are especially adapted for making small tools, test gages, dies, and other precision parts.

Duplicating lathe. Although the engine lathe is a versatile machine it is not widely used on quantity production jobs, as the setting and accuracy of each cut is largely dependent on the skill of the operator. Lathes provided with duplicating features eliminate hand setting of

Courtesy The Lodge & Shipley Machine Tool Company.

FIG. 4. Toolmaker Lathe 16- × 54-Inch Capacity.

Courtesy The American Tool Works Company.

FIG. 5. Duplicating Shaft from Standard Work Piece by Means of a Hydraulically
Controlled Cutting Tool.

the tools and frequent checking of measurements by having the tool controlled by a tracer point which follows a template mounted at the rear of the lathe. Figure 5 shows a hydraulically operated tracer controlling the cutting tool in the production of a shaft. A conventional turning tool is used, and the cut taken is a continuous uninterrupted one which duplicates the exact shape of the template. The template may be either flat or cylindrical, the latter design being more economical as it permits standard work pieces to be used as templates. One feature of this machine is having the tool rest at a 45-degree angle to the work axis. This permits cutting square shoulders as well as tapers' and radii by compensating for the continuous longitudinal movement of the carriage.

Advantages claimed for this type of lathe include lower production costs, accurate reproduction of parts, elimination of need for form tools, and reduction of setup time to a minimum. Work specially adapted for quantity production includes drive shafts, axles, valve stems, piston rods, arbors, and bevel-gear blanks. Flanged parts such as pump impellers, gas-turbine compressor wheels, and cylinder heads may be duplicated using the cross-feed and a flat template.

Lathe Construction and Operation

Lathe size. The size of a lathe is expressed in terms of the diameter of the work it will swing; thus, a 16-inch lathe is one having sufficient clearance over the bed rails to take work 16 inches in diameter. However, a second dimension is necessary to define further the size capacity of the machine in terms of work piece length. Some manufacturers express this in terms of the maximum work length in inches between the lathe centers, whereas others express it in terms of bed length in feet.

Lathe construction. In studying the construction of a lathe, reference to Figure 1 will be of assistance, as all the principal parts are labeled. All lathes receive their power through the *headstock,* which may be equipped either with a step-cone-pulley drive or a geared-head drive. Figure 6 shows a typical back-geared headstock equipped for a belt drive through a step-cone pulley. Four spindle speeds are available when the pulley is directly connected to the lathe spindle. If slower speeds are desired, the back gears are thrown in mesh with the two gears on either end of the cone pulley and the large gear to the right of the cone pulley is disengaged. Power then is transmitted through the train of four gears to the main spindle, providing four additional speeds.

Figure 2 shows the construction of a typical geared-head lathe where spindle-speed variations are obtained by regulating the levers on the side of the transmission.

The lathe *tailstock* can be adjusted along the bed of the lathe to accommodate different lengths of stock being turned. It is provided with a hardened center, which may be moved in and out by the wheel

Courtesy South Bend Lathe Works.

FIG. 6. Back-Geared Headstock with Gear Guards Removed.

adjustment, and is also equipped with setover screws at its base to be used for adjusting the alignment of the centers and for taper turning.

The *lead screw* is a long carefully threaded shaft, located slightly below and parallel to the bed and extending all the way from the headstock to the tailstock. It is geared to the headstock in such a way that it may be reversed and is fitted to the carriage assembly so that it may either engage or be released from the carriage during cutting operations. Figure 7 shows an end view of a lathe equipped with standard change gears. The top four gears shown are the *spindle gear*, two *reverse gears*, and the *stud gear*. These gears are fixed and are not changed to obtain various lead-screw speeds. When it is necessary to change the speed of the lead screw, the driving gear, idlers, and lead-screw gears are removed and the proper gears put in place. Most lathes today do not rely on manual gear changing but are equipped with a quick-change gearbox, located at the left end of the lead screw (see Figures 1 and 2). This box contains a number of gears so arranged that the lead screw can be driven at the proper speed to cut any of the standard threads. To change the feed it is necessary only to move the extending levers.

Courtesy South Bend Lathe Works.

FIG. 7.   End View of Standard-Change Gear Lathe.

The carriage assembly includes the *compound rest, tool post, saddle,* and *apron.* Since it supports and guides the cutting tool, it must be constructed with great accuracy and rigidity. Two hand feeds are provided to guide the tool on a crosswise motion. The upper hand wheel controls the motion of the compound rest, and, as this rest is provided with a swiveling adjustment protractor, it can be placed in various angle positions for short taper turning. A third hand wheel is used to move the carriage along the bed, usually to pull it back to starting position after the lead screw has carried it along the cut. The portion of the carriage that extends in front of the lathe is called an apron. On the face of the apron are mounted the various control wheels and levers. Figure 8 shows an interior view of an apron and the method of drive.

Lathes that are designed for toolroom use are provided with a *relieving attachment.* The function of this attachment is to relieve or back off the flutes of rotary cutters, taps, reamers, end mills, and dies. Figure 9 shows radial- and side-relieving attachments mounted on a

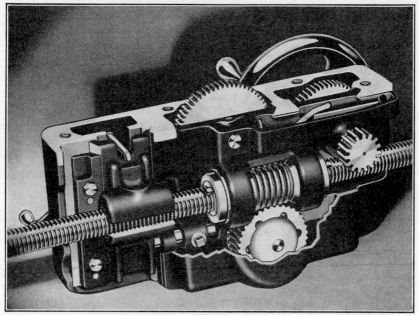

Courtesy South Bend Lathe Works.

Fig. 8. Interior View of Double-Wall Apron.

Courtesy Pratt & Whitney—Division Niles-Bement-Pond Company.

Fig. 9. Detail of Radial- and Side-Relieving Attachments with Cam Box Covers Open.

lathe and driven from a gearbox at the rear of the headstock. The radial attachment is mounted on the cross slide, while the side-relieving attachment is at the left. In radial relieving, motion is transmitted from the headstock to a cam in the attachment box which, in turn, causes the tool slide to move back and forth. This motion is synchronized with the spindle rotation and causes the tool to give proper relief to the part in question. The side-relieving attachment operates in a similar manner but gives the tool a longitudinal back and forth movement to produce side relief. It may be operated separately or with the radial attachment.

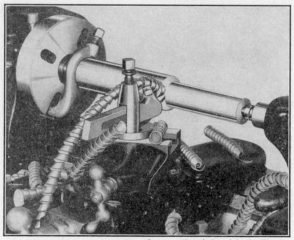

Courtesy South Bend Lathe Works.

Fig. 10.   Turning a Steel Shaft Mounted between Centers.

Supporting work between centers. The most common way to support work on a lathe is to mount it between centers, as shown in Figure 10. This method has the advantage of being able to resist heavy cuts and is convenient for long parts. Since the work is mounted between two tapered centers, it will not turn uniformly with the spindle unless it is attached in some further fashion. Such attachment is made through a pear-shaped forging known as a *dog*, which consists of a main body with an opening to accommodate the stock being turned, a setscrew at the lower end to fasten the work securely, and an elongated portion at the top (known as the tail) which is bent at a right angle—parallel with the stock—so that it may engage a slot in the face plate. After mounting, the tail of the dog is fitted into the face plate, the setscrew is tightened, and the work is ready to be turned, as shown in Figure 10. The center in the headstock turns with the work;

consequently, no lubrication of that center is necessary. The tailstock center, or dead center, acts as a conical bearing and for this reason must be kept clean and well lubricated. It should not be too tight against the work, nor should it be so loose that there is end play. A check should be made at frequent intervals, for, if it is too tight, the oil film will be broken down, and either the work or the center will be ruined.

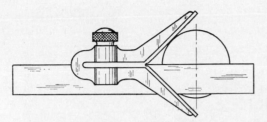

USE OF CENTER HEAD TO LOCATE CENTERS

DRILL & COUNTERSINK

CENTER HOLE IN SHAFT

SIZE OF CENTER HOLES			
DIA. OF WORK W	DIA. OF HOLE C	DIA. OF DRILL D	DIA OF BODY F
$\frac{3}{16}''$ TO $\frac{5}{16}''$	$\frac{1}{8}''$	$\frac{1}{16}''$	$\frac{13}{64}''$
$\frac{3}{8}''$ TO $1''$	$\frac{3}{16}''$	$\frac{3}{32}''$	$\frac{3}{10}''$
$1\frac{1}{4}''$ TO $2''$	$\frac{1}{4}''$	$\frac{1}{8}''$	$\frac{3}{10}''$
$2\frac{1}{4}''$ TO $4''$	$\frac{5}{16}''$	$\frac{5}{32}''$	$\frac{7}{16}''$

Fig. 11. Size of Center Holes and Method of Locating.

In preparing cylindrical work, care must be exercised in locating the center holes before they are drilled. Probably the most convenient method is with a combination square and scriber. The center head of the combination square should be held firmly against the shaft, as shown in Figure 11, and two intersecting lines scribed close to the blade. The intersection of the lines represents the center of the shaft, and this point should be center-punched to facilitate proper starting of the center drill. The sizes of center holes for various-size shafts are given in the table at the lower part of the illustration.

In turning long slender shafts, or boring and threading the ends of spindles, a *center rest* is used to give additional support to the work. The usual type of center steady rest is shown on the ends of the lathe beds in Figures 2 and 4. It is attached to the bed of the lathe and supports the work by means of the three jaws shown. Another rest, somewhat similar, is known as a *follower rest*. It is attached to the saddle of the carriage and supports work of small diameter that is likely to spring away from the cutting tool. This rest moves with the tool, whereas the center rest is stationary.

Cylindrical work that has been bored and reamed to size may be pressed on a steel *mandrel* and supported between centers for further machining. Lathe mandrels have hardened, ground surfaces and are available in all standard sizes. The surface is ground with a taper of about 0.0006 inch per inch in length, the small end being 0.0005 inch undersize to facilitate starting the work. The work should be pressed

Courtesy South Bend Lathe Works.

FIG. 12. Boring an Eccentric Hole on the Face Plate of a Lathe.

on the mandrel in an arbor press, as considerable pressure is needed in this operation. After the work is mounted on the mandrel, it is placed between the centers, and any further machining done is similar to other cylindrical turning.

Supporting work in chuck or on face plate. In addition to being held between centers, the work can also be held by being bolted to the *face plate,* by a jaw *chuck,* or by a draw-in *collet.* Figure 12 illustrates work supported by being bolted to a face plate. Such mounting is suitable for flat plates and parts of irregular shape. The figure illustrates the use of a boring bar for internal turning.

Lathe chucks are made in several designs, as shown in Figures 13 and 14, and may be classified as follows:

1. *Universal chuck.* The jaws all maintain a concentric relationship when the chuck wrench is turned.

2. *Independent chuck.* Each jaw has an independent adjustment.

3. *Combination chuck.* Each jaw has an independent adjustment and, in addition, has a separate wrench connection which controls all jaws simultaneously.

4. *Drill chuck.* A small universal screw chuck used principally on drill presses but frequently used on lathes for drilling and centering.

5. *Draw-in collet chuck.* Holds standard-shape bar stock in a centered position. A separate collet is necessary for each work size.

Lathe chucks are used for holding short pieces of stock of irregular shape that cannot be held between centers. For example, in making

Both Photos Courtesy Warner & Swasey Manufacturing Company.

Fig. 13. Four-Jaw Independent Chuck.

Fig. 14. Three-Jaw Geared Scroll Chuck.

a small gear blank from solid stock, the piece would first be mounted in the chuck and one side of it faced true. To produce a hole through the blank, the dead center should be removed from the tailstock and a drill chuck mounted in its place. Successive operations of centering, drilling, boring, and reaming can then be performed. The blank is then removed from the chuck and mounted on a mandrel for further machining.

Draw-in collet chucks are the most accurate of all types of chucks and are especially adapted for holding bar stock. In mounting a collet chuck attachment to a lathe, the live center is removed and a tapered sleeve bushing is put in its place. The proper-sized collet is placed in this sleeve and screwed to the draw bar extending through the spindle,

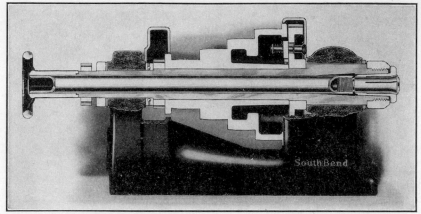

Courtesy South Bend Lathe Works.

FIG. 15. Cross Section of Headstock Showing the Construction of Draw-in Collet Chuck Attachment.

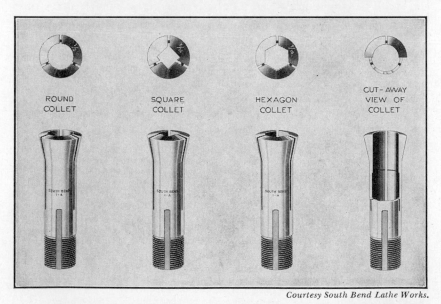

Courtesy South Bend Lathe Works.

FIG. 16. Side of End View of Various Types of Spring Collets.

as shown in Figure 15. Work can then be placed in the collet and held by turning the hand wheel on the end of the draw bar. This forces the collet back against the tapered surface of the sleeve and causes the collet jaws to grip the work. Collets are made for round, square, and other shapes, as shown in Figure 16. This means of holding stock is used in precision work for such parts as small tools, spindles, bushings, and screws. The work held by the collet must be the same size as the collet, or its accuracy will be impaired.

Taper turning. Many parts and tools made in lathes have tapered surfaces, varying from the short steep tapers found on bevel gears and lathe center ends to the long gradual tapers found on lathe mandrels. The shanks of twist drills, end mills, reamers, arbors, and other tools are examples of taper work. Such tools, supported by taper shanks, are held in true position and are easily removed.

There are several taper standards found in commercial practice. The following classification lists the standards commonly used:

1. *Morse taper.* Largely used for drill shanks, collets, and lathe centers. The taper is approximately 5⁄8 inch per foot.

2. *Brown & Sharpe taper.* Used principally in milling machine spindles: 1⁄2 inch per foot.

3. *Jarno and Reed tapers.* Used by some manufacturers of lathe and small drilling equipment. Both systems have a taper of 0.6 inch per foot, but the diameters are different.

4. *Sellers taper.* Used principally in equipment manufactured by William Sellers and Company. The taper is 3⁄4 inch per foot.

5. *Taper pins.* Used as fasteners. The taper is 1⁄4 inch per foot.

Each of these standards is made in a variety of diameters and designated by a number.

External tapers may be cut on a lathe in several ways:

1. By using a taper-turning attachment on the lathe, as illustrated in Figure 17. This attachment is bolted on the back of the lathe and has a guide bar which may be set at the desired angle or taper. As the carriage moves along the lathe bed, a slide over the bar causes the tool to move in or out, according to the setting of the bar. In other words, the taper setting of the bar is duplicated on the work. The advantages of this system are that the lathe centers are kept in alignment, and the same taper may be turned on various pieces, even though they vary in length.

2. By using the compound rest on the lathe carriage. This rest, which has a circular base, may be swiveled to any desired angle with the work. The tool is then fed into the work by hand. This method is especially adapted for short tapers such as truing up a lathe center.

3. By setting over the tailstock center. If the tailstock is moved horizontally out of alignment 1⁄4 inch, and a cylinder 12 inches long

is placed between centers, the taper will be ¼ inch per foot.   However, a cylinder 6 inches long will have a taper of ½ inch per foot.   Hence, the amount of taper obtained on a given piece depends on the length of the stock, as well as on the amount the center is set over.

4. By manually operating both hand feeds. This method is not recommended, as it is impossible to cut an accurate taper.

Courtesy The American Tool Works Company.

Fig. 17.   View of Ball-Bearing Taper Attachment on American Pacemaker Lathe.

Internal tapers can be machined on a lathe only by using the compound rest or the taper-turning attachment.   Small holes for taper pins are first drilled and then reamed to size with a taper reamer.

Lathe Tools

Single-pointed metal-cutting lathe tools consist of small pieces of rectangular tool steel rigidly supported in suitable holders.   The tool holder is held on the tool post of the lathe, and the work revolves against point of the tool.

In order to cut metal efficiently and accurately, the cutting tool must be properly ground to provide a keen cutting edge with correct angles for the kind of metal to be cut.   The shapes and angles of the tool vary considerably, depending on the type of cutting operation, kind of material being cut, tool material, and finish desired.

The *machinability*,* or ease with which a given material can be cut, is influenced greatly by the cutting tool. It must be recognized, however, that machinability is a relative term and is expressed only in such factors as length of tool life, power required to make the cut, and cost of removing a given amount of metal. Other factors influencing the machinability include cutting speed and feed and type of coolant used, a proper selection of which must be made to obtain optimum results for a given material.

Tool materials. Present-day production practices make rather severe demands on machine tools. To accommodate the many conditions imposed upon them, a wide variety of tool materials have been developed. No one of these materials is superior in all respects, but rather each has certain characteristics which limit its field of application. The selection of the proper tool material therefore depends on the type of service to which the tool will be subjected. Obviously the best material to use for a certain job is the one that will produce the machined part at the lowest unit cost. The principal materials used in cutting tools are as follows:

1. HIGH-CARBON STEELS. For many years, before the development of high-speed tool steels, carbon steels were used entirely for all cutting tools. With the carbon content ranging from 0.80 to 1.20%, these steels have good hardening ability and, with proper heat treatment, attain as great a hardness as any of the high-speed alloys. At maximum hardness the steel is quite brittle, and, if some toughness is desired, it must be obtained at the expense of hardness. Depth-hardening ability (*hardenability*) is poor, limiting the use of this steel to tools of small size. Because of the tendency of these tools to lose hardness at around 600 F, they are not suitable for high speeds and heavy-duty work, their usefulness being confined to work on soft materials such as wood. As a production-tool material for metal cutting, these steels are obsolete.

2. HIGH-SPEED STEELS. High-speed steels are high in alloy content, have excellent hardenability, and will retain a good cutting edge up to temperatures of around 1200 F. The ability of a tool to resist softening at high temperatures is known as *red hardness* and is a most desirable quality. The first tool steel that would hold its cutting edge to almost a red heat was developed by Frederick W. Taylor and M. White in 1900. This was accomplished by adding 18% tungsten and 5.5% chromium to steel as the principal alloying elements. Present-day

---

* For discussion of this subject see "Machinability of Steel," *Metals Handbook*, American Society for Metals, p. 360.

practice in the manufacture of high-speed steels still uses these two elements in nearly the same percentage. Other common alloying elements are vanadium, molybdenum, and cobalt. Although there are numerous high-speed steel compositions, they may all be grouped in the following three classes:

(*a*) *18-4-1 high-speed steel.* This steel containing 18% tungsten, 4% chromium, and 1% vanadium is considered to be one of the best all-purpose tool steels. In some steels of similar composition the percentage of vanadium is increased slightly in order to obtain better results in heavy-duty work.

(*b*) *Molybdenum high-speed steel.* Many high-speed steels use molybdenum as the principal alloying element since one part of this will replace two parts of tungsten. Molybdenum steels such as 6-6-4-2 containing 6% tungsten, 6% molybdenum, 4% chromium, and 2% vanadium have excellent toughness and cutting ability. For many applications, particularly drilling and tapping operations, molybdenum high-speed steels are better and cheaper than other types.

(*c*) *Superhigh-speed steels.* Some high-speed steels have cobalt added to them in amounts ranging from 2 to 15%, as this element increases the cutting efficiency, especially at high temperatures. One analysis of this steel contains 20% tungsten, 4% chromium, 2% vanadium, and 12% cobalt. Because of the greater cost of this material it is used principally for heavy cutting operations which impose high pressures and temperatures on the tool.

3. CAST NONFERROUS ALLOYS. A number of nonferrous alloys, containing principally chromium, cobalt, and tungsten, with smaller percentages of one or more carbide-forming elements as tantalum, molybdenum, or boron, are excellent materials for cutting tools. These alloys are cast to shape and have a high red hardness, being able to maintain good cutting edges on tools at temperatures up to 1700 F. Compared with high-speed steels, they can be used at twice their cutting speeds and still maintain the same feed. However, they are more brittle, do not respond to heat treatment, and can be machined only by grinding. Intricate tools can be formed by casting into ceramic or metal molds and then finished to shape by grinding. Their final properties are largely determined by the degree of chill given the material in casting. The range of elements in these alloys is 12 to 25% tungsten, 40 to 50% cobalt, and 15 to 35% chromium. In addition to one or more carbide-forming elements, carbon is added in amounts of 1 to 4%. These alloys have good resistance to cratering and can resist shock loads much better than carbides. As a tool

material they rank midway between high-speed steels and carbides for cutting efficiency.

4. CARBIDES. Carbide cutting-tool inserts are made only by powder-metallurgy technique; the metal powders of tungsten carbide and cobalt are pressed to shape, semisintered to facilitate handling and forming to final shape, then sintered in a hydrogen atmosphere furnace at 2800 F, being finished finally with a grinding operation. Carbide tools containing only tungsten carbide and cobalt (approximately 94% WC and 6% Co) are suitable for machining cast iron and most other materials except steel. Steel cannot be satisfactorily machined by this composition as the chips tend to stick or weld to the carbide surface and soon ruin the tool. To eliminate this difficulty titanium and tantalum carbides are added in addition to increasing the cobalt percentage. A typical analysis of a carbide suitable for steel machining is 82% tungsten carbide, 10% titanium carbide, and 8% cobalt. This composition has a low coefficient of friction and, as a result, has little tendency toward top wear or cratering. Since variation in composition alters the properties of carbide materials, several grades are available to accommodate the various types of work to be done.

Carbide tools are made by brazing or silver-soldering the formed inserts on the ends of commercial steel holders. The red hardness of carbide tool materials is superior to any other tool material, as it will maintain a cutting edge at temperatures over 2200 F. In addition, it is the hardest manufactured material and has extremely high compressive strength. However, it is very brittle, has low resistance to shock, and must be very rigidly supported to prevent cracking. Grinding is very difficult and can be done only with silicon carbide or diamond wheels. Clearance angles should be held to a minimum. Carbide tools permit cutting speeds from two to three times that of cast alloy tools, but at such speeds a much smaller feed must be used. From an economic point of view, carbide tools should always be used if possible. However, machines using carbide tools must be rigidly built, have ample power, and a range of feeds and speeds suitable for this material.

5. DIAMONDS. Diamonds used as single-point tools for light cuts and high speeds must be rigidly supported because of their high hardness and brittleness. They are used either for hard materials difficult to cut with other tool materials or for light high-speed cuts on softer materials where accuracy and surface finish are important. Diamonds are commonly used in the machining of plastics, hard rubber, pressed carbon, and aluminum with cutting speeds from 1000 to 5000 feet per

minute. In addition to being used for cutting tools, diamonds are also used for dressing grind wheels, for small wire-drawing dies, and in certain grinding and lapping operations.

Methods of supporting lathe tools. In most cases, the tools used in lathe work are small rectangular pieces of high-speed tool steel

A. Lathe Tool Holder for High-Speed Steel and Carbide Bits.

Both Photos Courtesy Robert H. Clark Company.

B. Tool Holder Used for Holding Boring Bar.

FIG. 18.

which are held in a tool holder. Because of the high cost of tool materials, it is much more economical to use these small inserts in special holders than to use solid forged tools. In Figure 18*A* is shown an adjustable tool holder capable of accommodating several different sizes of tool bits. The tool bit is securely clamped as near the cutting edge as possible and held by the setscrew and vise jaw with extreme rigidity. Internal lathe cuts can be made by clamping a boring bar in the holder as shown in Figure 18*B*. The tool post on the lathe carriage supports the tool holder in proper position for cutting. A variety of forged tool holders designed to hold the tool in correct position for directional cuts is available.

Tool shapes and angles.   In order to understand the cutting action in metal turning on a lathe, refer to Figure 19.   The view to the left center shows a cross section of the tool near its cutting end.   The

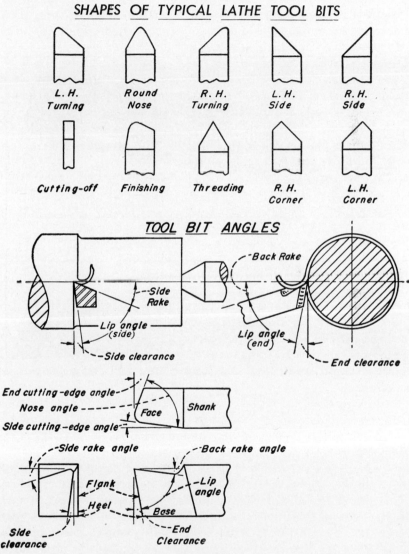

SHAPES OF TYPICAL LATHE TOOL BITS

| L. H. Turning | Round Nose | R. H. Turning | L. H. Side | R. H. Side |

| Cutting-off | Finishing | Threading | R. H. Corner | L. H. Corner |

TOOL BIT ANGLES

Back Rake

Side Rake

Lip angle (side)

Side clearance

Lip angle (end)

End clearance

End cutting-edge angle

Nose angle

Side cutting-edge angle

Face   Shank

Side rake angle   Back rake angle

Flank   Lip angle

Heel   Base

Side clearance   End Clearance

FIG. 19.   Recommended Shapes and Angles for Lathe Tools.

tool has been ground wedge-shaped, the included angle being called the *lip* or *cutting angle*.   The *side-clearance angle* between the side of the tool and the work is to prevent the tool from rubbing.   The angle is small, usually 6 to 8 degrees for most materials. The top angle, known as the *side-rake angle,* varies with the lip angle, which in turn depends on the type of material being cut. The view to the right center is a side view of the tool with similar angles indicated. If the tool is supported in a horizontal position, the *back-rake angle* is obtained by grinding. However, most tool holders are designed to hold the tool in approximate position for correct back rake. *End clearance* is also necessary to prevent a rubbing action on the flank of the tool. The complete nomenclature of the various parts of a tool is labeled on the finishing tool at the lower part of the figure.

In grinding tools it should be noted that the lip or cutting angle varies with the kind of material being cut. A properly selected cutting angle will have the cutting edge supported well enough to withstand heavy cuts and be capable of carrying away the heat generated, yet keen enough to cut well without requiring too much power. A compromise is necessary, and in general it is based on the hardness of the material. Hard materials require a cutting edge of great strength with a capacity for carrying away heat. Soft materials permit the use of smaller cutting angles, around 22 degrees for wood tools. Soft and ductile metals, such as copper and aluminum, require larger angles, ranging from 37 to 57 degrees, whereas brittle materials, where chips crumble or break easily, require still larger angles. An interesting variation in tool angles is that recommended for brass and duralumin. These materials work best with practically zero rakes, the cutting action being a scraping one. Because of the high ductility, the tool will dig in and tear the metal if a small cutting angle is used. Figure 20 illustrates suggested high-speed steel tool angles for various materials.

Carbide tools require slightly greater cutting angles than those shown in the figure because of the brittleness of the material. *Side-cutting-edge angles* of 5 to 20 degrees are recommended for these cutters. As the tool starts a cut, the load is not on the end but at a point back of the tip where the tool is stronger. Also, at the end of the cut there is a gradual reduction of the load. With the cutting edge at an angle, the length of the cutting edge is increased and the pressure per unit length decreased. An *end-cutting-edge angle* of 8 to 15 degrees with a small nose radius is recommended. This shape is a compromise between a point contact, which is apt to break, and a large nose radius, which results in a thin chip, excessive tool wear, and chatter.

Recent experience in the rough turning of artillery shells has demonstrated that carbide-tipped turning tools having a 5-degree negative side and back rake provide longer tool life before sharpening

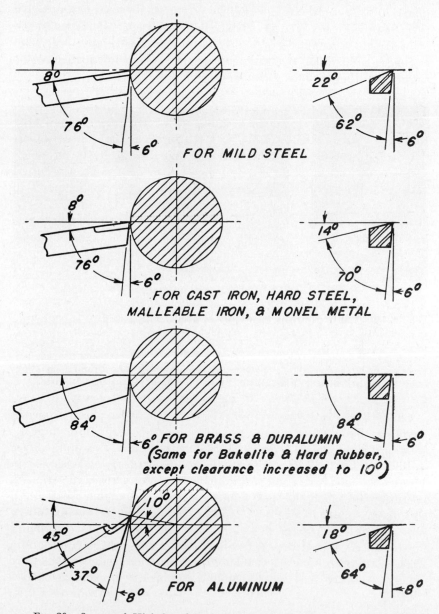

FOR MILD STEEL

FOR CAST IRON, HARD STEEL,
MALLEABLE IRON, & MONEL METAL

FOR BRASS & DURALUMIN
(Same for Bakelite & Hard Rubber,
except clearance increased to 10°)

FOR ALUMINUM

FIG. 20. Suggested High-Speed Steel-Tool Angles for Various Materials.

is necessary.* This is particularly true on roughing cuts, where materials are rough, scaly, or slightly eccentric, because with negative rake the surface irregularities strike the cutting edge of the tool back from the tip where the tool is much stronger. Naturally more heat is generated than by conventional turning; so an adequate coolant supply must be provided.

Courtesy Cincinnati Milling Machine Company.

A. Type 1. Discontin-uous or segmental chip.   *B.* Type 2. Continuous chip without built-up edge.   *C.* Type 3. Continuous chip with built-up edge.

Fɪɢ. 21. Basic Chip Types. Photomicrographs of cross sections taken through partially formed chips obtained, under various conditions, in machining operations such as turning, milling, planing, and broaching (according to Ernst).

Chip shape and formation. Much research has been done in studying the mechanics and geometry of chip formation, and the relationship of chip shape to such factors as tool life and surface finish. Ernst† has classified tool chips into three types as shown in Figure 21. Type 1, a discontinuous or segmental chip, represents a condition in which the metal ahead of the cutting tool is fractured into fairly small pieces. This type of chip is obtained in machining most brittle materials, such as cast iron and bronze. As these chips are produced, the cutting edge smooths over the irregularities, and a fairly good finish is obtained. Tool life is reasonably good, and failure usually occurs as a result of abrading action on the contact surface

* C. Edgar, "Negative Rake-Turning Tools Improve Roughing Cuts in Steel," *American Machinist*, August 16, 1945.

† H. Ernst, "Physics of Metal Cutting," *Machining of Metals*, American Society of Metals, 1938.

of the tool.   Discontinuous chips can also be formed on some ductile materials if the coefficient of friction is high.   However, such chips on ductile materials is an indication of poor cutting conditions.

An ideal type of chip, from the standpoint of tool life and finish, is the simple continuous chip (type 2), which is obtained in cutting ductile materials having a low coefficient of friction.   In this case the metal is continuously deformed and slides up the face of the tool without being fractured.   Chips of this type are obtained at high cutting speeds and are quite common when cutting is done with carbide tools. Because of their simplicity, they can be easily analyzed from the standpoint of the forces involved.

Type 3 chip is characteristic of those machined from ductile materials that have a fairly high coefficient of friction.   As the tool starts the cut, some of the material (because of its high friction coefficient) builds up ahead of the cutting edge.   As the cutting proceeds, the chips flow over this edge and up along the face of the tool.   Periodically a small amount of this built-up edge separates and leaves with the chip or is embedded in the turned surface.   Because of this action the surface smoothness is not so good as with the type 2 chip.   The built-up edge remains fairly constant during cutting and has the effect of slightly altering the rake angle.   However, as the cutting speed is increased, the size of the built-up edge decreases, and the surface finish is improved.   This phenomenon is also decreased by either reducing the chip thickness or increasing the rake angle, although on many of the ductile materials it cannot be eliminated entirely.

Chip control.   In high-speed production turning, the control and disposal of chips is important to protect both the operator and the tools.   This is best accomplished by breaking the chip into small lengths, which also facilitates its easy removal from the machine. Various means can be provided to accomplish this end.*

1. Grinding on the face of the tool along the cutting edge a small flat to a depth of about 0.020 inch.   This is known as a *chip breaker*, as it stresses the chips to their breaking point as they are formed.   The width varies according to the feed and depth of cut used.

2. Mechanical chip breaking, secured by brazing or screwing a thin carbide-faced plate on the face of the tool.   As the chip is formed, it hits the edge of the plate and is curled to the extent that it breaks in short pieces.

* "Selection and Application of Single-Point Tools," *American Machinist*, November 23, 1944.

3. Proper selection of tool angles, which control the direction of the curled chip and forces the chip into some obstruction which stresses the chip to its breaking point.

Grinding and setting tools. Experienced personnel with adequate grinding equipment are needed to obtain proper cutting angles on tools. Most uniform results are realized with special tool grinders which can be set to grind accurately any angle desired. If off-hand grinding is necessary, gages and templates should be used by the operator.

Tool bits should be removed from the holder before an attempt is made to grind them. The procedure for grinding the various faces is not of great importance, but it is suggested that the side-rake and side-clearance surfaces be prepared first. After these two angles are ground, the tool end may be given any shape desired. Shapes of typical lathe tool bits are shown in the upper part of Figure 19.

Aluminum oxide wheels are best for rough and finish grinding of high-speed steel tools, whereas silicon carbide and diamond wheels are necessary for cemented carbide tools. A final honing of the cutting edge is recommended to increase tool life.

In most cases it is assumed that the tip of the tool is in line with the center of the work, as shown in the various figures; however, some authorities recommend that the cutting edge of the tool point should be about 5 degrees above center, or $\frac{3}{64}$ inch per inch in diameter of the work. The position of the cutter bit must be taken into account when the various angles are being ground, as the height has considerable influence on the front clearance. For example, if the point is $\frac{1}{10}$ inch above the center lines in turning a 1-inch diameter, the front clearance practically disappears and the back rake is increased materially. All lathes are provided with spherical seats or rockers to assist in setting the tool properly with the work.

Tool life. The life of a tool is an important factor in production work, since considerable time is lost each time a tool is ground and reset. It is well to consider the following reasons for tool failure so that preventive measures can be taken where possible.

1. Improper grinding of tool angles. Cutting angles depend on the material to be cut; and their values are well established in handbooks, manufacturers' literature, and other sources.

2. Loss of tool hardness. This is brought about by excessive heat generated at the cutting edge. This situation is relieved by the use of coolants or by reducing the cutting speed.

3. Breaking or spalling of tool edge. This may be caused by taking too heavy a cut or by having too small a lip angle.

4. Natural wear and abrasion. All tools will gradually become dull by abrasion. In some cases this is accelerated by the development of a crater just back of the cutting edge. As the crater increases in size, the cutter edge becomes weaker and breaks off. This can be avoided by the proper selection of tool material.

5. Fracture of tool by heavy load. This condition will be reduced materially if the cutting tools are rigidly supported with a minimum of overhang.

Tool life can be prolonged by careful selection of tool angles, feed, cutting speed, and depth of cut, and by the use of proper coolant when the job is originally set up. Frequently a tool failure is caused by disregard of one or more of these factors. What has been said about lathe tools applies equally well to tools used by other machines.

Coolants. Coolants are various liquids, emulsions, or gases applied to the material being cut to improve the cutting operation. In addition to the fact that they cool the tank and the work, there are several other reasons for their use. Chips are washed away, and the finish of the machined surface is improved. Wear on the cutting edges is reduced, and tool life increased because of the lubrication of the tool. Also, less power is required. Finally, coolants reduce possible corrosion on both the work and the machines.

Coolants used should be capable of absorbing and carrying away heat. In addition, they must be free from odor, should not injure the skin of the operator, and should not corrode either the work or the machine. In most cases the coolant is recirculated by a small pump on the machine unless it is used in such small quantities that this arrangement is unnecessary. Best results are generally obtained when a generous supply of cutting fluid is directed on the tool and the work.

Various kinds of coolants are used, depending primarily on the kind of material being machined. Typical coolants used for various materials are:

Cast iron. Compressed air or worked dry. The use of compressed air necessitates an exhaust system to remove the dust caused by blowing the fine particles of iron.

Aluminum. Kerosene lubricant or soda water. Soda water consists of water with a small percentage of some alkali which acts as a rust preventive.

Malleable iron. Water-soluble oil lubricant. These coolants consist of a light mineral oil held in suspension by caustic soda, sulfurized oil, soap and other ingredients which form an emulsion when mixed with water.

Brass. Worked dry or paraffin oil.

Steel. Water-soluble oil, sulfurized oil, or mineral oil.

Wrought iron. Lard oil, or water-soluble oil.

In addition to these listed, many other coolants are used, the selection depending on the type of work being done. For example, lard oil would be very satisfactory for a tapping operation on steel, whereas, for high-speed cutting of the same steel on a turret lathe, a water-soluble oil emulsion would be better. Grinding operations use a water solution with some alkali such as soda or sodium carbonate to act as a rust preventive, a little oil being added to keep the soda in suspension.

Grinding coolants should not only cool efficiently but also keep the wheel clean. A poor coolant often contributes to wheel loading or glazing, resulting in the ineffective cutting action of abrasive particles. Coolants for grinding should be used in considerable volume and should not contain too much oil or gumming material.

The water-soluble oil emulsions, resembling milk in appearance, are widely used for all forms of operations. They are inexpensive, have high cooling properties, and have low viscosity which permits the oil to separate readily from the chips. In addition to the coolants mentioned, there is a wide variety of compounded mineral, fixed, and sulfurized oils that are used as cutting fluids.

Cutting Speeds and Feeds

Cutting speed is expressed in feet per minute and on a lathe is the surface speed or rate at which the work passes the cutter. It may be expressed by the simple formula: $CS = \pi DN$, where D is the diameter of the work in feet and N is the revolutions of the work per minute. The cutting speed in this expression is seldom unknown, since cutting speeds for various materials may be found in many textbooks and handbooks. In lathe work the unknown factor is the speed of the work, or the term N. Referring to Figure 22 we may note that, to maintain a recommended cutting speed of 90 feet per minute, it is necessary to increase the work revolution materially, as the diameter is decreased from 5 inches to 1 inch.

The term *feed* is used to express the distance that the tool moves for each revolution of the work and is sometimes expressed as chip thickness. Since so many factors must be given consideration, it is difficult to state definitely what the speed and feeds for a given

TABLE 7. CUTTING SPEEDS OF VARIOUS MATERIALS

Material	High-Speed Steel		Carbide	
	Rough	Finish	Rough	Finish
Cast iron	50– 60	80–110	120–200	350– 400
Semisteel*	40– 50	65– 90	140–160	250– 300
Malleable iron*	80–110	110–130	250–300	300– 400
Steel casting* (0.35 C)	45– 60	70– 90	150–180	200– 250
Brass (85–5–5)	200–300	200–300	600–1000	600–1000
Bronze (80–10–10)*	110–150	150–180	600	1000
Aluminum †	400	700	800	1000
SAE 1020*	80–100	100–120	300–400	300– 400
SAE 1050*	60– 80	100	200	200
Stainless steel*	100–120	100–120	240–300	240– 300

* Water-soluble oil lubricant.

† Kerosene lubricant.

material should be. In cutting steel, the color of the chip and the general feed of the machine are important indications, a blue chip indicating too much speed or feed. Vibration of the machine or rapid

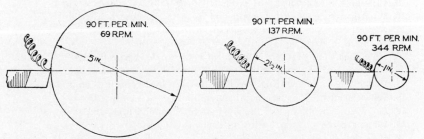

Courtesy Warner & Swasey Manufacturing Company.

FIG. 22. Relation of Rpm to Surface Speeds on Different Diameters.

dulling of the tool also indicates that the tool is overloaded. In general, the speed and feed are determined by the following factors:

1. Kind of material being cut. Materials vary greatly in hardness and other physical properties which affect the cutting speed and life of the tool.

2. Kind of material in the cutter. Carbon-steel cutters can take about one-half the cutting speed of a high-speed tool-steel cutter. Stellite and carbide cutters will stand still greater speeds.

3. Types of finish desired. In general, high speeds with fine feeds give the best finish.

4. Rigidity of the machine. No work should be done at speeds and feeds that cause vibration in the machine.

5. Kind of tool being used. Forming tools, taps, and other tools that are expensive and difficult to sharpen should be operated at speeds and feeds that insure long life.

6. Type of coolant used.

Table 7, prepared by the Warner & Swasey Company, gives recommended cutting speeds of various materials for turret lathes.

Review Questions

1. What types of surfaces can be machined on an engine lathe?
2. What is a speed lathe, and for what type of work is it used?
3. How is the size of a lathe determined?
4. Name three methods of turning accurate tapers on a lathe.
5. What is an engine lathe? A geared-head lathe?
6. What is the purpose of each of the following lathe parts: Face plate, center rest, compound rest, lead screw, and back gears?
7. Describe the operation of a duplicating lathe.
8. What is wrong with a lathe that turns a slightly tapered surface instead of a cylinder? Assume the small diameter to be on the tailstock end.
9. How does a toolroom lathe differ from an ordinary engine lathe?
10. What is a relieving attachment, and for what purpose is it used?
11. Name four types of chucks used in lathe work.
12. How are internal tapers turned on an engine lathe?
13. How does a Morse taper differ from a Brown & Sharpe taper?
14. Sketch a tool bit, and indicate the lip angle, top rake, and side rake.
15. Define the term "cutting speed." How is it determined on a lathe?
16. What is meant by machinability, and how is it expressed?
17. For what type of work is the single-point diamond tool used?
18. What are the principal alloying elements in high-speed steel?
19. How does a tool bit for cutting brass differ from one for cutting mild steel?
20. What desirable properties should a coolant possess?
21. Why are chip breakers used on some tools, and how are they constructed?
22. In what ways do cutting tools fail?
23. What factors determine the speed and feed to use in metal cutting?

References

BOSTON, O. W., *Metal Processing*, 2d edition, John Wiley & Sons, 1951.

CLASS, GEORGE M., "Tool Life in Metal Turning," *American Machinist*, December 25, 1940.

COLVIN, FRED H., *Running an Engine Lathe*, McGraw-Hill Book Company, 1941.

EDGAR, C., "Negative Rake Turning Tools for Roughing Steel," *American Machinist*, August 16, 1945.

HINE, C. R., *Machine Tools for Engineers,* McGraw-Hill Book Company, 1950.

How to Run an Engine Lathe, South Bend Lathe Company, 1943.

JONES, F. D., *Machine Shop Training Course,* Industrial Press, 1940.

JUDKINS, MALCOLM F., "Metal Cutting," *Mechanical Engineering,* May 1937.

Machining—Theory and Practice, American Society for Metals, 1950.

Metals Handbook, American Society for Metals, 1948.

MOIR, H. L., and O. W. BOSTON, "A New Study in Cutting Fluid Recommendations," *SAE Journal,* 1940.

WILLIAMS, W. J., "How Carbide Tools Reduce the Cost of Machining Steel," *Machinery,* February 1941.

15

TURRET AND AUTOMATIC LATHES

Turret and automatic lathes possess special designs and features which particularly adapt them to production work. The "skill of the worker" has been built into these machines, making it possible to reproduce identical parts with operators in charge who have little skill. In contrast to this, the engine lathe requires a highly skilled operator and more time to reproduce many parts which are dimensionally the same. The principal characteristic of this group of lathes is that the tools for consecutive operations can be continuously set up in readiness for use in the proper sequence. Although considerable skill is required to set and adjust the tools properly, once they are correct, little skill is required to operate them. Furthermore, many parts can be produced before adjustments are necessary. Eliminating the setup time between operations reduces the production time tremendously. The high development of turret and automatic lathes has made interchangeable manufacture what it is today.

Classification

The following classification of turret and automatic lathes, made according to single outstanding design characteristics, will serve as an outline of the discussion that is to follow.

1. Turret lathe
   (a) Horizontal
      (1) Ram-type.
      (2) Saddle-type.
   (b) Vertical
      (1) Single-station.
      (2) Multistation.
   (c) Automatic.

2. Automatic lathe
   (a) Horizontal.
   (b) Vertical.

3. Automatic screw machine
   (a) Single-spindle.
   (b) Multispindle.

This classification may be further subdivided according to special features, such as method of drive, method of chucking, capacity, and number and arrangement of tool slides. These details and other special features are explained in the discussion of the various types of machines.

Turret Lathes

Horizontal turret lathe. These lathes are frequently listed according to the type of work they do. In appearance and general design the *bar* and *chucking* machines are much alike, as may be observed in Figures 1 and 2. Their principal difference is in the tools they use and in the manner in which the stock is held. Bar machines do not

Courtesy Jones & Lamson Machine Company.

Fig. 1.   Universal Ram-Type Turret Lathe Equipped with Hydraulic Bar Feed and Chucking Mechanism.

require the built-in rigidity that chucking machines do, as in most cases the bar tools can be made to support the work. Chucking tools overhang and do not support the work, thus causing greater strain on both work and tool support; hence, chucking machines must have the greatest possible rigidity.

Both the types of turret lathes previously mentioned may be made in either *ram* or *saddle* type. The ram type is so named because of the manner in which the turret is mounted. In these machines the turret is placed on a slide or ram which moves back and forth on a saddle clamped to the lathe bed. This arrangement permits quick and easy movement of the turret and is specially recommended for bar and light work. The saddle, although capable of adjustment, does not move in the operation of the turret. The saddle-type

Courtesy Warner & Swasey Manufacturing Company.

FIG. 2.   No. 5 Universal Turret Lathe Equipped with Chucking Tools.

Courtesy Warner & Swasey Manufacturing Company.

FIG. 3.   Saddle-Type Turret Lathe Equipped with Standard Tools for Chucking Work.

machine has the turret mounted directly on a saddle which moves back and forth with the turret in its operation. This design permits more rigid support of the tools, so necessary in heavy chucking work.

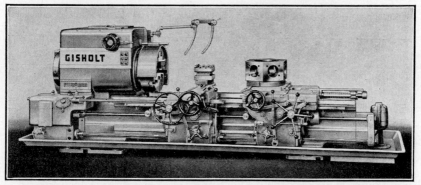

FIG. 4. Saddle-Type Turret Lathe for Heavy Production Work Shown without Tooling.

The stroke also is much longer, which is an advantage in long turning or boring cuts. Saddle-type turret lathes are illustrated in Figures 3 and 4.

Construction. Turret lathes have many features similar to those of modern engine lathes. The headstock in most cases is geared with provision for 6 to 12 spindle speeds. The various spindle speeds, as well as forward and reverse movement, are all controlled by levers extending from the head. The drive motor is usually located in the motor leg below the headstock and connected to the geared-head pulley by means of a belt. Early-design turret lathes were frequently belt-driven through step pulleys, but this arrangement is no longer used. Some few machines, designed for light work, are driven by a multiple-speed motor mounted directly on the spindle inside the headstock housing. High speeds, up to 3600 rpm, are possible on these machines.

The *cross-slide* unit, on which the tools are mounted for facing, forming, and cutting off, is somewhat different in construction from the tool-post and carriage arrangement used on lathes. It is made up of four principal parts: the cross slide, the square turret, the carriage, and the apron. These parts are readily discernible in the various turret-lathe illustrations. Some of the cross slides are supported entirely on the front and lower front ways, permitting more swing clearance for the work. This arrangement is frequently utilized on saddle-type machines which are to be used for large-diameter chucking jobs. The other arrangement for mounting has the cross slide riding on both upper bedways and further supported by a lower way. This is used on machines engaged in bar work and other applications where a large swing clearance is not necessary. An advantage of this type is the added tool post in the rear, frequently used in cutting-off operations.

On top of the cross slide is mounted a *square turret* capable of holding four tools in readiness for use. If several different tools are required, they are set up in sequence and can be quickly indexed and locked in correct working position. In order that cuts may be duplicated, the slide is provided with either a positive stop or a feed trip. Likewise, the longitudinal position of the entire assembly may be accurately controlled by positive stops on the left side of the apron. Cuts may be taken with square-turret tools simultaneously with tools mounted on the hexagon turret.

The outstanding feature of a turret lathe is the use of a *hexagon turret* in place of the usual lathe tailstock. This turret, mounted on either the sliding ram or the saddle, carries the tools for the various operations. The tools are mounted in proper sequence on the various faces of the turret so that, as it indexes around between operations, the proper tools are brought into position. For each set of tools there is provided a stop screw which controls the distance the tool will feed. When this distance is reached, an automatic trip lever stops further movement of the tool by disengaging the drive clutch.

Differences between turret and engine lathes. The main difference between these two machines is that the turret lathe is adapted to quantity-production work, whereas the engine lathe is primarily used for miscellaneous jobbing, toolroom, or single-operation work. The essential features of a turret lathe which make it a quantity-production machine are these:

1. Tools may be permanently set up in the turret in the proper sequence of their use.
2. Each tool is provided with a stop or feed trip so that each cut of a tool is the same as its previous cut.
3. Combining cuts can be made—that is, tools on the cross slide can be used at the same time that tools on the turret are cutting.
4. Extreme rigidity in the holding of work and tools is built into the machine.

When a turret lathe is once set up for a certain job, many parts may be machined identically, without further adjustment of the tools. All types of work that can be done on an engine lathe can likewise be done on a turret lathe and, in many cases, can be done quicker: bar and chuck work, thread cutting, taper turning, drilling, reaming, and many other similar operations. Although we now have many other production machines, the turret lathe has been largely responsible for the development of interchangeable manufacture as we know it today.

Methods of Holding Stock

As the turret lathe is a production machine, special attention is given to methods of holding the work so that it can be done quickly and accurately. Since the operation is usually simple, extreme rigidity can be built into such equipment so that heavy cuts can be made. The usual devices for holding work are *collets, arbors, chucks,* and *special holding fixtures.*

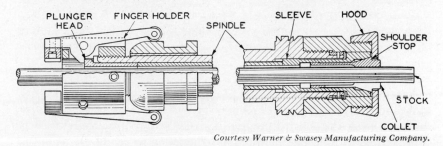

Courtesy *Warner & Swasey Manufacturing Company.*

FIG. 5. Stationary-Type Spring Collet.

Collets. Collets, commonly used for bar-stock material, are made with jaws of standard sizes to accommodate round, square, and hexagon stock. For large stock, collets of the parallel closing type are sometimes used, but in most cases collets of the spring type are recommended. These collets are solid at one end and split on the other end, which is tapered. The tapered end contacts with a similarly tapered hood or bushing, and, when the tapered end is forced into the hood, the jaws of the collet tighten around the stock. Spring collets are made in three designs: The *pushout type,* the *draw-in type,* and the *stationary type.* In each, however, the operation is similar to that just described. A cross section of a stationary type is shown in Figure 5. With this type there is no movement of the stock when it is tightened in the collet, since the latter is held in place against the hood. As the tapered surface of the plunger sleeve is pushed against a similar surface on the collet, the jaws are forced against the work. For work that must be accurately located endwise, this type of collet assembly is best. Pushout-type collets are recommended for bar work, as the slight movement of the stock pushes it against the bar stop. This type is of the same construction as shown in Figure 5 except that there is no hood to stop the forward movement of the bar stock. Draw-back-type collets are not widely employed for bar stock, but are useful when the collets are of extra-capacity size and are utilized for holding short pieces, as shown in Figure 6. The slight back motion in closing forces the work against the locating stops.

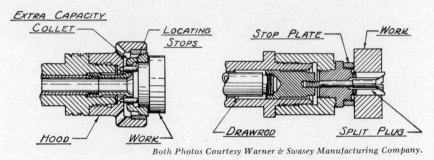

Both Photos Courtesy Warner & Swasey Manufacturing Company.

FIG. 6.   Draw-Back Extra-Capacity   FIG. 7.   Expanding Plug-Type
Collet.   Arbor.

Arbor. Expanding or threaded arbors are used to hold short pieces of stock that have a previously machined accurate hole in them. The action in holding the work is controlled by a mechanism very similar to that used with collets. An expanding plug-type arbor is shown in Figure 7. The work is placed on the arbor against the stop plate, and, as the draw rod is pulled, the tapered pin expands the partially split plug and grips the work. The threaded arbor operates in a similar fashion except that the work is screwed on the arbor by hand and is then forced back against a stop tube or flange.

Both collets and arbors may be power-operated by pneumatic, hydraulic, or electrical means located at the end of the spindle. Such an arrangement is frequently used on high-production work to provide quicker and easier operation.

Chucks. Chucks are used for holding large and irregularly shaped parts and, in general, are the same types as employed in engine-lathe work. Illustrations of the *universal, independent,* and *combination* types are shown in Chapter 14. These chucks are either bolted or screwed to the spindle and have a very rigid mounting.

In addition to standard chucks, there are several other special types adapted for holding work of irregular shape. One of these, known as a two-jaw box chuck, is designed to hold work with parallel flat sides. Both jaws, on opposite sides of the chuck, move in and out together.

Another special chuck, known as a revolving jaw, is adapted for finishing small parts where several faces must be machined. After a cut is made, the work can be indexed to the next position, usually 90 degrees, and another cut can be taken. The revolving-jaw chuck is used principally for the machining of pipe fittings.

Power chucks operated by air, hydraulic means, or electricity to relieve the operator of the effort involved in tightening and loosening the work are available for production jobs. This is a distinct advantage if the work is large. An additional advantage of the power chuck is that it is quick acting.

It is difficult to mount all types of work on standard equipment; therefore, many special chuck jaws or holding fixtures must be devised. Standard face plates are frequently used for mounting such fixtures. The holding device is held to the face plate either by bolting or by means of the T slots on the face of the plate.

All these work-holding devices can be used equally well with both automatic and turret lathes.

Tools and tooling principles. As has been stated, once a turret lathe is properly tooled, an experienced machinist is not required to operate it. However, skill is required in the proper selection and mounting of the tools. In small-lot production it is important that this work be done in as short a time as possible so as not to consume too much of the total production time. This time is made up of four factors: setup time, work-handling time, machine-handling time, and cutting time. Consideration must be given to all these factors in the original setup if the final production time is to be as short as possible.

Setup time can be reduced by having all necessary tools in condition and readily available. A thorough knowledge of the tools and the machine is also important. For short-run jobs a permanent setup of the usual tools on the turret is an excellent means of reducing time. In Figure 8 is shown a permanent setup for bar work with the tools mounted in the logical sequence for their use. The tools selected are standard tools and the ones most commonly used in this type of work. Permanently mounted, they may be quickly adjusted for various jobs. A similar setup can be prepared for chucking jobs.

The *work-handling time,* that time consumed in mounting or removing the work, is largely dependent on the type of work-holding devices used. For bar work this time is reduced to a minimum by having quick means for advancing the stock built into the machine.

The time it takes to bring the respective tools into cutting position is the *machine-handling time*. This can be reduced by having the tools in proper position and sequence for convenient use, and also by taking multiple or combined cuts whenever possible.

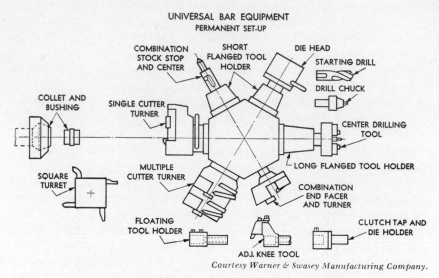

Courtesy *Warner & Swasey Manufacturing Company.*

Fig. 8.   Permanent Setup for Universal Bar Equipment.

The actual *cutting time* for a given operation is largely controlled by the use of proper cutting tools, feeds, and speeds.   However, addi-

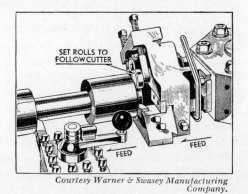

Courtesy *Warner & Swasey Manufacturing Company.*

Fig. 9.   "Combined Cuts" on Bar Work.

tional time may often be saved by combining cuts as shown in Figure 9. *Combined cuts* refers to the simultaneous use of both slide and turret tools.   In bar work combined cuts are especially desirable, as additional support is given to the work, thereby eliminating spring and chatter. In chucking work internal operations, such as drilling

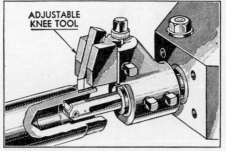

Courtesy Warner & Swasey Manufacturing Company.

FIG. 10. "Multiple Cuts" from Hexagon Turret.

or boring, may frequently be combined with turning or facing cuts from the square turret. Time also may be saved by taking *multiple*

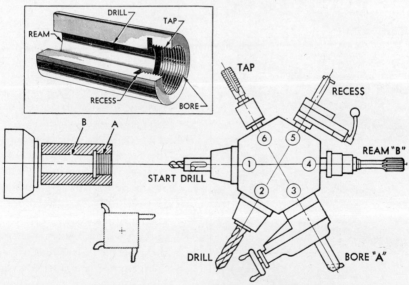

Courtesy Warner & Swasey Manufacturing Company.

FIG. 11. Basic Hexagon-Turret Setup Illustrating the Correct Sequence of Operations to Handle Required Internal Cuts on Threaded Adapter Shown in Insert.

cuts—that is, having two or more tools mounted on one tool station. Figure 10 shows both boring and turning tools set up on one station of the turret.

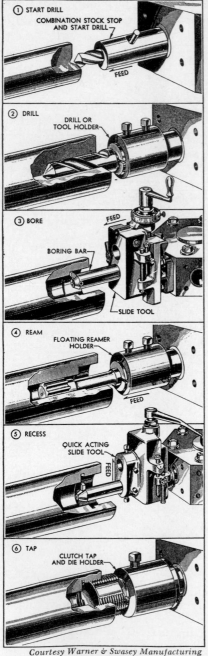

① START DRILL

COMBINATION STOCK STOP
AND START DRILL

FEED

② DRILL

DRILL OR
TOOL HOLDER

③ BORE   FEED

BORING BAR

SLIDE TOOL

④ REAM

FLOATING REAMER
HOLDER

FEED

⑤ RECESS

QUICK ACTING
SLIDE TOOL

FEED

⑥ TAP

CLUTCH TAP
AND DIE HOLDER

Courtesy Warner & Swasey Manufacturing Company.

FIG. 12. Setup for Machining Internal Operations on Threaded Adapter.

To illustrate the method of tooling and sequence of operations for a given job, a basic hexagon-turret setup is shown in Figure 11 for making necessary internal cuts on a threaded adapter. Figure 12 shows the details of the internal cuts required to machine the adapter. With reference to the sequence shown in the figure, the various operations are as follows:

1. The bar stock is advanced against the combination stock stop and start drill and clamped in the collet. The start drill is then advanced in the combination tool, and the end of the work is centered.

2. The hole through the solid stock is drilled the required length.

3. The thread diameter is bored to correct size for the threads specified. A stub boring bar in a slide tool is used.

4. The drilled hole is reamed to size with the reamer supported in a floating holder.

5. A groove for thread clearance is recessed. For this operation a quick acting slide tool is used with a recessing cutter mounted in a boring bar.

6. The thread is cut with a tap held in a clutch tap and die holder. For odd-size threads a single-point tool may be used. This operation is followed by a cutting-off operation not shown in the figure.

Another example of tooling is illustrated in Figure 13. In this case the tool setup is for a shoulder stud shaft made of 2½-inch bar stock. The tooling shown is for a quantity of these parts and is slightly

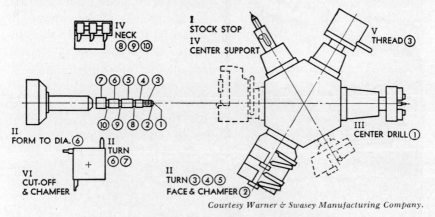

Courtesy Warner & Swasey Manufacturing Company.

Fig. 13. Tool Setup for Shoulder Stud Shaft.

more complicated than a setup for producing only a few. With one exception all operations are external cuts. As shown in the figure, the tools used for the respective operations are as follows:

OPERATIONS AND TOOLS USED

Operation	Hexagon Turret	Square Turret
I	Feed stock to stop	
II	Turn (3), (4), and (5) diameter	Turn (6) and (7) to diameter
	Face and chamfer (2)	
III	Center drill (1)	
IV	Support (1) with center	Neck cuts (8), (9), and (10) with back tools
V	Thread (3)	
VI		Cut-off and chamfer

Based on an output of 120 pieces the time per piece is estimated to be:

Setup time per piece	1 min
Work-handling time per piece	½ min
Machine-handling time per piece	½ min
Cutting time per piece	5½ min
Total production time	7½ min per piece

A few of the typical tools used in turret-lathe work have been illustrated in Figure 12. These tools are so designed that they may be quickly mounted in the turret and adjusted for use. In addition to the usual operations of drilling, boring, reaming, and internal threading shown in the figure, various other threading, centering, and turning tools are available. Internal threading is frequently done with collapsible taps to facilitate quick removal of the tool. For the same reason automatic die head cutters which open at the end of the thread are used for external threads.

For outside turning a *box tool,* shown in Figure 14, has been developed. As bar stock is supported only at the collet, additional

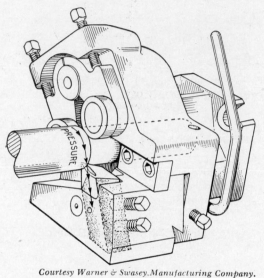

Courtesy Warner & Swasey Manufacturing Company.

Fɪɢ. 14. Box Tool for Bar Stock.

support must be provided in order for heavy cuts to be taken. This is done by means of two rollers which contact the outside diameter of the stock and take up the thrust of the cutting tool. Adjustment of the rolls for varying diameter work is controlled by two setscrews at the top of the holder. When the rolls are set slightly behind the cutting tool, they tend to smooth out or burnish the surface. However, if the turned diameter must be concentric with the adjacent surface, the rolls are set ahead and adjusted to its diameter. For light cuts, a similar box tool which supports the work by means of a V-back rest can be used. Cutters are held in position by two setscrews, and the lever at the back of the assembly is for the purpose of withdrawing the cutter from the work on the return stroke to prevent marking.

Many small standard tools are also used in turret-lathe work. Drills, boring tools, reamers, and lathe-type turning tools can be rigidly supported in the various tool-holding devices. Cutting angles and speeds for these tools are the same as those described for lathe and other machine-tool operation.

Controlled spindle turret lathe. A turret lathe, designed for machining nonferrous metals and known as an electrocycle lathe, is shown in Figure 15. This lathe is arranged so that all spindle speeds and headstock operations can be preset and automatically controlled

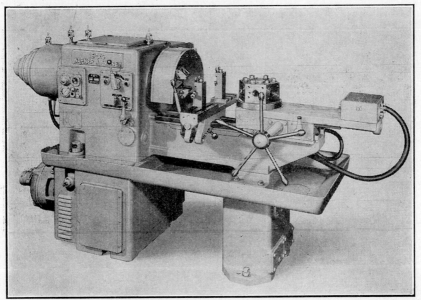

Courtesy Warner & Swasey Manufacturing Company.

FIG. 15. Electrocycle Turret Lathe Especially Designed for Machining Nonferrous Metals.

through a complete cycle of operations. The cycle is actuated and controlled by the hexagon turret as it is moved to successive stations by the operator. At the beginning of the cycle, the headstock spindle is started as the turret moves forward, and, from then on, all spindle operations such as speed changes, reversing, stopping, and positioning of spindle are automatic in accordance with the prearranged cycle. By controlling the cycle, the machine handling time of a job is reduced and the operator is relieved of a considerable amount of work. Experienced operators are not essential.

Automatic horizontal turret lathe. The automatic turret lathe in Figure 16 resembles in appearance the standard saddle-type machine. However, this machine is completely automatic in operation to the extent that one operator may handle two or more machines. The hexagonal turret is hydraulically operated and is provided with rapid traverse and automatic changeover to the proper feed at any point. There are two cross slides which may be operated singly or together. The movement of these slides is controlled by cams actuated by the forward movement of the turret. Machines of this type are used on long-run chucking jobs, where the expense of setting up and tooling can be spread over many parts. The advantages of automatic opera-

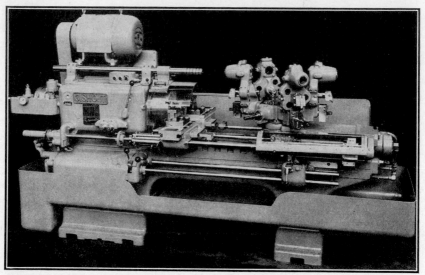

Courtesy Gisholt Machine Company.

Fig. 16. Automatic Turret Lathe.

tion are elimination of human element from the time cycle, possibility for operator to attend several machines, and faster rate of production.

Vertical turret lathe. A vertical turret lathe is a machine resembling a vertical boring mill, but having the characteristic turret arrangement for holding the tools. It consists of a rotating chuck or table in horizontal position, with the turret mounted above on a cross slide. In addition, there is at least one side head provided with a square turret for holding tools. All tools mounted on the turret or side head have their respective stops set so that the length of cuts can be the same in successive machining cycles. It is, in effect, the same as a turret lathe standing on the headstock end, and it has all the features necessary for the production of duplicate parts. This machine was developed to facilitate the mounting, holding, and machining of heavy parts. Only chucking work is done on this kind of machine.

In Figure 17 is shown a 30-inch vertical turret lathe. This machine is constructed with two cutter heads, the swiveling main turret head, and the side head. The turret head is mounted on a saddle held on the horizontal rail and is provided with both vertical and horizontal screw feed. For angle cuts it may be swiveled up to 45 degrees on either side of vertical. The side head has rapid traverse and feed

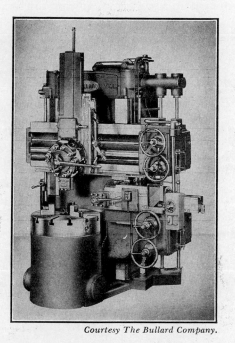

Courtesy The Bullard Company.

Fig. 17. 30-Inch Cut Master Vertical Turret Lathe.

independent of the turret head and provides for simultaneous machining, adjacent to operations performed by the turret, without interference. Larger machines of this type are frequently equipped with an additional ram-type head mounted on the left-hand side of the horizontal rail, which can be operated separately or in conjunction with the other two. The table of this machine is supported rigidly by tapered bearings and driven by spiral bevel gears. Work tables usually have a chuck built into them, although a plain table with T slots is sometimes preferred.

Automatic vertical turret lathe. The Man-Au-Trol vertical turret lathe, shown in Figure 18, is of the same general design as a standard vertical turret lathe. The outstanding feature of this machine is that each head can be automatically controlled in all its functions. These functions include such things as rate and direction of feed, change in spindle speed, indexing of turret, starting, and stopping. Once a cycle of operations is preset and all tools are properly adjusted, the operator need only load, unload, and start the machine. The pro-

Courtesy The Bullard Company.

Fig. 18. Man-Au-Trol Vertical Turret Lathe.

duction rate of these machines is greatly increased over that of those manually operated, because this machine operates almost continuously and makes all changes from one operation to another without hesitation or fatigue. By reducing the handling time and making the cycle automatic, an operator can attend more than one machine.

Automatic vertical multistation lathe. Machines of this type are designed for high production and are usually provided with either six or eight stations. In a six-station machine there would be five working spindles and a loading position. All varieties of machining operations can be performed, including milling, drilling, threading, tapping, reaming, and boring. The advantage of this type of machine is that all operations can be done simultaneously. In actual operation all tools are fed to the work, held in chucks or fixtures, at the respective loading stations. When all operations are complete, the tools or work

Courtesy The Bullard Company.

Fig. 19. Six-Spindle Mult-Au-Matic Vertical Lathe with Chucking Capacity up to 8 Inches.

move vertically out of the way, the work table indexes one station, and the operations are repeated. The time between indexing operations is controlled by the time of the longest single operation.

In Figure 19 is shown an 8-inch six-spindle Bullard Mult-Au-Matic, automatic production machine of this type. It is made in several sizes, accommodating work up to $17\frac{1}{2}$ inches in diameter, with either six or eight spindles. This machine is designed to accommodate all classes of machine work on castings, forgings, or cut-off bar stock. Several types of heads are provided for this machine. The plain vertical head of one-piece construction is combined with the saddle and permits only vertical movement with 8-inch strokes. The plain compound slide has a single slide mounted on the saddle, permitting a 4-inch horizontal movement. By using a standard universal head, the tool may be fed vertically, horizontally, or in any angular direction. Standard double-purpose heads have two slides. The left slide operates only in a vertical direction, while simultaneously the right-

Courtesy The Cleveland Hobbing Machine Company.

FIG. 20. Eight-Spindle Rotary Rigid-Turning Machine Setup for Shell Turning.

hand slide moves left in a horizontal direction. With these motions available, cuts may be taken in any desired direction. Feed for the tools is controlled by cam action, and various spindle speeds may be obtained at each station. Parts to be machined, after being chucked, are indexed from one station to another, as previously described.

Eight-spindle machines can be equipped with either single or double indexing. With single indexing seven operations can be performed in the cycle; with double indexing only three operations are possible. In the second case two pieces are completed in each cycle.

An eight-spindle rotary "rigid-turning" machine, operating on a

A. Single-Spindle Rigidturner Machine Adapted to Turning Multiple Diameters on a Wide Variety of Work.

Both Photos Courtesy The Cleveland Hobbing Machine Company.

B. Sequence of Operations on Mold Turning Illustrating Type of Cutter Used.

Fig. 21.

different cutting principle from that of the previous multiple-spindle machine, is shown set up for shell turning in Figure 20. In this machine, the work is rotated and fed past a stationary single-point tool, clearly shown in the insert next to the figure. This cutting tool is controlled by a profile cam which imparts the form to the work. Only turning operations are performed on this machine. Other production machines, similar in appearance to this one, are designed for spline cutting on axle shafts, gear hobbing, or mold turning.

A mold-turning machine, also known as a "Rigidturner," utilizes a different method of turning from the usual single-point tool method and is specially adapted to turning multiple diameters on a wide variety of production work. A special form cutter is supported on a short horizontal shaft, and the work is held between centers in a vertical position. The type of tool used in mold cutting and the method employed in its operation is illustrated in Figure 21. The work advances past the cutter, which is rotated in a variable timed relation, thus producing the various diameters. The entire operation is automatic except for loading and unloading the work from the machine. Machines of this type are built with both single and multiple spindles.

Automatic Lathes

Lathes that have their tools automatically fed to the work and withdrawn after the cycle is complete are known as *automatic* lathes. Most lathes of this type require that the operator place the part to be machined in the lathe and remove it after the work is complete, and so are perhaps incorrectly called automatic lathes. Lathes that are fully automatic are provided with a magazine feed so that a number of parts can be machined, one after the other, with little attention from the operator. Machines in this group differ principally in the manner of feeding the tools to the work. Most machines, especially those holding the work between centers, have front and rear tool slides. Others, adapted for chucking jobs, have an end tool slide located in the same position as the turret on the turret lathe. These machines may also have the two side-tool slides. Still another construction employs a flat table in front of the chucking spindle, on which can be mounted tool slides at any angle or in any position. Each tool slide has individual feed and receives its power from individual drive shafts at the end of the machine. Several types of automatic lathes are described in the following paragraphs.

A 16-inch Fay automatic lathe setup for machining SAE 8620 drive pinions between centers is shown in Figure 22. This machine has

A. Tooling for Turning Automotive Drive Pinion.

Both Photos Courtesy Jones & Lamson Machine Company.

B. 16-Inch Fay Automatic Lathe.

FIG. 22.

both front and rear tool carriages mounted on heavy cylindrical bars. All turning tools are mounted on the front carriage and receive their longitudinal motion from the forward and reverse cams located beneath the headstock. These tools may be given a tilting motion, by means of the former slide in front of the machine, in order to turn tapers or relieve the tools at the end of the cut. In multiple tooling it is advisable to have some automatic means of relieving cutting pressure of the tools at the points where the cuts are matched. This

Courtesy The Lodge & Shipley Machine Tool Company.

FIG. 23*A*. Duomatic Lathe Tooled to Finish Turn and Face Gear End of Automotive Pinion.

is obtained by moving the former slide down the angle of the guide. This action relieves the tool pressure at the desired rate to insure definite matching of all cuts without undercutting or marking on the return stroke. All facing, forming, and chamfering tools are carried on the rear carriage. These tools move into the work in a transverse plane controlled by a rear former slide which is moved by cylindrical cams beneath the machine.

A view of the tooling setup for this job is shown in Figure 22*A*. The pinion and shaft are chamfered by tools on the back arm while the front carriage turns the several diameters. Carbide tools are used with a cutting speed of 1185 surface feet per minute, and the actual cutting time amounts to only 8½ seconds. Other products commonly machined on this lathe include shells, oil-well tool joints, airplane-engine cylinders, and rear-axle housings.

Figure 23*B* shows a Duomatic automatic lathe, so named because of its two independently operated carriages, one in front and one in the rear. Both carriages have cross tool slides which can be swiveled to any desired angle for power feed as well as independent lead screws to provide power feed for their respective carriages during turning or boring operations. Both carriages can be used simultaneously in turning operations, as is the case in the machining operation shown in

Courtesy The Lodge & Shipley Machine Tool Company.

FIG. 23B. Duomatic Lathe with Air-Operated Tailstock Spindle Operation.

the figure. Either one or both may be used in facing or grooving operations by using the tool slides mounted on the carriages. The independent control boxes, which regulate tool feeds and stop and return tools to the commencement of cycle, are located at front and rear of the headstock end of the lathe. When once set up, the lathe is entirely automatic from the time of loading to the end of the machining cycle.

The setup for finish turning and facing the gear end of an automatic pinion is shown in Figure 23A. In this operation, the front tools turn the right-hand bearing and tapered pinion surface while the rear tools chamfer the end of shaft and both sides of bevel pinion. The production rate on this job is around 50 units per hour. Chucking jobs can be done on this machine, as well as those having the work between centers.

An automatic lathe, known as a *platen-type* Simplimatic, is shown in Figure 24. This machine, designed primarily for chucking jobs, is provided with front and rear tool slides mounted on the platen or table

Courtesy Gisholt Machine Company.

FIG. 24. Platen-Type Automatic Lathe Setup for Machining Bevel Gear Blank.

end of the machine. In operation all tools feed simultaneously, performing all turning, facing, boring, and chamfering operations at one time. Power for feeding the tools comes to the tool slides from one end through universal couplings and drive shafts. At the end of the cycle the slides retract, and the platen moves back to facilitate unloading. The entire operation of the machine is automatic, and the operator has only to load and unload the machine. Platen-type machines have considerable flexibility in the mounting of the various tool slides and can be adapted to a variety of jobs.

A vertical-head lathe, specially designed for the machining of flywheels and similar work, is shown in Figure 25. This machine is a development from the platen-type machine just described and has a cutting head which moves into the work for either plunge cutting or the positioning of slides for radial work. The tools are placed on the face of the vertical head around the work and all cut simultaneously. Cam segments, on a single master drum, actuate and feed the tool slides at their proper rate. The operation of the machine is automatic except for loading and unloading the work. The production rate on this job is 45 flywheels per hour.

Courtesy Gisholt Machine Company.

FIG. 25. Machining Flywheel on Vertical-Head Simplimatic Lathe.

A small fully automatic lathe, designed for spindle speeds up to 5000 rpm, is shown in Figure 26. In this setup a magazine feed is substituted for the rear slide, and the regular tailstock is replaced by a special centering device for supporting the bronze coupling during machining operations. The front slide turns the outside diameter, while the vertical slide turns a spherical form on one end and squares the shoulder back of the formed section. One feature of this machine is the compact design of the tailstock which permits the free passage of turning tools on the front slide. This lathe has many tooling possibilities and is used for machining pistons, bushings, shells, armatures, valve guides, and numerous other similar parts.

A single-spindle automatic chucking machine, of somewhat different design, is shown in Figure 27. This machine uses two cross slides and an overhead pentagonal turret for holding the tools. All are operated by cams which are permanently set and do not have to be changed at any time. Automatic control of the spindle speeds, feeds, indexing, and length of cutting stroke is provided by adjustable trips

Courtesy Seneca Falls Machine Company.

Fig. 26.   Automatic Lathe with Loading Device.

in a selector drum. One feature of this machine is the accessibility of all tools and controls which reduces setup time to a minimum.

Automatic lathes have been developed primarily for quantity production and have done much to reduce machining costs of many parts. All the machines described are rugged in construction and are capable of using modern high-speed cutting tools. Versatility is sacrificed in some machines, but this is not an important consideration in long-run jobs. The selection of the proper machine for a given job must be carefully considered and is influenced by such factors as work size and shape, type of machining to be done, ease of setting up tools, and quantity of parts to be machined.

Courtesy Warner & Swasey Manufacturing Company.

FIG. 27. Single-Spindle Automatic Chucking Machine.

Automatic Screw Machines

The automatic screw machine was invented by Christopher N. Spencer of the Billings & Spencer Company about 75 years ago. The principal feature of the invention was to provide a controlling movement for the turret so that tools could be fed into the work at desired speeds, withdrawn, and indexed to the next position. This was all accomplished by means of a cylindrical or drum cam located beneath the turret. Another feature, also cam-controlled, was a mechanism for clamping the work in the collet, releasing it at the end of the cycle, and then feeding the bar stock up against the stop. These features are still used in about the same way as originally worked out.

An automatic screw machine is essentially a turret lathe designed to use only bar stock. It is so named, because the first machines of this type were used mainly for manufacturing bolts and screws. Since it can produce parts, one after the other, with little attention from the operator, it is naturally called automatic. Most automatic screw machines not only feed in an entire bar of stock but also are provided with a magazine so that several bars can be fed through the machine automatically.

Automatic screw machines may be classified according to the type of turret used or the number of spindles the machine has. Multispindle machines, however, are not usually spoken of as screw machines, but rather as multispindle automatics. The type of work that the two machines do is the same, although there is considerable difference in the design and production capacity.

Courtesy Brown & Sharpe Manufacturing Company.

Fig. 28.   Automatic Screw Machine.

Single-spindle automatic. In Figure 28 is illustrated an automatic screw machine designed for bar work of small diameter. This machine has a cross slide, capable of carrying tools both front and rear, and a turret mounted in a vertical position on a slide with longitudinal movement. The two disk cams controlling the cross slide are directly underneath and are driven by the front drive shaft. Also mounted on this same drive shaft are three disk-shaped carriers, upon which are mounted dogs to engage various trip levers to control the operation of the machine. The one to the extreme right controls the indexing of the turret, the center one controls the collet and feeding of the stock, and the one to the left the rotation and speed of the spindle. The various tools used in the machine are mounted around the turret in a vertical plane in line with the spindle. This is more clearly illustrated in Figure 29 which shows the turret setup for making a small aluminum coupling. All usual machining operations, such as turning, drilling, boring, and threading, can be done on these machines. The type of bar stock used, whether round, square, hexagonal, or of some special shape, is determined by the cross section preferred in the finished product. Collets for any commercial shape are available.

The machine shown in the figure is usually equipped with an automatic rod magazine to keep it supplied with material for a period of time. When a rod of material is completely used, the machine stops, and another rod is fed into the collet up to the stop. The machine then automatically resumes operation. In addition to attending several machines, the operator checks the work and tools and sees that the magazines are supplied with materials.

Courtesy Brown & Sharpe Manufacturing Company.

FIG. 29. Automatic Screw Machine Setup for Making Aluminum Coupling.

Swiss-type screw machine. In Figure 30 is shown the end view of a Swiss-type screw machine developed for precision turning of small parts. The single-point tools used on this machine are placed radially around the carbide-lined guide bushing through which the stock is advanced during machining operations. Most diameter turning is done by the two horizontal tool slides while the other three are used principally for such operations as knurling, chamfering, cutting off, and recessing. During operations, the stock is held by a rotating collet in the headstock back of the tools, and all longitudinal feeds are accomplished by a cam which moves the headstock forward as a unit. This forward motion advances the stock through the guide bushing and to the single-point tools which are controlled and positioned by cams. By coordinating their movement with the forward movement of the stock, any desired shape can be turned. Diameters on slender parts can be held to tolerances ranging from 0.0002 to 0.0005 inch.

American-made machines of this type vary in sizes from 3/32 to 1/2 in maximum capacity. Their use is fairly well limited to slender work pieces that would be difficult to do on ordinary automatic screw machines. These machines excel in small precision work and can frequently complete jobs that by other means would require several

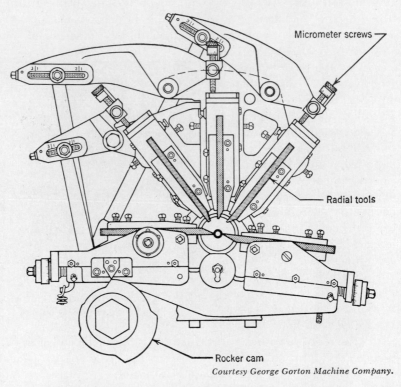

Courtesy George Gorton Machine Company.

Fig. 30. End View of Swiss-Type Screw Machine Showing Rocker Cam and Tool-Control Mechanism.

machine settings. Pinion shafts, gear blanks, pivots, and balance staffs, are typical of the small parts made for watches and instruments.

Multiple-spindle automatic. Multiple-spindle automatic machines are the fastest type of production machines for bar work. They are fully automatic in their operations and are made in a variety of models, with two, four, five, six, or eight spindles. In these machines all spindles operate simultaneously, and one piece is completed each time the tools are withdrawn and the spindles indexed.

The general construction of a multiple-spindle automatic is shown in Figure 31. The spindles carrying the bar stock are all held and

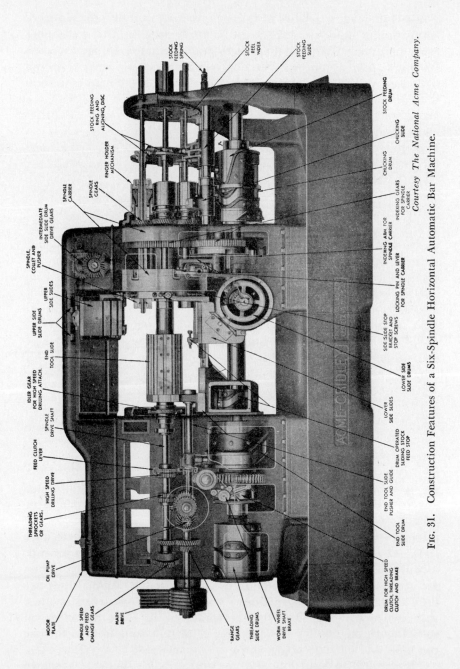

STOCK FEEDING SPRING

STOCK REEL INDEX

STOCK FEEDING SLIDE

STOCK FEEDING RING AND ALIGNING DISC

STOCK FEEDING DRUM

FINGER HOLDER MECHANISM

CHUCKING DRUM

CHUCKING SLIDE

SPINDLE CARRIER

SPINDLE GEARS

SPINDLE CARRIER

INTERMEDIATE SIDE DRUM DRIVE GEARS

INDEXING GEARS FOR SPINDLE CARRIER

SPINDLE, COLLET AND PUSHER

INDEXING ARM FOR SPINDLE CARRIER

UPPER SIDE SLIDES

LOCKING PIN AND LEVER FOR SPINDLE CARRIER

UPPER SIDE SLIDE DRUMS

SIDE SLIDE STOP BRACKET AND STOP SCREWS

END TOOL SLIDE

IDLER GEAR FOR HIGH SPEED DRILLING ATTACH.

LOWER SIDE SLIDE DRUMS

SPINDLE DRIVE SHAFT

LOWER SIDE SLIDES

FEED CLUTCH LEVER

DRUM OPERATED SLIDING STOCK FEED STOP

HIGH SPEED DRILLING DRIVE

END TOOL SLIDE PUSHER AND GUIDE

THREADING SPROCKETS OR GEARS

END TOOL SLIDE DRUM

OIL PUMP DRIVE

DRUM FOR HIGH SPEED CLUTCH, THREADING CLUTCH AND BRAKE

MOTOR PLATE

SPINDLE SPEED AND FEED CHANGE GEARS

MAIN DRIVE

RANGE GEARS

THREADING SLIDE DRUMS

WORM WHEEL DRIVE SHAFT BRAKE

ACME-GRIDLEY

Courtesy The National Acme Company.

FIG. 31.   Construction Features of a Six-Spindle Horizontal Automatic Bar Machine.

rotated in the spindle carrier. Opposite each spindle are mounted the necessary tools for the respective operations. Most of the tools are supported on the end tool slide, which is centrally located with reference to all spindles. This tool slide does not index or revolve with the spindle carrier but slides forward and back on the stem shaft to carry the end working tools to and from contact with the revolving bars of stock. Both above and below the spindle carrier and end tool slide are two cross slides on which side-cutting tools can be mounted. In six- and eight-spindle models there are two additional intermediate or side slides available. All slides are independently operated and are used in combination with end-slide tools for such operations as form turning, knurling, thread rolling, slotting, and cutting off.

Bars of stock are loaded into each spindle when it has been indexed to the first position. If automatic stock feeding is used, it is done in the lower spindle position at the rear of the machine. In operation, the spindle carrier is indexed by steps to bring the bar of stock in each of the work spindles successively in line with the various tools held on the tool slides. All tools in the successive positions are at work on different bars at the same time. The time to complete one part is equal to the time of the longest operation plus the time necessary for withdrawing the tools and indexing to the next position. This time can frequently be reduced to a minimum by dividing the long cuts between two or more operations.

The drive for the multiple-spindle automatic is somewhat complicated, as all tool operations and machine movements are automatically controlled. The motor, mounted on the end of the machine opposite the spindles, operates the entire machine. The main drum shaft is located below the spindles and extends the full length of the machine. This shaft, with its several drum cams and gear connections, controls all tool movements, indexing, stock feeding, and timing of operations.

In Figure 32 is shown a six-spindle automatic screw machine tooled for a simple turning and drilling job. In this machine the respective cross slides provided for each spindle are distributed radially about the spindle carrier. These slides hold the tools for turning, knurling, and cutting off, and each is operated by a separate cam. The balance of the tools for such operations as drilling and threading are mounted on the main center slide which is moved to the point where the feed starts through an intermittent gear. Bar stock may be fed in at two stations to permit the completion of two pieces in one cycle, or, if desired, the machine can be equipped with magazine feed.

To show how a multiple-spindle automatic is set up, an operation sheet for the production of differential pinions is shown in Figure 33. Before a machine is set up for a new job, it is first necessary to make several preliminary calculations. These will include choice of tools, sequence of operations, spindle speeds and tool feeds for the stock and tools, selection of the proper gears and cams, and estimation of the production. This preliminary calculation is usually a function

Courtesy Greenlee Bros. & Company.

Fig. 32. Close-up of Tooling Arrangement on 6-Spindle Machine.

of the production-planning department, and, when it is completed, a sheet, similar to the one in the figure, is turned over to the setup man for his guidance. In making out such a sheet it should be kept in mind that the time to make one piece can never be less than the longest operation. However, if it is possible to split the longest operation between two or more stations, the time to produce one piece can be reduced. Reference to the figure will show that this procedure has been followed in the planning of this job. Space on the figure does not permit including all the information normally included on such a sheet. In addition to the data shown, there should be indicated the tools used for each operation, spindle speeds, tool feeds, change gear sizes, cam descriptions, and kind of material to be used.

Multiple-spindle automatics are not limited to bar stock but may

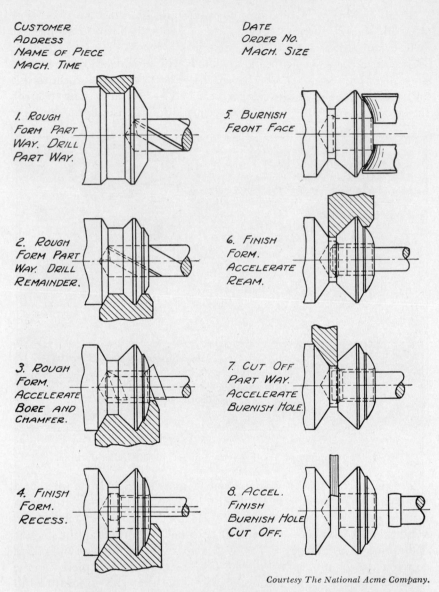

CUSTOMER
ADDRESS
NAME OF PIECE
MACH. TIME

DATE
ORDER NO.
MACH. SIZE

1. ROUGH FORM PART WAY. DRILL PART WAY.

5. BURNISH FRONT FACE

2. ROUGH FORM PART WAY. DRILL REMAINDER.

6. FINISH FORM. ACCELERATE REAM.

3. ROUGH FORM. ACCELERATE BORE AND CHAMFER.

7. CUT OFF PART WAY. ACCELERATE BURNISH HOLE.

4. FINISH FORM. RECESS.

8. ACCEL. FINISH BURNISH HOLE CUT OFF.

Courtesy The National Acme Company.

FIG. 33. Operation Sheet for Differential Pinion.

be provided with hydraulic or air-operated chucks for holding individual pieces. In some cases the chucks are loaded by the operator; in others magazine feeders are arranged to load the machine at one of the lower stations. Machines of this type are known as multiple-

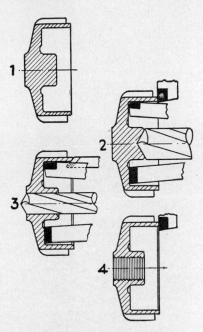

A. Operation for Machining Cast-Iron
Gear.

1—Loading station.
2—Rough face end. Rough bore large
hole. Rough face bottom. Spot.
3—Drill small hole. Finish bore large
hole. Finish face bottom. Chamfer
inside large hole.
4—Finish face end. Tap.

Courtesy The National Acme Company.

B. Machining Cast-Iron Cylinder Gear on a 4-Spindle Automatic.

Fig. 34.

spindle automatic chucking machines and are similar to the bar machines except for the stock-holding equipment.

The four-spindle automatic chucking machine, shown in Figure 34, is machining cast-iron gears according to the operation schedule listed in the insert above. By using combined and multiple cuts, as is done at the second and third station, the number of operations required is reduced to a minimum.

A great many attachments to permit almost any type of machine operation are available for these machines. Both solid and self-opening dies and taps may be applied in position to suit the work. Taper turning, combined taper turning and taper boring, or recessing attachments are applied to the end tool slide. A spindle-stopping mechanism can be arranged for such operations as milling, slotting, and cross drilling. Many machines are provided with a small chip conveyor which picks up the chips beneath the tooling area and dumps them into a container at the end of the machine. To assist in production records, a chronolog can be used to count the production and record the idle time of the machine.

A great variety of parts can be produced by a multiple-spindle automatic, the only limiting factor being the capacity of the machine. However, long-run jobs are necessary to offset the high initial investment, high maintenance, and expensive tooling costs. Both single-spindle automatics and hand-turret lathes have wide application and in short- and medium-run work prove to be economical in operation. Each machine is good in its field, but care must be taken in making the initial selection.

Review Questions

1. Prepare a classification of turret and automatic lathes.
2. How does a turret lathe differ from an engine lathe?
3. Distinguish between the ram and saddle types of turret lathe.
4. What advantages are to be gained in the use of a controlled spindle turret lathe?
5. List the various devices for holding stock on a turret lathe.
6. What type of spring collet is recommended for bar work?
7. What are some of the distinguishing characteristics of automatic lathes that make them different from engine lathes?
8. What four factors make up the total production in turret lathe operation?
9. What is meant by the terms "combined cuts" and "multiple cuts"?
10. How is bar stock supported so that it will not deflect when being cut?
11. Show by sketch the tool setup for making ½-by-2½-inch hexagon-head machine bolts.
12. Prepare an operation sheet for the bolt described in Problem 11.
13. What is the purpose of the following: box tool, automatic die head, square turret, spring collet, and bar stop?

14. What type of work is done on a vertical turret lathe?

15. Explain the operation of a vertical automatic multistation lathe.

16. What type of work is done on a platen-type automatic lathe?

17. Describe the construction and operation of a Swiss-type automatic screw machine.

18. Describe the operation of an automatic multiple-spindle screw machine.

References

BOLZ, R. W., *Production Processes,* Vol. 1, Penton Publishing Company, 1949.

How to Machine Parts on a Turret Lathe, Warner & Swasey Company, 1944.

LONGSTREET and BAILEY, *Turret Lathe Operators Manual,* Operators' Service Bureau, Warner & Swasey Company, 1940.

Tool Engineers Handbook, American Society of Tool Engineers, McGraw-Hill Book Company, 1949.

THREADS AND THREAD CUTTING

A *screw thread* is a ridge of uniform section, in the form of a helix, on the surface of a cylinder. The terminology relating to screw threads is clearly illustrated in Figure 1. Screw *sizes* are expressed by the outside or major diameter and the number of threads per inch. Thus a

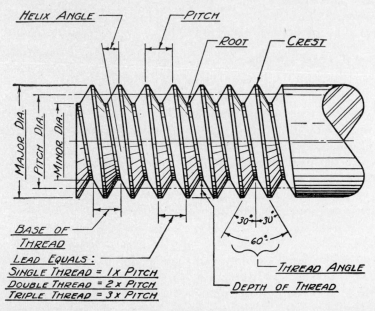

FIG. 1. American National Form Thread.

½-inch 13-thread stud indicates a screw ½ inch in diameter and having 13 threads per inch. *Pitch* is expressed by a fraction with 1 as the numerator and the number of threads per inch as the denominator. Thus, a screw having 16 single threads per inch has a pitch of ¹⁄₁₆. It should be kept in mind that only on single-threaded screws does the pitch equal the lead. By definition the *lead* is the amount a screw advances axially in one revolution. Hence, on a double-threaded

404

screw the lead is twice the pitch, on a triple-threaded screw the lead is three times the pitch, and so on.

Screw threads are used principally on fasteners such as machine bolts, stove bolts, and wood screws. Threads of this nature are simple in design and easy to produce. The usual form is a V, although there are several slight variations of this form.

Another use for screw threads is to transmit power. The mechanical advantage obtained in the ordinary screw jack illustrates this application. Closely associated with this is the use of threads for transmitting motion, such as the lead screw on a lathe.

Finally, screw threads are employed for such measuring devices as micrometers. Screw threads sometimes fulfill several of these uses. For example, the screws controlling the work table of a milling machine may be used either for accurate measuring or for controlling the table movement. The form in which the screw is made is naturally influenced by the function it has to fulfill.

Types of Screw Threads

Screw threads have been standardized according to their cross-sectional form. Figure 2 shows the common forms in use and the relationships that exist between the pitch and the principal dimensions. All bolts and similar fasteners have *V-shaped threads,* as shown in *A* of the figure. There are two standards in the United States that utilize this form of thread: namely, the *National Coarse Screw Thread* and the *National Fine Screw Thread.* The National Fine series differs from the National Coarse series only in having more threads per inch for a given size. Such threads have been adopted by the automotive and aeronautical industries, since there is less tendency for them to work loose because of vibrations they may be subjected to. This type of thread is characterized by a small flat on top and at the root of the thread, which adds to its strength. V-type threads without these flats, shown at *B,* have a greater tendency to fail at the sharp root corners when subjected to loading conditions. The *International Standard Metric Thread* shown in *D* is essentially the same as the National Standard except for a smaller flat at the root and a different number of threads per unit distance. From a standpoint of design, the *Whitworth Standard* used in England is perhaps better than any of those already mentioned, as the filleted top and root add strength to the thread by eliminating sharp corners where fatigue cracks may start. This thread is shown at *C* in the figure; however, it is gradually being replaced by the Unified Standard shown in Figure 3. The Acme thread shown at *F* is principally used for the transmission of power and motion. It has an advantage over other similar screws in that wear may be compensated for by adjusting the half nuts in contact with the screw. This would be impossible with the square threads shown at *E*.

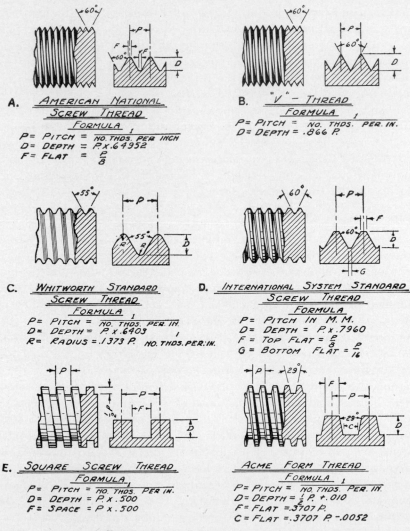

A. AMERICAN NATIONAL SCREW THREAD
FORMULA
P = PITCH = $\frac{1}{NO. THDS. PER INCH}$
D = DEPTH = P x .64952
F = FLAT = $\frac{P}{8}$

B. "V" - THREAD FORMULA
P = PITCH = $\frac{1}{NO. THDS. PER. IN.}$
D = DEPTH = .866 P.

C. WHITWORTH STANDARD SCREW THREAD
FORMULA
P = PITCH = $\frac{1}{NO. THDS. PER. IN.}$
D = DEPTH = P x .6403
R = RADIUS = .1373 P. $\frac{1}{NO. THDS. PER: IN.}$

D. INTERNATIONAL SYSTEM STANDARD SCREW THREAD
FORMULA
P = PITCH IN M.M.
D = DEPTH = P x .7960
F = TOP FLAT = $\frac{P}{8}$
G = BOTTOM FLAT = $\frac{P}{16}$

E. SQUARE SCREW THREAD
FORMULA
P = PITCH = $\frac{1}{NO. THDS. PER IN.}$
D = DEPTH = P x .500
F = SPACE = P x .500

ACME FORM THREAD
FORMULA
P = PITCH = $\frac{1}{NO. THDS. PER. IN.}$
D = DEPTH = $\frac{1}{2}$ P. + .010
F = FLAT = .3707 P.
C = FLAT = .3707 P. -.0052

FIG. 2. Standard Screw-Thread Forms.

Another advantage of the Acme over the square thread is that it may be cut with suitable taps and dies. *Square threads* are more suitable for transmitting power where there is a large thrust on one side of the thread.   These threads, however, cannot be cut with taps and dies and must be machined on a lathe.   Another type, similar to the square thread, is known as a *buttress thread*.   It has one side that is sloping 45 degrees while the other is perpendicular.   The principal application of this thread is for the transmission of power, although it has the disadvantage that the thrust can be in only one direction.   *Worm threads* are similar to the Acme Standard except that they have a greater depth. This form of thread is used exclusively for worm-gear drives.

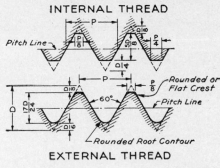

FIG. 3.   Unified Screw-Thread Standard.

The new *unified screw-thread* standard, shown in Figure 3, was adopted recently by Britain, Canada, and the United States.   It is very similar to the present American Standard and in most applications will be interchangeable with it.   The greatest change in tooling will occur in Britain since they have changed from the 55-degree angle of the Whitworth system to the 60-degree American Standard angle.   The basic width of the nut is $\frac{1}{4}$ pitch whereas that of the screw is $\frac{1}{8}$ pitch. This increased flat on the nut facilitates tapping and at the same time has proved to be just as serviceable.   The shape of the thread crest and root is not mandatory and may be either flat or rounded.   Actually it approximates the shape obtained from a worn tool and is very similar to many threads produced under the American Standard.

Pipe threads have been standardized according to the American National Standard shown in Figure 4.   To insure tight joints, the thread has a taper of $\frac{3}{4}$ inch per foot.   The threads have the conventional V shape, except for the last four or five, which have flat tops. These last threads all have imperfect bottoms, as shown in the figure. The usual method of cutting these threads is with suitable taps and dies, although they may also be cut on a lathe using the taper attachment.

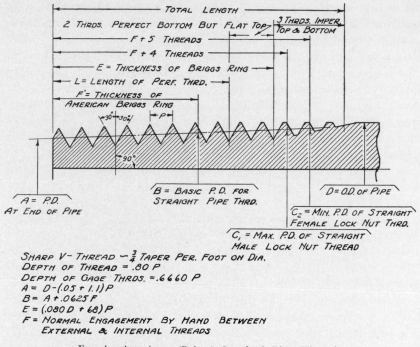

Sharp V-Thread ‒ ¾ Taper Per. Foot on Dia.
Depth of Thread = .80 P
Depth of Gage Thrds. = .6660 P
A = D‒(.05 + 1.1)P
B = A + .0625 F
E = (.080 D + 68)P
F = Normal Engagement By Hand Between
      External & Internal Threads

Fig. 4. American (Briggs) Standard Pipe Thread.

Methods of Making Threads

External threads may be produced by the following manufacturing processes:

1. Cutting to shape on an engine lathe.
2. Using die and stock (manual).
3. Automatic die head (turret lathe).
4. Milling machine.
5. Threading machine (plain or automatic).
6. Rolling between dies (flat or circular).
7. Die casting.
8. Grinding.

Internal threads may be produced by:

1. Cutting to shape on an engine lathe.
2. Using tap and holder.
3. Automatic collapsible tap.
4. Milling machine.

Cutting threads on a lathe. The lathe is the most versatile of all machine tools for cutting threads, since on this machine it is possible to cut all forms of threads; however, the lathe is usually selected when only a few threads are to be cut or when special forms are desired. The form of the thread is obtained by grinding the tool to the proper shape. To insure getting the proper shape, a suitable gage or templet should be used. Figure 5 shows a cutter bit ground for cutting 60-degree V threads and the gage which is used for checking the angle of the tool. This gage is known as a *center gage,* as it is also used for gaging lathe centers. Special form cutters as shown in Figure 7 can also be used for cutting these threads. These cutters are previously shaped to the correct form and are sharpened by grinding only on the top face.

In setting up the tool for V threads, there are two methods of feeding the tool. First, the tool may be fed straight into the work and the threads formed by taking a series of light cuts, as shown at *A* in Figure 5. With this method there is cutting action on both sides of the tool bit. The disadvantage of this method is that it is impossible to provide any side rake on the cutting tool, although some back rake may be obtained. On materials such as cast iron or brass, where little or no side rake is recommended, this method is satisfactory. However, in cutting steel threads it is advisable to use a side rake on the tool. This necessitates feeding the tool in at an angle, as shown at *B* and *D*. To do this, the compound rest is turned to an angle of 29 degrees, and, by using the cross-feed on the compound rest, the tool is fed into the work so that all cutting is done on the left-hand side of the tool. The tool bit, being ground to an angle of 60 degrees, allows 1 degree of the right-hand side of the tool to smooth off that side of the thread.

It is necessary that the tool be given a positive feed along the work at the proper rate to cut the desired number of threads per inch. This is accomplished by a train of gears located on the end of the lathe, which drive the lead screw at the required speed with relation to the headstock spindle. This gearing may be changed to cut any desired pitch of screw. The lead screw, in turn, engages the half nuts on the apron of the lathe, which provides a positive drive for the tool.

The older-type standard change-gear lathes require that the gears be changed manually. Referring to Figure 6, one may see the usual arrangement of gears on such lathes. The *spindle gear* drives through the small *reversing gears* to the *stud gear*. As shown in the figure, both the reversing or tumble gears are in mesh. When the hand lever is raised, one of the gears is thrown out of mesh, and, if one gear is eliminated from the train, the rotation of the lead screw is reversed.

The speed ratio from spindle gear to stud gear is 1 to 1, or, in other words, there is no increase or decrease in the rotational speed of the

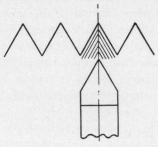

A. STRAIGHT FEED

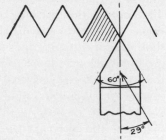

B. FEED AT ANGLE

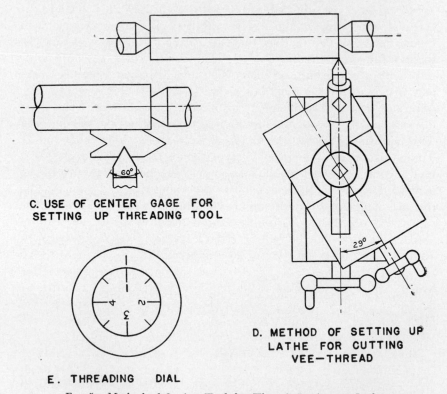

C. USE OF CENTER GAGE FOR SETTING UP THREADING TOOL

D. METHOD OF SETTING UP LATHE FOR CUTTING VEE—THREAD

E. THREADING DIAL

Fig. 5. Method of Setting Tool for Thread Cutting on Lathe.

stud gear. Keyed to the stud gear is another gear called the *driving gear*. It connects with the *lead-screw gear* by means of an *idler*. In simple gearing the only two gears to be changed are the driving and lead-screw gears. The correct selection of these gears depends on the number of threads to be cut and the pitch of the lead screw.

Assume, as an example, that it is desired to cut a thread with 13 threads per inch on a lathe having a lead screw with 8 threads per inch. If the ratio from driving gear to lead-screw gear is 1 to 1, the tool will advance $\frac{1}{8}$ inch for each revolution of lead screw and will cut 8 threads per inch. In order to cut 13 threads per inch, the lead-screw speed must be slowed down somewhat in relation to the spindle

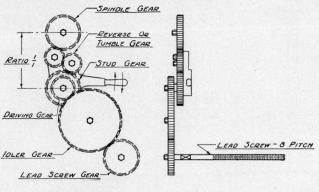

SIMPLE GEARING AT END OF LATHE

FIG. 6.

speed. The ratio that must exist in this case is 8 to 13. Hence, a driving gear and a lead-screw gear having this ratio will cut the desired thread. The rule for determining the proper gear ratio is:

$$\frac{\text{Number of threads on lead screw}}{\text{Number of threads to be cut}}$$

In this case the ratio is 8 to 13.

By multiplying both the numerator and denominator by a number, the ratio may be expressed as numbers of teeth in each gear. Hence,

$$\frac{8 \times 3}{13 \times 3} = \frac{24T}{39T} \quad \begin{array}{l}\text{(driving gear)}\\\text{(lead-screw gear)}\end{array}$$

If no gears are available with these numbers of teeth, some other multiplier must be used, or, if the ratio is too large, compound gearing is necessary.

All the newer-type lathes are provided with quick-change gearboxes, as shown in Figures 1 and 2 of Chapter 14. No computation is necessary, as the chart on the cover of the gearbox states the correct position of levers needed to obtain the number of threads per inch desired.

After the lathe is set up, the cross-feed screw is set at some mark on the micrometer dial, and a light cut is taken to check the pitch of the thread.   At the end of each successive cut, the tool is removed from the thread by turning back the cross-feed screw.   This is necessary, as any back play in the lead screw would prevent the tool from returning in

FIG. 7.   Thread Cutting on a Lathe.

its previous cut.   The tool is returned to original position, the cross-feed screw is set at the same reference mark, the tool is fed the desired amount for the next cut, and another cut is taken.   These operations are repeated until the thread is cut to a proper depth.   To check the work a ring thread gage or a standard nut is used.   Figure 7 illustrates the tool setup for thread cutting on a lathe.

Most lathes are equipped with a *thread dial indicator* as shown in Figures 5 and 8.   Close by the dial is a lever (shown in Figure 8) which is used to engage and disengage the lead screw with a matching set of half nuts in the carriage.   At the end of each cut, the half nuts are disengaged and then re-engaged at the correct time so that the tool always follows in the same cut.   The indicator is connected to the lead screw by means of a small worm gear, and the face of the dial which revolves is numbered to indicate positions at which the half nuts

may be engaged.   The position at which the half nuts should be closed
depends on the size of thread, as follows:

1. For even-number threads: any line on dial.
2. For odd-number threads: any *numbered* line.
3. For threads involving half threads: any odd-numbered line.
4. For threads involving quarter threads: return to original starting
   point each time.

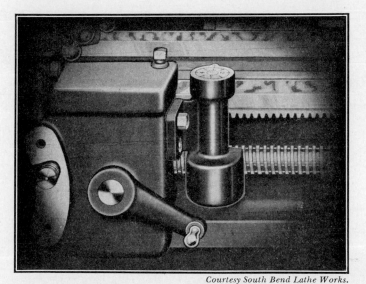

Courtesy South Bend Lathe Works.

Fig. 8.   Threading Dial on Lathe.

Taps and dies.   Taps are used principally for the manual production of internal threads, although with proper mounting they may also
be used in machine threading.   Figure 9 is a graphic illustration of a
tap with the various parts of the tool labeled.   The tool itself is a
hardened piece of carbon or alloy steel resembling a bolt, with flutes
cut along the side to provide the cutting edges.   For hand tapping
these are furnished in sets of three for each size, as shown in Figure 10.
In starting the thread, the *taper tap* should be used, since it insures
straighter starting and more gradual cutting action on the threads.   If
it is a through hole, no other tap is needed.   For closed or blind holes
where it is desired to have threads to the very bottom, the *taper, plug,*
and *bottoming taps* should all be used in the order named.   Many
other taps are available and are usually named according to the kind
of thread they are to cut.

In all cases, where a hole is to be tapped, the hole that is drilled before the tapping operation must be of such size as to provide the necessary metal for the threads. Such a hole is said to be a *"tap-size"* hole. Referring to Table 8, note that, if a ⅜-inch 16-thread hole is to be cut, the tap-size drill is listed as being $\frac{5}{16}$ inch in diameter.

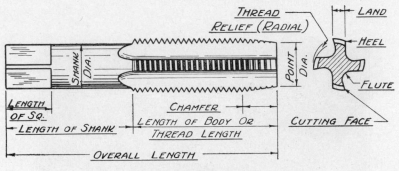

FIG. 9.   Tap Nomenclature.

This is equivalent to the root diameter of a ⅜-inch 16 standard screw and allows sufficient metal in the hole for the threads.

In order to cut external threads, *dies* similar to those shown in Figure 11 are used. The most common type is the adjustable die, as it can be made to cut slightly undersize or oversize. When used for hand cutting, the die is held in a die stock which provides the necessary leverage to turn the die in making a cut.

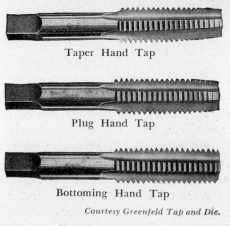

Taper Hand Tap

Plug Hand Tap

Bottoming Hand Tap

Courtesy Greenfeld Tap and Die.

FIG. 10.   Hand Taps.

For successful operation of either taps or dies, some consideration must be given to the nature of the material to be threaded. The shape and angle of the cutting face influence the performance, since no tool can be made to work successfully for all materials. Another important factor is proper lubrication of the tool during the cutting operation. This insures longer life of the cutting edges and results in smoother threads. Since no one lubricant can be recommended for all cases, it is advisable to consult specialists or handbooks in making a selection.

Both the taps and dies described may also be used in the machine cutting of threads. Because of the nature of the cutting operation, they must be held in a special holder so designed that the tap or die can be withdrawn from the work without injury to the threads. This is frequently accomplished by reversing the rotation of the tool or work after the cut has been made. Numerous tapping attachments are available for internal thread cutting on a drill press. These attach-

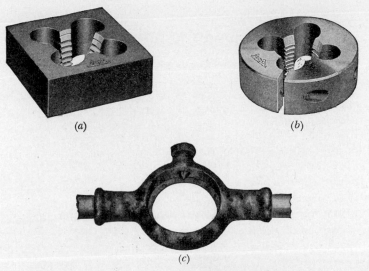

(a)   (b)

(c)

Courtesy Greenfield Tap and Die.

FIG. 11. (a) Square Die, (b) Round Die, and (c) Stock.

ments are usually provided with two spindles which operate in opposite directions. The tap is rotated into the work at the proper cutting speed until the threads are made. As soon as the tap is raised upward, the other spindle is engaged by means of a ball or friction clutch, and the rotation of the tap is reversed, thus removing it from the work. The withdrawing speed is usually much faster than the cutting speed. The same procedure is used in cutting external threads with non-opening dies.

In small production work on a turret lathe, the tap is held by a special holder, which prevents the tap from turning as the threads are cut. Near the end of the cut the turret holding the tool is stopped, and the tap holder continues to advance until it pulls away from a stop pin a sufficient amount to allow the tap to rotate with the work. The rotation of the work is then reversed, and, when the tap holder is withdrawn, it is again engaged with the stop and held until the work is rotated from the tap. External threads may also be cut with a die utilizing this same procedure, although in most cases such threads are cut with self-opening dies.

TABLE 8. STANDARD SCREW-THREAD PITCHES AND RECOMMENDED TAP-DRILL SIZES

American National Coarse-Thread Series Standard Thread (NC) Formerly US Standard					American National Fine-Thread Series Standard Thread (NF) Formerly SAE Thread				
No. or Diam.	Thr'ds Per Inch	Outside Diam. of Screw	Tap Drill Sizes	Decimal Equivalent of Drill	No. or Diam.	Thr'ds Per Inch	Outside Diam. of Screw	Tap Drill Sizes	Decimal Equivalent of Drill
1	64	0.073	53	0.0595	0	80	0.060	$\frac{3}{64}$	0.0469
2	56	0.086	50	0.0700	1	72	0.073	53	0.0595
3	48	0.099	47	0.785	2	64	0.086	50	0.0700
					3	56	0.099	45	0.0820
4	40	0.112	43	0.0890					
5	40	0.125	38	0.1015	4	48	0.112	42	0.0935
6	32	0.138	36	0.1065	5	44	0.125	36	0.1040
					6	40	0.138	33	1.1130
8	32	0.164	29	0.1360					
10	24	0.190	25	0.1495	8	36	0.164	29	0.1360
12	24	0.216	16	0.1770	10	32	0.190	21	0.1590
					12	28	0.216	14	0.1820
$\frac{1}{4}$	20	0.250	7	0.2010					
$\frac{5}{16}$	18	0.3125	F	0.2570	$\frac{1}{4}$	28	0.250	3	0.2130
$\frac{3}{8}$	16	0.375	$\frac{5}{16}$	0.3125	$\frac{5}{16}$	24	0.3125	I	0.2720
					$\frac{3}{8}$	24	0.375	Q	0.3320
$\frac{7}{16}$	14	0.4375	U	0.3680					
$\frac{1}{2}$	13	0.500	$\frac{27}{64}$	0.4219	$\frac{7}{16}$	20	0.4375	$\frac{25}{64}$	0.3906
$\frac{9}{16}$	12	0.5625	$\frac{31}{64}$	0.4843	$\frac{1}{2}$	20	0.500	$\frac{29}{64}$	0.4531
					$\frac{9}{16}$	18	0.5625	0.5062	0.5062
$\frac{5}{8}$	11	0.625	$\frac{17}{32}$	0.5312	$\frac{5}{8}$	18	0.625	0.5687	0.5687
$\frac{3}{4}$	10	0.750	$\frac{21}{32}$	0.6562	$\frac{3}{4}$	16	0.750	$\frac{11}{16}$	0.6875
$\frac{7}{8}$	9	0.875	$\frac{49}{64}$	0.7656	$\frac{7}{8}$	14	0.875	0.8020	0.8020
1	8	1.000	$\frac{7}{8}$	0.875	1	14	1.000	0.9274	0.9274
$1\frac{1}{8}$	7	1.125	$\frac{63}{64}$	0.9843	$1\frac{1}{8}$	12	1.125	$1\frac{3}{64}$	1.0468
$1\frac{1}{4}$	7	1.250	$1\frac{7}{64}$	1.1093	$1\frac{1}{4}$	12	1.250	$1\frac{11}{64}$	1.1718

For large-diameter internal threads it is common practice to use a *collapsing tap*. In Figure 12 is shown such a tap, widely used on automatic screw machines, drill presses, and other machines which have facilities for rotating the threading tool. This tap revolves while the threads are cut. Collapsing is automatic when the proper length of thread has been cut, and resetting is by means of an outside yoke. Similar taps are devised for stationary spindles. The collapsing in this type is also automatic, but the resetting is by means of a handle which must be moved by the operator.

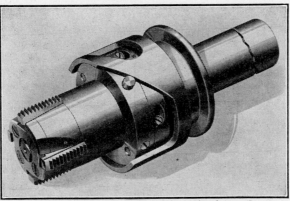

Courtesy The National Acme Company.

FIG. 12.   Revolving Tap—Collapsing Type.

Courtesy Landis Machine Company.

FIG. 13.   Receding Circular Chaser Collapsible Tap.

In Figure 13 is shown a receding circular chaser collapsible tap which was specially designed for production tapping of line pipe, casing, and drill-pipe couplings in the tube mills.   It produces a high-quality thread well within all API tolerance specifications on seamless, welded steel, or wrought-iron pipe. The head of the tap is a self-contained unit that is detachable from the body, which permits using heads covering a thread range of 4 to 12 inches. Any taper thread from 0 to ¾ inch per foot can be obtained by a cam adjustment. For manual operation, the tap is expanded by a short movement of the crank handle, to bring the tripping ring into contact with the face of the coupling, thus bringing into operation the receding mechanism as

Courtesy The National Acme Company.

FIG. 14.   Revolving Die Head.

the tap is fed into the coupling. At the end of the thread the tap is collapsed, which permits it to be removed without interference with the threads.

Two types of *automatic die heads* are shown in Figures 14 and 15. In one type the cutters or chasers are mounted tangentially; in the other, they are in a radial position. The die head shown in Figure 14 is for use on machines having revolving spindles. Those commonly used on turret lathes and screw machines are of the stationary type (see Figure 15), requiring the work to rotate, but in general appearance there is not much difference. In all cases the chasers open automatically at the end of the cut and may be withdrawn from the work without damage to the threads. Dies of this type may be adjusted to various diameters within practical limits; and, in addition, they have micrometer adjustments to control the thread size.

Tapping machines. Production tapping machines for threading nuts and similar parts are made in several types, depending on the nature of the product and number to be threaded. A fully automatic nut-tapping machine equipped with four spindles is shown in Figure 16. Nut blanks are automatically fed to working plates from two motor-driven oscillating hoppers. Each hopper feeds two blanks to working position through adjustable chutes. The blanks are then clamped in working position, and the four tapping spindles are fed to the work by individual lead screws. When the operation is finished, the spindles

Courtesy Warner & Swasey Manufacturing Company.

FIG. 15. Stationary Tangent Die Head.

are reversed at approximately double the tapping speed, and the nuts are discharged to individual containers. The capacity of the machine depends on such factors as tap size, nut thickness, type of material; however, for small-size nuts a production close to 9000 per hour can be attained.

Another type of threading machine is equipped with a dial feed arrangement and is provided with several vertical spindles for performing successive operations. Drilling, milling, tapping, and screw inserting can all be done if desired, as the part is indexed from one station to another. These machines are semiautomatic; the operator has only to place the work in position.

A common type of tapping machine, usually a multispindle arrangement, is provided with taps having extra long shanks. The tap is advanced through the nut by the lead screw and, upon completion of the threading, continues downward until the nut is released. The spindle then returns to its upper position with the tapped nut on its

Courtesy The Bodine Corporation.

FIG. 16. Four-Spindle Automatic Nut-Tapping Machine.

shank. When the shank has been filled with nuts, the tap is removed and the nuts are emptied into a container.

Threading machines. In Figure 17 is shown a double-spindle threading machine of 1½-inch capacity. Tangential threading tools provided with eight rotational speeds are used. Parts to be threaded are held by vises mounted on the carriage, clearly illustrated in the figure. Of the two hand wheels shown, one controls the double-acting vises while the other regulates the movement or positioning of the carriage. The lever at the rear locks the carriage to the lead screw located beneath and feeds the work to the revolving die. For absolute accuracy in pitch of threads, the use of a lead screw for feeding

Courtesy The Hill Acme Company, Acme Machinery Division.

FIG. 17. 1½-Inch Double-Spindle Threading Machine.

the carriage is recommended, especially for threads of large diameter. Very often no mechanical positive feed is used for small threads, as the lead on the threading die feeds the work at the proper rate. With proper adjustment of the rod stop at the side of the carriage, the die opens automatically when the required length of thread is cut.

Machines of this type may also be used for tapping nuts by using a tap chuck in the die head and gripping the nut in the vise. A long-shank tap is used for this work and, as the nuts are tapped, they feed back onto the shank of the tap.

Thread milling. Accurate threads of large size, both external and internal, can be cut with standard or hob-type cutters. For long external threads a threading machine is used which is similar in appearance to a lathe.   Work is mounted either in a chuck or between centers, and the milling attachment is at the rear of the machine.   In cutting a long screw a single cutter is mounted in the plane of the thread angle and fed parallel to the axis of the threaded part.

A planetary-type thread-milling machine* intended for mass production of short internal or external threads is shown in Figure 18.

Fig. 18.   Enlarged View of Cutter Head for Outside Threads.

The figure shows the cutter-head setup for external threads using annular milling cutters which cover the full length of the cut.

In operation, a work-holding fixture is mounted on the machine table which holds the work rigidly.   The milling head carrying the hob is revolved eccentrically about the work and is simultaneously rotated on its own axis, advancing by means of a lead screw for a sufficient distance to produce the desired thread.   The cutter spindle, after completing the milling operation, automatically returns to center position.   A reversing switch is then contacted, and the sleeves are brought back to the original starting position.   The depth of the thread is controlled by adjustment in the eccentricity of the spindle sleeve.   After proper adjustment the entire cycle of operation is automatic.

Rolling screw threads.   A large proportion of the standard bolts and screws manufactured have their threads formed by being rolled between suitable dies.   In this process both cold- and hot-working methods are employed.   Cold rolling of threads up to 1 inch in diameter has proved successful.   In this process the metal on the cylinder is cold-forged under considerable pressure into the desired shape; and, as a result of this cold working of the metal, such threads have greater strength than cut threads.   Slightly less material is required for bolts made in this fashion, as the outer parts of the threads are forced into the die.   The diameter of the stock used should be approximately equal to the pitch diameter of the screw.   Both the

* See Chapter 19 for additional information on planetary milling.

accuracy and uniformity of rolled threads are excellent if the blanks are held to correct size. The burnishing effect from the rolls produces very smooth threads with a good finish.

There are two different methods employed in the rolling of threads. In one case the bolt is rolled between two flat dies, each being provided with parallel grooves cut the size and shape of the thread. One die is held stationary while the other reciprocates and rolls the blank between the dies. This operation is shown diagrammatically in Figure 19.

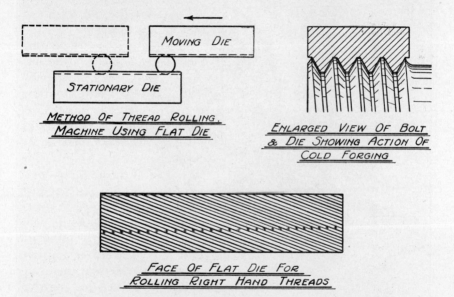

METHOD OF THREAD ROLLING.
MACHINE USING FLAT DIE

ENLARGED VIEW OF BOLT
& DIE SHOWING ACTION OF
COLD FORGING

FACE OF FLAT DIE FOR
ROLLING RIGHT HAND THREADS

FIG. 19. Sketch Illustrating the Principle of Rolling Threads with Flat Dies.

The process may be illustrated by rolling a screw between two soft boards under pressure. On examination of the boards, we note that each has impressed into its surface a series of angular, parallel lines. By reversing this illustration and starting with similar grooves in hardened steel, threads will be rolled into a piece of soft steel rod placed between them. The other process employs three grooved rollers held in a radial position with reference to the stock. In appearance the die used resembles an ordinary die head with circular chasers. As the stock is fed between these rolling dies under pressure, the metal is forced into the grooves of the dies, thus forming the threads. A machine of this type is shown in Figure 20. A similar machine employing two cylindrical-die rollers may also be used. In this case the unthreaded blank is placed between two parallel rollers which are hydraulically fed to the proper depth and then opened for removal of the screw.

In general, flat dies are recommended for small-diameter screws and most commercial bolts as their operation is faster. Small screws may be produced on automatic machines at the rate of 175 per minute. Cylindrical-die machines are best for precision work and larger-diameter (up to 2½-inch) screws. They can also handle short threads and

Fig. 20. Roll-Threading Machine Employing Three Roller Dies.

hollow parts which are impractical on flat-die machines. Thread-rolling machines can produce all commercial standard screw-thread forms as well as pipe threads, drive screws, wood screws, and special thread forms.

Thread grinding. Grinding is used as either a finishing or a forming operation on many screw threads where accuracy and smooth finish are required. This process is particularly applicable for threads that have been heat-treated to eliminate possible errors resulting from the treatment.

In general, there are two types of wheels used in thread grinding, as illustrated in Figure 21. The method shown at *A* employs a single wheel, shaped to correct form, which traverses the length of the screw. The wheel is rotated against the work, usually at speeds ranging from 7500 to 10,000 surface feet per minute, and at the same time traverses the length of the screw at a speed determined by the pitch of the thread. The surface speed of the work is determined by many factors such as depth of cut and kind of material, but for most cases it ranges from 1½ to 10 surface feet per minute. It is possible to cut a complete thread by one pass of the wheel; however, most threads are formed by two or more passes, the last one removing only a few thousandths in the

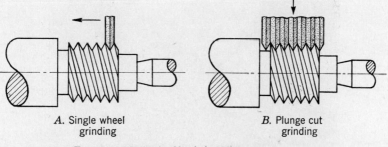

A. Single wheel   B. Plunge cut
grinding   grinding

FIG. 21. Methods Used in Thread Grinding.

interest of accuracy and finish. The form of the grinding wheel must be dressed periodically by a diamond truing device to compensate for gradual wear. The movement of the diamonds is controlled either from template formers or through a pantograph mechanism. Although the truing action is automatic, it must be predetermined by the operator.

Short threads may be ground by the plunge-cut method, as shown at *B* in the figure. With this method the wheel is fed in the entire depth of the thread before the work is started. The work then makes one revolution while it traverses a distance equal to one pitch, thus completing the thread. A little overtravel is provided to insure a perfect thread over the entire length. Multiribbed wheels may be used to traverse-grind as is done with single wheels, but this is not recommended owing to the greater wear on the leading ribs. The dressing of plunge-cut wheels is usually done by a *crush-roll process* as illustrated in Figure 22. The operation consists of slowly rolling the grinding wheel in crushing contact with a hardened roller which has on it threads the same as will appear on the work. This method of dressing is rapid and accurate and provides the wheel with sharp cutting edges so essential for good grinding. The process is limited to the use of vitrified wheels, and there is a gradual decrease in roll accuracy as repeated dressings are made.

Most thread-grinding machines are characterized by having an operating cycle that is entirely automatic from the time the operation starts until the thread is complete. Compensating devices are usually provided to allow for the decreased diameter of the wheel after dressing so that the work size is not altered and no resetting of the wheel is necessary. A similar arrangement is often provided to compensate for

Courtesy Sheffield Gage Corporation.

FIG. 22.   Crush-Roll Dressing of Grinding Wheel for Thread Grinding.

backlash so that the wheel may traverse back and forth for rapid cutting. Thread grinding lends itself to the production of threads on either hard or soft material. The process also produces a high degree of accuracy and finish which is so important for precision and highly stressed screw threads.

Review Questions

1. Name and sketch five standard screw threads. Indicate angle on each thread.
2. To what various uses may screw threads be put?
3. Distinguish between lead and pitch on a screw thread.
4. What advantages does an Acme thread have over a square thread?
5. List the various methods by which external threads can be made.
6. Briefly describe the new unified screw-thread standard.
7. How do the American National Pipe threads differ from the National Coarse threads?
8. What methods can be used for cutting internal threads?
9. How are threads cut on a turret lathe?
10. Sketch the gears on the end of an engine lathe, and, assuming the pitch of the lead screw to be 8, indicate the number of teeth in the driving and lead-screw gears necessary to cut 11 threads per inch.

11. What is a thread dial indicator, and how does it work?
12. What is a tap? Name six kinds.
13. How would you cut an internal square thread?
14. How are threads cut on a turret lathe?
15. What type of threading equipment should be used for cutting internal threads on a drill press?
16. What three methods are employed in rolling threads?
17. What types of screw threads may be produced by rolling?
18. Describe the operation of a planetary-type thread-milling machine.
19. Describe two methods of producing threads by grinding.

References

FLANDERS, RALPH E., "American Thread Grinding Practice," *Machinery,* September 1939.

GAILLARD, JOHN, "New American Standard for Screw Threads Presents Unified Series," *Modern Machine Shop,* May 1949.

KENT's *Mechanical Engineers' Handbook,* 12th edition, John Wiley & Sons, 1950.

PETERKA, A. E., *Bolts, Nuts, and Screws,* Lamson & Sessions Company, 1941.

Screw Thread Cutting Manual, Geometric Tool Company, 1946.

Tool Engineers Handbook, American Society of Tool Engineers, McGraw-Hill Book Company, 1949.

CHAPTER
17

SHAPERS AND PLANERS

A *shaper* is a machine having a reciprocating cutting tool, of the lathe type, which takes a straight-line cut. By moving the work across the path of this tool, a plane surface is generated, regardless of the shape of the tool. This method of producing a flat surface has the advantage that its perfection is not dependent on the accuracy of the tool, as is the case in using a milling cutter for the same type of work. By means of special tools, attachments, and devices for holding the work, a shaper can also cut external and internal keyways, spiral grooves, gear racks, dovetails, T slots, and other miscellaneous shapes.

Classification of Shapers

According to general design, shapers can be classified as follows:

1. Horizontal—push cut
   (*a*) Plain (production work).
   (*b*) Universal (toolroom work).
2. Horizontal—draw cut.
3. Vertical
   (*a*) Slotter.
   (*b*) Keyseater.
4. Special purpose, as for cutting gears.

Power can be applied to the machine by an individual motor either through gears or belt, or by step-cone pulley from the lineshaft. The reciprocating drive of the tool can be arranged in several ways. Some of the older shapers were driven by gears or by feed screw, but most shapers are now being driven by an oscillating arm and crank mechanism, as illustrated in Figure 3.

Horizontal-Type Shapers

Construction. Figure 1 shows a plain horizontal type of shaper commonly used for production and general-purpose work. This shaper, consisting of a base and frame which supports a horizontal ram, is quite simple in construction. The *ram,* which carries the tool, is given a reciprocating motion equal to the length of the stroke desired. The *quick-return mechanism* driving the ram is designed so that the return stroke of the shaper is faster than the cutting stroke. The purpose of such an arrangement is to reduce the idle time of the machine to a minimum. The tool head at the end of the ram can

Courtesy The Cincinnati Shaper Company.

FIG. 1. Plain Horizontal Shaper.

be swiveled through an angle and is provided with means for feeding the tool into the work. On it is fastened the *clapper-box tool holder* which is pivoted at the upper end to permit the tool to rise on the return stroke so as not to dig into the work. The construction of this tool holder is clearly shown in Figure 2.

The work table is supported on a crossrail in front of the shaper. By means of a lead screw in connection with the crossrail, the work can be moved crosswise or vertically by either hand or power drive. A *universal* shaper has these same features and, in addition, is provided with swiveling and tilting arrangements to permit accurate machining at any desired angle. The swiveling adjustment takes place about an axis that is parallel to the motion of the ram. The tilting feature is in the table top which provides a means to set the table at an angle to

Courtesy The Cincinnati Shaper Company.

Fig. 2. A Heavy-Duty Shaper Taking a Deep Cut.

the swiveling axis. Both adjustments are equipped with protractors to assist the operator in setting the table at any desired angle.

The work on a shaper is held by bolting it to the work table or by fastening it in either a vise or some special fixture. The table is provided with T slots which permit bolts to be inserted to facilitate the holding of work or fixtures. Reference to the illustrations shows clearly how this is accomplished.

Quick-return mechanism. Several types of quick-return mechanisms have been developed for shapers, but the most common type is the *pillar* or *oscillating-arm* type shown diagrammatically in Figure 3. It consists of a rotating crank driven at a uniform speed which is connected to an oscillating arm by a sliding block. Referring to the figure, we note that the cutting stroke takes up 220 degrees of the crank revolution while the return is made through only 140 degrees movement of the crank.   Hence the ratio,

$$\frac{\text{Cutting stroke}}{\text{Return stroke}} = \frac{220}{140} = \frac{1.57}{1}$$

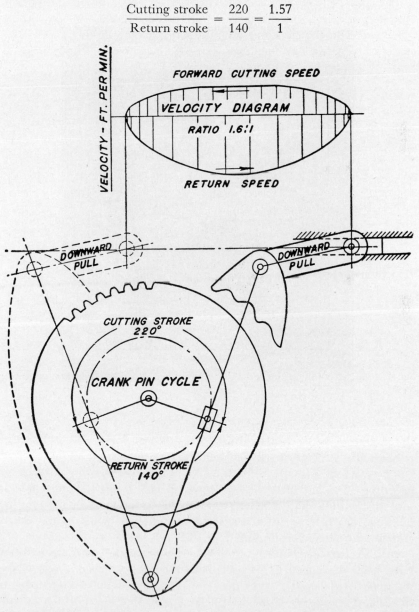

FIG. 3. Pillar-Type Quick-Return Mechanism for Shaper.

The quick return is due to the crank end, with the sliding block, being close to the arm fulcrum during the lower half of rotation. The stroke length is varied by changing the length of the crank.

The quick-return and drive mechanism for a typical oscillating-arm type shaper is illustrated in Figure 4.   In this construction the sliding block works in the center of the rather massive oscillating arm.   The crank is contained in the large gear and may be varied by a screw

Courtesy The Hendey Machine Company.

Fig. 4.   Quick-Return Drive Mechanism Used on a Hendey Horizontal Push-Cut Shaper.

mechanism.   The crank gear is driven by the transmission gears, as shown in the figure.   To change the position of the stroke, the clamp holding the connecting link to the screw is loosened, and the hand wheel at the end of the screw is turned.   As the screw is fastened to the ram, it can be moved backward or forward by turning this wheel.

Draw-cut shaper.   This shaper is so named, because the tool is pulled across the work by the ram instead of being pushed.   In Figure 5 is shown a machine of this type equipped with a small jib crane and hoist.   Horizontal draw-cut shapers are especially recommended for heavy cuts, being widely used for cutting large die blocks and machining large parts in railroad shops.   During the cut, the work is drawn against the adjustable back bearing or face of the column, thereby reducing the strains on the crossrails and saddle bearings.   There is

FIG. 5. 32-Inch High-Duty Draw-Cut Shaper.

little tendency for vibration, as a tensile strength is exerted in the ram during the cut. This permits the use of large forming tools without resulting tool chatter marks on the work.

Hydraulic shaper. The hydraulic shaper is similar in appearance to those driven by some form of mechanism, as may be noted in Figure 6. One of the principal advantages claimed for this type of shaper is that the cutting speed and pressure in the ram drive are constant from beginning to end of the cut. Both the cutting-stroke length and its position relative to the work may be changed quickly without stopping the machine, by the use of two small handles at the side of the ram. Another feature is that the ram movement can be

Courtesy Rockford Machine Tool Company.

Fig. 6. Hydraulic Shaper, 16-to-28-Inch Stroke.

reversed instantly anywhere in either direction of travel. The hydraulic controlled feed is accomplished while the tool is clear of the work. The maximum ratio of cutting stroke to return stroke is about 2 to 1.

Vertical Shapers

Vertical shapers or *slotters* (see Figure 7) are used principally for internal cutting and planing at angles, and for operations that require vertical cuts because of the position in which the work must be held. Operations of this nature are frequently found on die work, metal molds, and metal patterns. The shaper ram operates vertically and has the usual quick-return feature like the horizontal-type machines.

FIG. 7*A*. Vertical Shaper Setup for Cutting Spline in Flange.

Courtesy Pratt & Whitney—Division Niles-Bement-Pond Company.

FIG. 7*B*. 6-Inch Vertical Shaper.

Work to be machined is supported on a round table having a rotary feed in addition to the usual table movements. The circular table feed permits the machining of curved surfaces, which is particularly desirable for many irregular parts that cannot be turned on a lathe. Plane surfaces are cut by using either of the table cross-feeds. An interesting special machine, known as a universal vertical miller-shaper, has been developed for machining irregular punch and die shapes and other parts requiring both milling and shaping operations.

A special type of vertical shaper known as a *keyseater* is especially designed for cutting keyways in gears, pulleys, flywheels, and similar parts. The work is clamped to a horizontal table, and the tool is reciprocated in a vertical position through its center. The work is fed to the cutter by table adjustments.

Courtesy G. A. Gray Company.

FIG. 8. Planing a Machine Table on a Double-Housing Planer.

The Planer and Its Work

A *planer* is a machine tool designed to remove metal by moving the work in a straight line against a single-edged cutting tool. The type of work it does is very similar to that done on a shaper except that a planer is adapted to much larger work (illustrated in Figure 8) in the planing of the ways on a large machine table. The cuts are all plain surfaces, but they may be horizontal, vertical, or at an angle. In addition to machining large work, this planer is frequently used in production work to machine multiple small parts held in line on the platen.

Differences between planer and shaper. Although both the planer and shaper are adapted to the machining of flat surfaces, there is not much overlapping in their fields of usefulness; they differ widely in construction and in method of operation. When the two machines are compared in construction, operation, and use, the following differences may be seen:

1. The planer is specially adapted to large work; the shaper can do only small work.

2. On the planer the work is moved against a stationary tool; on the shaper the tool moves across the work, which is stationary.

3. On the planer the tool is fed into the work; on the shaper the work is usually fed across the tool.

4. The drive on the planer table is either by gears or by hydraulic means. The shaper ram can also be driven in this manner, but in most cases a quick-return link mechanism is used.

5. Most planers differ from shapers in that they approach constant-velocity cuts.

Planer and shaper size. The usual method of designating the size of planers and shapers is as follows:

Shaper—Maximum length of work that can be machined (inches).
Vertical shaper or slotter—Maximum length of stroke × diameter of work table (dimensions in inches).
Planer—Width of table (inches) × distance from table to rail (inches) × length of table (feet).

Classification of planers. Planers may be classified in a number of ways, but according to general construction there are four types:

1. Double-housing planer (Figure 8).
2. Open-side planer (Figure 10).
3. Pit-type planer (Figure 11).
4. Edge or plate planer (Figure 12).

Planer drive. Each of the above types may vary, according to the method of drive. In such a classification there are gear drive (both spur gear and spiral), hydraulic drive, screw drive, belt drive, variable-speed motor drive, and crank drive. The first two mentioned are the types most generally used. The screw drive is employed principally on plate planers, whereas the crank drive is found only on some small planers. Variable-speed-reversing motors, controlled by stops at each end of the stroke, are used on some planers.

Hydraulic drives have proved most satisfactory for planers for several reasons. First, uniform cutting speed is attained throughout the entire cutting stroke. The acceleration and deceleration of the table take place in such a short distance of travel that they need not be considered as a time element. A second advantage is that the inertia forces to be overcome are less in a hydraulic planer than in the conventional gear-driven planer. The gear-driven planer, with its fast-revolving parts, including the rotor of the drive motor, has several times more inertia force to overcome than the simple piston rod and piston of the hydraulic drive. Overcoming inertia consumes energy, and, with rapid short strokes, the difference in power consumption is noticeable. Further advantages of hydraulic drives are uniform cutting pressure, quick table reversal, rapid means of varying the stroke, and less noise in operation.

Double-housing planer. This type of planer consists of a long heavy base on which the table or platen is reciprocated. At the side of the base near the center is located the upright housing. This supports the crossrail upon which the tools are fed across the work. Figure 8, a double-housing planer, illustrates clearly how the tools are supported and the manner in which they can be adjusted for angle cuts. These tools may be fed manually or by power in either a vertical or a crosswise direction. The motor drive is usually at one side or the planer near the center, and the drive mechanism is located under the platen.

The accuracy of a planer is determined largely by its rigidity and the manner in which the ways in the bed are machined. Most medium-sized planers have one flat and one double-V way which allow for unequal bed and platen expansions. Large planers having three ways will have a double-V way at the center and flat ways at each side. The controls for operation are all at the upright housing. Adjustable dogs at the side of the bed control the stroke length of the platen.

Large planers, as shown in Figure 9, are available for handling heavy and massive machine work. Planers of this type are similar to other planers and differ principally in size. On the machine shown there are four tool supports, two located on the upper crossrails and two on the side housings.

Open-side planer. A variation in housing construction is shown in Figure 10. This type, having the housing on one side only, is known as an *open-side* planer and is adapted to handle wide work. A jib crane and electric hoist are frequently provided with planers for handling the work where they are not served by a traveling crane. The planer shown in the figure is hydraulically driven.

Courtesy William Sellers & Company.

Fig. 9. Large Heavy-Duty Planer.

Both double-housing and open-side planers can be equipped with duplicating attachments for machining irregular surfaces. To do this it is necessary that a master form be mounted on one side of the table

Courtesy Rockford Machine Tool Company.

FIG. 10. Open-Side Planer.

Courtesy Mesta Machine Company.

FIG. 11. Pit-Type Planer.

so that, as the tracer moves over the surface, the cutting tool is moved accordingly. Such devices are usually hydraulically operated and are similar in operation to the duplicating units used on other machine tools.

Pit-type planer. A pit-type planer is massive in construction and differs from an ordinary planer in that the bed is stationary and the

Courtesy Consolidated Machine Tool Corporation, William Sellers & Company Division.

FIG. 12. Plate or Edge Planer.

tool is moved over the work. Figure 11 shows such a planer designed for work up to 14 feet in width and 35 feet in length. Two ram-type heads are mounted on the crossrail, and each is furnished with double clapper block tool holders for two-way planing. The two reversing housings, which support the crossrail, slide on ways and are screw-driven from an enclosed worm drive at one end of the bed. All feeds are automatic and reversible and are designed to operate either at both ends of the planing stroke or at one end only.

Plate or edge planer. For the fabrication of heavy steel plates for pressure vessels and armor plate, a special type of planer, known as a *plate* or *edge planer,* has been devised. Such a planer is shown in Figure 12. The plate is stationary and is clamped to a large bed on one

side of the housing.   To further insure having the work securely held,
a series of clamps come down from the cross housing and hold the plate
edge in place.   The cutting tool is attached to a carriage which is supported on the heavy ways of the planer.   A large screw drive is used

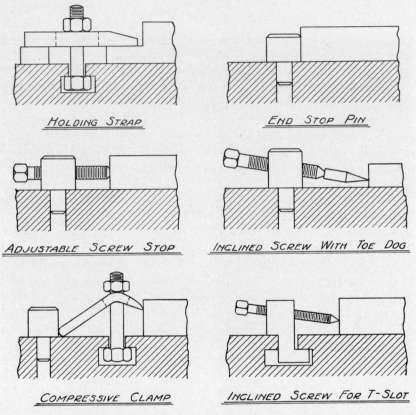

HOLDING STRAP   END STOP PIN

ADJUSTABLE SCREW STOP   INCLINED SCREW WITH TOE DOG

COMPRESSIVE CLAMP   INCLINED SCREW FOR T-SLOT

FIG. 13.   Methods of Holding Work on Planer Table.

for moving the carriage carrying the operator and tools along the work.
The size of the plates that can be edge-machined is limited by the width
and height of the machine opening.   However, there is no limit to the
length the plate may extend behind the machine.

Tools and Work-Holding Devices

The tools used in shaper and planer work are of the same general
type as those used on a lathe, but heavier in construction.   Some forged
tools are used, but generally tool holders with removable bits are more
satisfactory, as heavy tools are required on the large machines.   The

holder should be designed to hold the bit near the center line of the holder or the pivot point rather than at an angle as is customary with lathe tool holders. With the tip of the tool back, there is less tendency for it to dig into the metal and cause chatter.

On the shapers and small planers high-speed steel tools have wide use, as the cutting speeds are generally suitable for this type of material. In planer work, where heavier cuts are required, the carbide tool is more popular. However, caution must be exercised in using carbide tools on machines not equipped with an automatic lifting device for the tool on the return stroke. If the tool is permitted to rub the work, the cutting edge is very apt to be chipped.

Planer and shaper tools are ground with about the same cutting, rake, and clearance angles, but they vary somewhat in shape according to the way they are to be held. A tool ground with straight cutting edges and a small corner radius is preferred for most general-purpose work.

Work tables on planers and shapers are constructed with T slots on their surfaces to provide means for holding and clamping down parts that are to be machined. On large machines it is very important that work be securely held because of the heavy cuts that are taken. A heavy-duty vise held by bolts engaging T slots in the work table is suitable for small objects and is the usual method of holding work on a shaper. On planers most work is held by clamping directly to the platen, and a wide variety of clamps, stop pins, and holding devices have been developed for this purpose, as shown in Figure 13. Note that several of these arrangements are adapted to holding down plates so that the entire surface may be machined.

Review Questions

1. What type of work can be done on a shaper?
2. Show by sketch how the quick-return motion is accomplished on a shaper.
3. If a shaper makes 36 complete strokes a minute and the length of stroke is 9 inches, what is the cutting speed in feet per minute? The ratio of return stroke to cutting stroke is 2 to 3.
4. For what type of work is a draw-cut shaper used?
5. What advantages are claimed for hydraulic drives on shapers and planers?
6. What kind of work is done on a vertical shaper?
7. How does a planer differ from a shaper?
8. List the various types of metal planers.
9. What is the main feature of an open-side planer, and why is it so constructed?
10. How is the quick-return motion on a planer accomplished?
11. Describe the operation of a pit-type planer.
12. What is a plate planer, and how does it operate?

13. What kind of cutting tools are used on shapers and planers?
14. How is the cutting tool supported on a planer?
15. How is the work held on a planer bed?

References

BOLZ, R. W., *Production Process,* Vol. 1, Penton Publishing Company, 1949.
MURPHY, J. J., "The Shaper as a Manufacturing Tool," *Machinery,* June 1949.
Tool Engineers Handbook, American Society of Tool Engineers, McGraw-Hill Book Company, 1949.

DRILLING AND BORING MACHINES

One of the simplest machine tools used in production and toolroom work is the ordinary *drill press*. It consists of a spindle which imparts rotary motion to the drilling tool, a mechanism for feeding the tool into the work, a table on which the work rests, and a frame. It is essentially a single-purpose machine, although a number of similar machine operations can be performed with the addition of appropriate tools.

The operation of *drilling* consists of producing a hole in an object by forcing a rotating drill against it. The same results are accomplished in some machines by holding the drill stationary and rotating the work: An example of this is drilling on a lathe with the work held and rotated by the chuck.

Other methods of producing a hole are by punching, flame cutting, and coring. The punching process is very rapid and specially adapted to thin materials. It produces accurate holes, but the punches and dies are expensive. Oxyacetylene cutting or the oxygen lance will cut holes through any thickness of commercial material, but these holes are not accurate in either size or shape. Coring is used principally on large holes in castings to save metal and reduce machining costs.

Boring is the operation of enlarging a hole that has already been drilled or cored; it is principally an operation of truing a hole that has previously been drilled. A single-point lathe-type tool is used. To perform this operation on a drill press requires a special holder for the boring tool.

Counterboring refers to enlarging one end of a drilled hole. The enlarged hole, which is concentric with the original one, is flat on the bottom. The tool for this operation is similar to an end mill and is provided with a pilot pin which fits into the drilled hole to center the cutting edges. Counterboring is used principally to set bolt heads and nuts below the surface. When it is required to finish off a small surface around a drilled hole, the operation is known as *spot facing*. This is a customary practice on rough surfaces to provide smooth seats for bolt heads. If the top of a drilled hole is beveled to accommodate the conical seat of a flat-head screw, the operation is called *counter-sinking*.

Reaming is the operation of enlarging a machined hole to accurate size with a smooth finish. A reamer is an accurate tool and is not designed to remove much metal; hence, the allowance for reaming should not exceed 0.015 inch. Although this operation and those previously mentioned can be done on a drill press, other machine tools are equally well adapted to perform them.

Classification of Drilling Machines

Drilling machines are classified according to their general construction:

1. Portable drill.

5. Gang drilling machine.

2. Sensitive drilling machine
   (*a*) Bench mounting.
   (*b*) Floor mounting.

6. Multiple-spindle drilling machine
   (*a*) Single unit.
   (*b*) Way-type.

3. Upright drilling machine
   (*a*) Light duty.
   (*b*) Heavy duty.

7. Automatic-production drilling machine
   (*a*) Indexing table.
   (*b*) Transfer type.

4. Radial drilling machine
   (*a*) Plain.
   (*b*) Semiuniversal.
   (*c*) Universal.

8. Deep-hole drilling machine
   (*a*) Vertical.
   (*b*) Horizontal.

These drilling machines vary considerably in size, method of feeding the drills, and application of power.

Portable and sensitive drills. Portable drills are small compact drilling machines used principally for such drilling operations as cannot be conveniently done on a regular drill press. The simplest of these is the hand-operated drill. Most portable drills, however, are equipped with small electric motors. These drills operate at fairly high speeds and accommodate drills up to ½ inch in diameter. Similar drills, using compressed air as a means of power, are used in cases where sparks from the motor may constitute a fire hazard.

The *sensitive* drilling machine is a small high-speed machine of simple construction similar to the ordinary upright drill press. It consists of an upright standard, a horizontal table, and a vertical spindle for holding and rotating the drill. Machines of this type are hand-fed, usually by means of a rack and pinion drive on the sleeve holding the rotating spindle. These drills may be driven directly by a motor, by a belt, or by means of a friction disk. The friction-disk drive has considerable speed regulation, although it is not suitable for slow speeds and heavy cuts. Sensitive drill presses are suitable only for light work and are seldom capable of rotating drills over ⅝ inch in diameter.

Upright drills. *Upright* drills are similar to sensitive drills except that they have power-feeding mechanisms for the rotating drills and are designed for heavier work. Figure 1 shows a 21-inch machine with a box-type upright. A box-column machine is more rigid than a round-column machine and consequently is adapted to heavier work. This machine is provided with nine spindle speeds offered in several speed ranges from 75 to 3500 rpm. Feed rates of 0.004, 0.008, 0.014, and 0.020 inch per revolution are controlled by a single feed lever. The feed clutch is automatically controlled so that the spindle will be disengaged when it reaches its upper or lower limit of travel. It also can be set to disengage at any predetermined depth if the feed trip dial on the left of the sliding head is set. This machine can be used for tapping as well as for drilling.

Radial drilling machine. The *radial* drilling machine is designed to be used for large work where it is not feasible for the work to be moved around if several holes are to be drilled. Such a machine is shown in Figure 2. It consists of a vertical column supporting an arm

Courtesy Cincinnati Bickford Tool Company.

Fig. 1. 21-Inch Upright Drill.

which carries the drilling head. The arm may be swung around to any desired position over the work bed, and the drilling head has a radial adjustment along this arm. These adjustments permit the operator to locate the drill quickly over any desired point on the work. *Plain* machines of this type will drill only in the vertical plane. On *semi-universal* machines the head may be swiveled on the arm to drill holes at various angles in a vertical plane. *Universal* machines have an additional swiveling adjustment in either the head or the arm and can drill holes at any angle.

The machine illustrated has 32 spindle speeds in geometrical progression, ranging from 20 to 1600 rpm. Sixteen selective power feeds

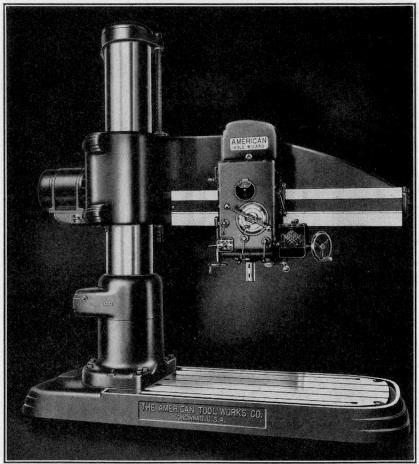

Courtesy The American Tool Works Company.

Fig. 2. Radial Drilling Machine.

from 0.003 to 0.087 inch per revolution are available, and the machine is also equipped with a tapping attachment. There is an elevating mechanism for raising the arm as well as a rapid traversing means for moving the drilling head.

Gang drilling machine. When several drilling spindles are mounted on a single table, it is known as a *gang drill*. There are two types: those with spindle units permanently spaced along the table, and those with an adjusting feature permitting the spindles to be spaced at various distances. The first and most common type is adapted to production work where several operations must be performed. The work is usually held in a jig which can be easily slid

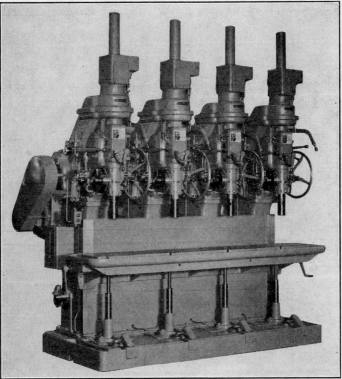

Courtesy Barnes Drill Company.

FIG. 3. Four-Spindle Gang Drilling Machine.

on the table from one spindle to the next. If several operations must be performed, such as drilling two different-sized holes and reaming them, four spindles are set up for this purpose. With automatic feed control, two or more of these operations may be going on simultaneously, attended by only one operator. The arrangement is similar to operating several independent drill presses, but much more convenient because of its compactness. A four-spindle machine of this type is shown in Figure 3. This machine has separate motors for each spindle and is equipped with power feed and lead-screw tapping arrangement.

When the job demands that several holes be drilled in line on a long piece, it is necessary to have spindle units that can be adjusted to give the desired hole spacing. Machines of this type are used for any straight-line multiple-hole drilling applications, as in pipes, channels, castings, angles, and plates.

Courtesy Moline Tool Company.

Fɪɢ. 4. Hydraulic Feed Driller with 16 Universal Joint-Type Spindles and a 30-Inch-Diameter Drilling Area.

Multiple-spindle drilling machine. *Multiple-spindle* drilling machines have been developed for the purpose of drilling several holes simultaneously. These machines are essentially production machines and, when once set up, will drill many parts with such accuracy that all parts are interchangeable. In some applications drilling jigs are unnecessary, but in most cases a plate provided with hardened bushings is essential to guide the drills accurately into the work. Multispindle drilling machines differ principally in the way the drills are held and in the way the feed is accomplished.

Most machines are vertical machines, as shown in Figure 4. This machine is provided with a maximum of 16 drill spindles covering an area 30 inches in diameter. Each lower drill spindle is driven from the upper drill spindle through two universal joints and a tubular driving shaft, the tube being splined at the upper end to permit

Courtesy Barnes Drill Company.

FIG. 5. Special Unit for Drilling, Chamfering, and Tapping Operations, Consisting of Three Vertical Production Drilling Machines with Indexing Table.

maximum adjustment of the drill. The head assembly carrying the spindles is mounted on a carriage which travels on vertical double-V ways. The feed is hydraulically operated, and this is accomplished by feeding the head assembly with the drills to the work. In operation, the drilling cycle consists of rapid advance of drills to the work, proper feed, and rapid return of drills to the starting position. The approximate capacity of this machine is sixteen $\frac{7}{8}$-inch holes in soft steel.

Multiple drilling machines frequently use a table feed in place of the one just described, thus eliminating the movement of the heavy geared-head mechanism which rotates the drills. This may be done in several ways: by rack and pinion drive, by lead screw, or by a rotating plate cam. The last method is well adapted to provide varying motions which give rapid approach, uniform feed, and quick return to the starting position.

Courtesy Baker Bros.

FIG. 6. Vertical Hydraulic Drilling Machine Equipped with Indexing Table and Two Horizontal Way-Type Units.

A special 3-unit vertical machine with a 4-station indexing table is shown in Figure 5. This machine is arranged to hold two clutch housing castings in each station, and at successive stations the parts are drilled, chamfered, spot-faced, and tapped. Indexing is automatic from the start of the cycle until its completion. This unit is made up of three standard hydraulic production machines with the specially provided indexing table. Reaming, facing, and, in some cases, milling operations can be performed on these machines in addition to those operations mentioned above.

Way-type semiautomatic drilling machines are used extensively in production work. These are usually two-, three-, or four-way drilling machines designed principally for single-purpose jobs. Engine block castings and similar parts, requiring the drilling of many holes, are typical examples of the work done on these machines. A large three-way drilling machine of this type is illustrated in Figure 6. The drilling machine in this figure is an example of building up a multiple drilling machine by utilizing a standard heavy-duty vertical machine and two horizontal way-type units. The vertical drill is hydraulically operated and can be used either with a single drill up to 3 inches or with a multiple-spindle head operating several smaller drills. The two horizontal way-type machines are each equipped with portable hydraulic feed units. This special machine is used for production jobs requiring holes on three sides; however, if used with an indexing table, other type jobs are possible.

Automatic-transfer processing machine. Automatic-transfer processing machines are designed to complete a series of machining operations at successive stations, and to transfer the work automatically from one station to the next. They are, in effect, a production line of connected machines which are synchronized in their operation so that the work piece, after being loaded at the first station, progresses automatically and without manual handling through the various stations to its completion. Although most of the operations performed at the various stations are of the type done on a drilling machine, milling operations can also be included.

In Figure 7 is shown a 15-station unit for processing automobile cylinder heads. In this case the cycle time of 37.2 seconds is based on the time consumed by the longest series of operations performed at one of the stations and includes the time for transfer and for clamping and unclamping the work, as well as the time for tool movements and operation. Some 96 holes are processed at the various stations, and at one a milling operation is performed. Provision is made at the fourth and eighth station for a 360-degree turnover fixture for dumping chips; parts may also be removed at these stations if necessary. The production rate for the machine is 77 pieces per hour when it is operating at a normal efficiency of 80%.

Automatic-transfer machines range from comparatively small units having only two or three stations to long straight-line machines with as many as 80 stations. They have been used primarily in the automobile industry where, by high production schedules, it is possible to offset their high initial cost by savings in labor. Products processed by these machines include cylinder blocks, cylinder heads, refrigeration compressor bodies, axle housings, and similar parts.

Courtesy Greenlee Bros. & Company.

FIG. 7. 15-Station Automatic-Transfer Machine for Processing Automobile Cylinder Heads.

Deep-hole drilling machine. Several problems not encountered in ordinary drilling operations arise in the drilling of long holes in rifle barrels, long spindles, connecting rods, certain oil-well drilling equipment, and many other similar applications. As the hole length increases, it becomes more and more difficult to support the work and the drill properly. The rapid removal of chips from the drilling operation becomes necessary to insure the proper operation and accuracy of the drill. Rotational speeds and feeds must be carefully determined, since there is greater possibility of deflection than when a drill of ordinary size is used.

To overcome these problems, deep-hole drilling machines have been developed which are especially adapted to this type of machine work. In design these machines may be of either the horizontal or the vertical type; they may be of single-spindle or multispindle construction; and they may vary as to whether the work or the drill is caused to revolve.

In Figure 8 is illustrated a two-spindle machine of the horizontal type. The work is supported at one end in the headstock and on the other end by the work carriage at the center of the machine. Rotation is given to the work from the headstock spindles. The work carriage supports the drills by means of hardened bushings at a point just

Courtesy Pratt & Whitney.

FIG. 8. Two-Spindle Horizontal Deep-Hole Drilling Machine.

adjacent to where they enter the work. The other end of the drill is supported by the drill carriage at the right, and, if necessary, center supports are also used. The feeding of the drill is obtained from the lead screw which forces it slowly into the rotating work. The drill feed must be very light to avoid deflecting the drill.

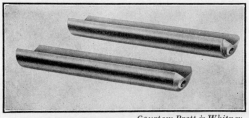

Courtesy Pratt & Whitney.

FIG. 9. Single-Fluted Drills for Deep-Hole Drilling.

Kinds of Drills

A typical drill used with deep-hole drilling machines is shown in Figure 9. This drill has only a single cutting edge. In the lip of the drill is a hole to carry the oil to the drill point. The chips are carried out of the hole along the flute of the drill as rapidly as they are formed. Twisted drills with oil holes and two flutes are also available for this type of drilling. In most cases the drill is held stationary to facilitate pumping the oil through the drill. Holes drilled in these machines are accurate and concentric with the diameter. Additional finish may be given by special reamers or broaching tools.

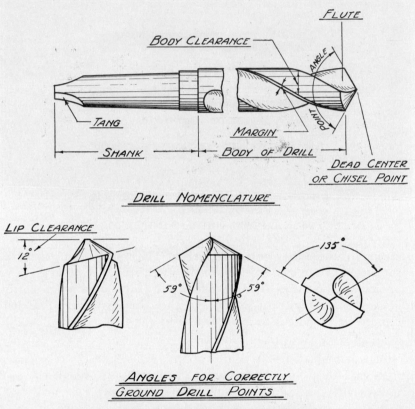

FIG. 10. Twist-Drill Nomenclature and Angles.

The most common type of drill used is the *twist drill,* having two flutes and cutting edges. In Figure 10 the nomenclature of this drill, as well as the usual point, clearance, and end angles, is shown. The drill is held and properly centered in the socket of the drilling-machine spindle by means of the *tapered shank.* This has a Morse Taper of approximately 5⁄8 inch per foot, which is standard for drills, reamers, and other similar tools. The *tang* at the end of the taper fits into a slot in the socket to prevent slipping of the tapered surface. Straight-shank drills are held and properly centered in a drill chuck.

These drills are cheaper than those having a tapered shank; and such construction is common for small drills.

A number of different kinds of drills is shown in Figure 11, the principal variation among them being the number and angle of the flutes. Straight-fluted drills have several special applications, one of them being the drilling of soft metals where there is a tendency for a regular drill to "dig in." These are successful, because there is no

Taper Square Shank

Taper Shank Twist Drill

Three-Groove Drill

Straight Shank Twist Drill

Drill for Molded Plastics

Courtesy National Twist Drill and Tool Company.

Fig. 11. Types of Drills.

rake angle to the cutting edge. Similar drills of this type are used in drilling brick or tile and also in deep-hole drilling. Two-fluted drills with either interior or exterior oil channels are frequently used on turret-lathe-production drilling. Three-fluted drills are used principally for enlarging holes previously punched, drilled, or cored. Various drills with different flute angles have been developed to give improved drilling to special materials and alloys. In addition, some drills are made in combination with other tools, as, for example, the combination drill and tap or the drill and countersink.

For drilling large-size holes in pipe or sheet metal twist drills are not suitable. The cut is too large, or the drill tends to dig into the work, or the hole is too large to be cut by a standard-size drill. Round holes are easily cut in thin metal by means of a hole cutter, as shown in Figure 12. *Saw-type* cutters of this design can be obtained for a wide range of sizes. When in use they are mounted in a drill press.

For very large holes in thin metal a cutter known as a *fly cutter* is used. Such a cutter, shown in Figure 13, consists of tool bits held in a horizontal holder and capable of being adjusted to accommodate a wide range of diameters. Both cutters cut in the same path, but one is set slightly below the other.

Courtesy Armstrong-Blum Manufacturing Company.

FIG. 12. Cutter for Making Round Holes in Thin Metal.

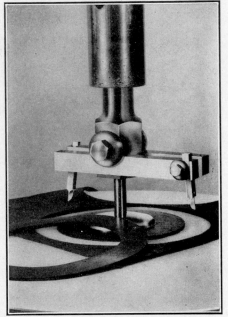

Courtesy Robert H. Clark Company.

FIG. 13. Cutting with a Fly Cutter.

A drill developed by the Black Drill Company is designed for hardened steel. The drill operates at high speed and develops sufficient friction to anneal the steel and permit cutting without softening the drill point. This drill has a triangular section with three flutes, although for counterboring work a flat end can be used. The point angle for best results is 130 degrees. Drills of this type are used for carburized stock, spring steel, die sections, knives, and similar hard materials.

Drill Performance

To obtain good service from a drill, it must be properly ground. The point angle should be correct for the material that is to be drilled:

for steel, aluminum, brass, and most materials, 118 degrees has proved very satisfactory; for plastics, this angle should be reduced to 90 degrees or under; whereas some of the harder steel alloys use angles greater than 118 degrees. In grinding this angle, care must be exercised to get the lips the same length as well as to have the angle the same on each side of the drill center line. The clearance angle (see Figure 10) should be 12 degrees.

The *cutting speed,* expressed in feet per minute, is a measure of the peripheral speed of the drill. For high-speed drills on ordinary steels this value is about 110 feet per minute. Cutting speeds vary from 20 to 250 feet per minute, depending on the material hardness. Carbon-steel drills should be operated at about one-half the speeds recommended for high-speed steel drills.

To obtain best performance and long life for the cutting edges, some coolant should be used. A few of the suggested coolants are listed below:*

Aluminum—⅔ lard oil, ⅓ kerosene.
Brass—⅔ lard oil, ⅓ kerosene.
Bronze—Soluble oil.
Copper—Soluble oil.
Cast iron—Dry.
Glass—Kerosene.
Magnesium—Dry.
Malleable iron—Soluble oil.
Steel—Soluble oil.
Tool steel—Lard or soluble oil.

Drill performance is also affected by the helix angle of the flutes. Although this angle may vary from 0 to 45 degrees, the usual standard for steel and most materials is 30 degrees. The smaller this angle is made, the greater is the torque necessary to operate a given feed. As the angle is increased appreciably, the life of the cutting edge is reduced. Some materials are drilled more efficiently by drills with special helix angles. For example, an angle of 45 degrees works very satisfactorily for zinc alloys and aluminum, whereas a 20-degree angle is recommended for Bakelite.

In evaluating drill performance, the material of which the drill is made must not be overlooked. It has been previously stated that high-speed steel tools (18-4-1 type) will stand about twice the cutting speed of carbon-tool steel. For hard and extremely abrasive materials, drills tipped with tungsten carbide give excellent service. Stellite and other nonferrous hard-surfacing alloys are also being used for similar difficult materials. Many drills are now chrome-plated to provide a hard wearing surface.

Drill feeds are expressed in inches per revolution. In making the proper selection, the cutting speed of the metal being worked on and

* From *Tool Engineers Handbook,* American Society of Tool Engineers, McGraw-Hill Book Company.

the drill material must both be taken into consideration. Feeds for high-speed drills below 1 inch usually range from 0.0025 to 0.012 inch per revolution; however, reference should be made to feed tables in handbooks dealing with the subject for the proper feeds and speeds to use for various situations.

Procedure for Producing Accurate Holes

Drilling accuracy depends to a large extent on the proper grinding of the drill point. Slight variations in the angles and lip lengths

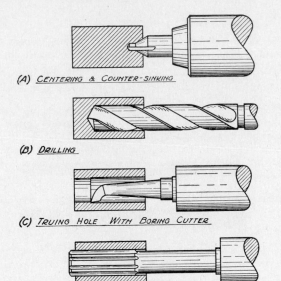

(A) *CENTERING & COUNTER-SINKING*

(B) *DRILLING*

(C) *TRUING HOLE WITH BORING CUTTER*

(D) *FINAL SIZING WITH REAMER*

Fig. 14. Procedure for Producing Accurate Holes.

cause the hole to be oversize or off center. Because of the bluntness of the drill point, it is difficult to start a drill properly or accurately without a centering hole. Furthermore, when finish and accuracy in size are paramount, a drilled hole is not suitable. To eliminate these difficulties, it is frequently necessary to employ several operations to produce an accurate hole. Figure 14 illustrates the procedure recommended. Four steps are involved: locating and centering the hole, the actual drilling, truing the hole with a boring tool, and reaming the hole to accurate size. This is common practice for producing accurate holes on lathes and milling machines as well as on drill presses. If drilling jigs are used, the centering and boring operation may be omitted.

Reamers and Miscellaneous Tools

A *reamer* is a tool used to finish a hole previously drilled or bored. The material removed by this process should be around 0.015 inch and for very accurate work should not exceed 0.005 inch. Because of the small stock removed by this process, reamed holes are perfectly round and have a smooth surface. Any tolerance is above the nominal size. In some cases it is desirable to have the hole a fraction of a thousandth oversize in order to produce certain fits.

A number of types of reamers are available for different materials and applications. They are:

1. Hand reamer.
2. Chucking reamer.
3. Shell reamer.
4. Taper reamer.

5. Expansion reamer.
6. Adjustable reamer.
7. Special-purpose reamer.

Illustrations of several types of reamers are shown in Figure 15. The *hand reamer* is a finishing tool for very accurate holes. Only a few thousandths of an inch of metal should be removed. It is slightly

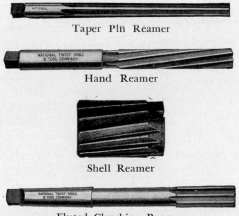

Taper Pin Reamer

Hand Reamer

Shell Reamer

Fluted Chucking Reamer

Courtesy National Twist Drill and Tool Company.

Fig. 15. Types of Reamers.

tapered at the end to facilitate starting and has very little clearance on the flutes. This type, as well as most of the others, is made with both straight and spiral flutes. *Chucking reamers* are designed to be power-driven at slow speeds and are made in two general types: rose and fluted reamers. *Rose reamers* do all their cutting on the beveled end. There is no relief on the lands of the flutes, and they have a very slight taper toward the shank to prevent binding. *Chucking fluted reamers* do their cutting on the straight flutes, which are backed off or relieved the entire length. Both these reamers are made with

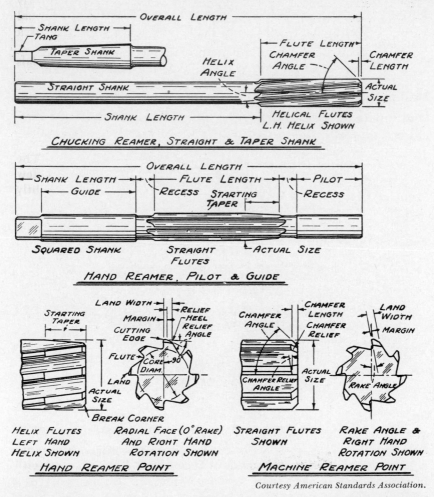

Courtesy American Standards Association.

FIG. 16. Sketch Illustrating Terms Applying to Reamers, American Standard B5.14–1941.

straight or taper shanks. A reamer, when set up on a machine, should be "floating" so as to center itself properly with the hole. *Shell reamers* are made in both types. A shell reamer consists of a shell end mounted on an arbor. This construction results in an economy where high-priced alloys are used, since the arbor can be salvaged when the reamer is worn out. *Expansion reamers* are those reamers that can be adjusted either to compensate for wear or purposely to ream oversized holes. *Adjustable reamers* differ from them in that they can be manipulated to take care of a considerable range in sizes. *Taper* and other special-purpose reamers are similar to those described, except that they are shaped for some special job. The sketches shown in Figure 16 illustrate terms applying to reamers as proposed by the American Standards Association.

Drilling Jigs

In production work, where many parts are to be drilled and interchangeability is desired, it is essential to provide means for quickly

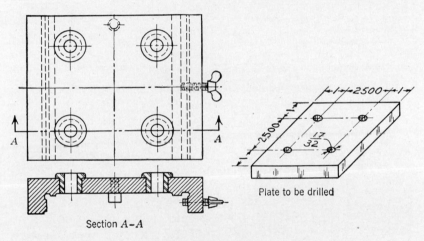

Section *A-A*

Fig. 17. Plate Drilling Jig.

and accurately locating the drill with reference to the work. This is accomplished by building a *jig* which holds the part and guides the cutting tool to the proper location. Such a device is a good example of the transfer of skill from a mechanic to an accessory part of a machine, thus permitting the operation to be accurately accomplished by an unskilled operator. This is well illustrated in the drilling of four holes in a plate by using a plate or channel jig similar to the one shown in Figure 17. The jig is made with hardened steel bushings which accurately locate the positions of the four holes. Any number of plates may be clamped in this jig, and each part will be identical with the other.

Jigs all perform the same function but differ widely in appearance according to the shape and design of the part to be worked on. Their classification is based on their general appearance and construction. In Figure 18 is shown a box-type jig with open sides arranged for

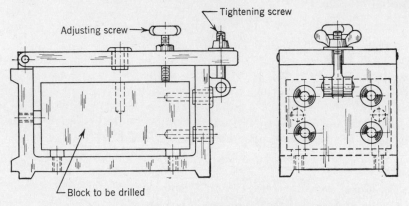

FIG. 18.   Box-Type Jig for Drilling Two Sides of a Block.

drilling two sides of a block.   Figure 19 illustrates a table-type jig for drilling four holes in a flange.   Other types in general use include templet, open, indexing, diameter, and universal.

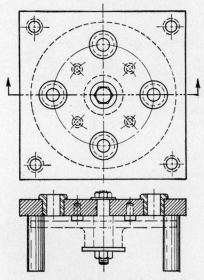

FIG. 19.   Table-Type Jig for Drilling Flange Holes.

An important consideration in the design of any jig is to provide quick and easy loading and unloading so that the operator will not lose much time in these operations. Likewise clamping devices must be positive, and the design should be such that there is no question about the proper location of the part in the jig. Clearance is usually provided under drill bushings to allow chips to escape without having to go through them. This is important if much metal is to be removed. In addition, provision should be made for rapid cleaning of chips from the jig. Most jigs made utilize the many standard parts that are available for their construction. Such standardized parts include drill bushings, thumb screws, knobs, rest buttons, toggle clamps, springs, jig bodies, and numerous other parts. Jigs are not limited to drilling operations but are also used on tapping, counterboring, and reaming operations.

Boring Machines

Several machines have been developed that are especially adapted to boring work. One of them, known as a *jig borer,* is constructed for precision work on jigs and fixtures. This machine, which is similar in appearance to a drill press, will do both drilling and end-milling work in addition to boring. Two other machines, the *vertical boring mill* and the *horizontal boring machine,* are adapted to large work. Although the operations that these machines perform can be done on lathes and other machines, their construction is justified by the ease and economy obtained in holding and machining the work.

Jig boring machine. In Figure 20 is shown a machine designed for locating and boring holes in jigs, fixtures, dies, gages, and other precision parts. Machines of this type consist of a rigid frame, a fixed precision spindle for holding the various tools, and a movable table provided with accurate measuring devices upon which the work rests. On the machine shown in the figure table measurements are made by precision end measures, each slide being equipped with one of these devices. Even inches are measured with solid end measures graduated in inches and fractions by an inside micrometer. At the end of the device is a dial indicator which acts as a pressure gage and maintains the zero reading with constant pressure. This means of measuring permits readings to an accuracy of 0.0001 inch. Another method of measuring used on some jig boring machines is by means of micrometer lead screws. This method is accurate for small machines and is advantageous in that the work is both moved and measured simultaneously. For long lead screws some sort of compensating device is necessary to take care of known screw inaccuracies.

A jig borer, to give best service, must be well equipped with proper small tools and accessories. The time in boring holes is so short that setting up is often the longest part of the job. Much time can be saved by using spotters or locating tools, reamer drills, and end reamers with the same-size straight shank. These tools can be held in a collet and quickly changed. Additional tools and accessories should include boring bits, adjustable boring chucks, rotary table, collets for tools, and the necessary bolts and straps to hold the work.

Because of the speed and accuracy with which jig boring machines can perform, they are frequently used on short-run production jobs. Using this machine for such work eliminates the expense of a jig.

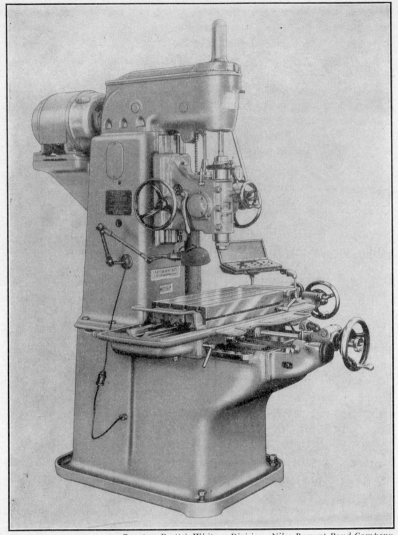

Courtesy Pratt & Whitney Division—Niles-Bement-Pond Company.

FIG. 20.   Precision Jig Borer.

Vertical boring mill.   The vertical boring mill is so named because the work rotates on a horizontal table in a fashion similar to the old potter's mill.*   The cutting tools are stationary, except for feed movements, and are mounted on the adjustable-height crossrail.   These

* See also discussion of vertical turret lathe in Chapter 15.

tools are of the lathe and planer type and are adapted to horizontal facing work, vertical turning, and boring.   This machine is sometimes called a rotary planer, and its cutting action on flat disks is identical

FIG. 21.   Vertical Boring Mill.

with that of a planer.   It may also be compared to a lathe placed in a vertical position with the rotating chuck or face plate horizontal.   The cutting action would be the same in turning the outside diameter of a large cylinder.   These machines, rated according to their table diameter, vary in size from 3 to 40 feet.   The large machine shown in Figure 21 is a typical example.

The vertical boring mill is able to hold large heavy parts, since the work can easily be placed on the table with a crane and does not require much bolting down to hold it in place. It also takes up very little floor space compared with other machines that might do the same work. Examples of the type of work machined on a vertical boring mill are large pulleys, grinding disks for glass plants, large

Courtesy Ex-Cell-O Corporation.

Fig. 22. Vertical Precision Boring Machine.

flange fittings, vertical housings for pumps and motors, flywheels, and numerous other circular-shaped parts. Very accurate work can be done on these machines because of their extreme rigidity and simplicity of design.

Cylinder boring machine. Boring machines, similar to the one shown in Figure 22, are specially constructed for precision boring of automobile cylinders, both straight and V type. These machines bore all cylinders simultaneously, and accurate alignment is maintained between all holes. Boring and facing connecting rods, boring valve holes, and other similar operations on crankcases and cylinder heads can also be done on this machine.

Horizontal Boring Machine

The horizontal boring machine differs from the vertical boring mill in that the work is stationary and the tool is revolved. Furthermore, it is adapted to the boring of horizontal holes, as can be seen by

Courtesy Defiance Machine Works.

FIG. 23. Horizontal Boring Machine.

reference to Figure 23. The horizontal spindle for holding the tool is supported in an assembly at one end which can be adjusted vertically within the limits of the machine. This movement and the rotary motion given the tool are the only movements the tool usually has. A work table having longitudinal and crosswise movements is supported on ways on the bed of the machine. In some cases the table is capable of being swiveled to permit indexing the work and boring holes at desired angles. At the other end of the machine is an upright to support the outer end of a boring bar when boring through holes in large castings. On some machines designed for work on extremely large parts, the parts are bolted to a large face plate permanently mounted on the floor. The upright carrying the boring spindle is then mounted on ways to provide means of crosswise adjustment with the work. The longitudinal feed of the rotating spindle is accomplished by having two spindles, one inside the other, the inside one having an independent traverse feed.

A smaller horizontal boring machine, specially designed for drilling and boring work on jigs, fixtures, and various machine parts, is shown

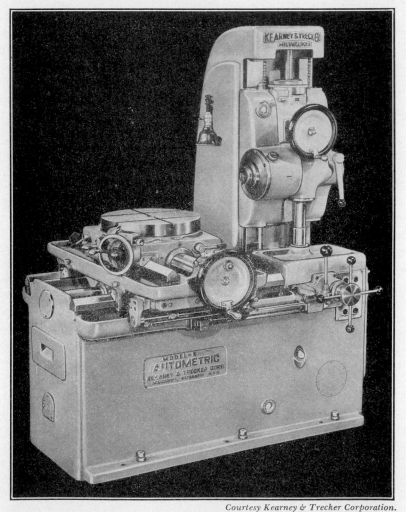

Courtesy Kearney & Trecker Corporation.

FIG. 24. Autometric Horizontal Precision Boring Machine.

in Figure 24. Work is mounted on an indexing table having both longitudinal and crosswise motions. This machine is capable of boring holes perpendicular or parallel to finished surfaces or parallel to a finished surface but at angles with one another.   The tool is held by the horizontal head mounted parallel to the top surface of the work table, and the machining operation is similar to boring or end-mill work on the ordinary knee-type milling machine. Micrometer dials are used for measurement, and movements of the table are accurate within a tolerance of 0.0001 inch in any 12 inches in length. The type of work done on this machine is very similar to that done on the jig borer. The machine is also adapted to production jobs requiring close accuracy.

Boring Tools

The process of boring is the enlarging of holes previously drilled or cored. Drilled holes are frequently bored to eliminate any possible eccentricity and to enlarge the hole to a reaming size. Boring tools may also be used to finish holes to correct size. This is frequently done on large holes or on odd-sized holes for which no reamer is available. Also, where the expense of core drills or reamers is great, a boring cutter may prove to be the economical tool to use.

The boring tool most commonly used is a single-pointed tool supported in a manner that permits its entry into a hole. A boring tool of this type is shown in Figure 25A. This tool is forged at the end and then ground to shape. It is supported in a separate holder which fits into a lathe tool post. For turret lathes slightly different holders and forged tools, similar to the one shown at B, are used. A modification of this tool is the boring bar shown at C, which is designed to hold a small high-speed steel tool bit at the end. The bar supporting the tool is rigid and may be adjusted according to the hole length. Although the clearance, rake, and cutting angles of these tools should be similar to those recommended for lathe work, these angles cannot be used if the holes are small. Greater end clearance is necessary, owing to the curvature of the hole surface, and back rake is almost impossible to attain because of the position of the tool. This may be seen by reference to the illustration showing the tool in working position. The side-rake and side-clearance angles have no restrictions placed on them and may be ground correctly. As the internal diameter is increased and large boring machines of the vertical and horizontal type are used, turning tools and holders of the lathe type are possible. Because of the decrease in surface curvature, properly shaped tools with correct angles can be used.

In production work boring cutters with multiple-cutting edges are widely used. These cutters, shown at F, somewhat resemble shell reamers in appearance, but are usually provided with inserted tooth cutters. The cutters may be adjusted radially to compensate for

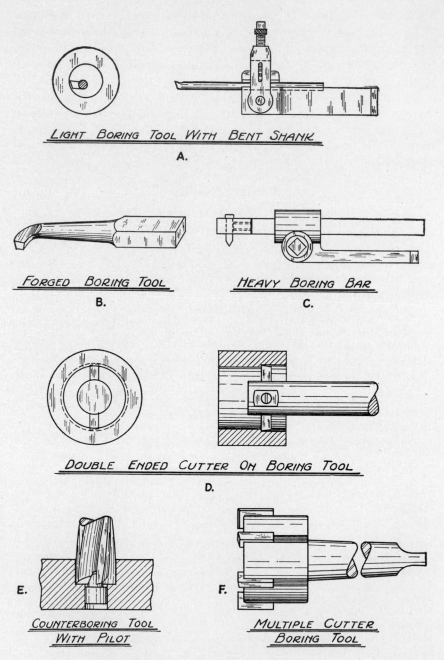

LIGHT BORING TOOL WITH BENT SHANK
A.

FORGED BORING TOOL
B.

HEAVY BORING BAR
C.

DOUBLE ENDED CUTTER ON BORING TOOL
D.

E.

COUNTERBORING TOOL
WITH PILOT

F.

MULTIPLE CUTTER
BORING TOOL

FIG. 25. Types of Boring Tools.

wear and variations of diameter. Boring tools of this type have longer life than single-pointed tools and, hence, are more economical for production jobs. The counterboring tool at *E* is designed to recess or enlarge one end of a hole. These tools are provided with pilots to insure concentric diameters.

For precision boring work on milling machines, jig borers, or drill presses, it is necessary to use a tool having micrometer adjustment. This tool differs from those previously described in that its position is fixed in the machine and it rotates. Hence, any increase in hole size must be obtained by adjusting the tool radially from its center.

Review Questions

1. Distinguish among drilling, boring, counterboring, and reaming.
2. Prepare a classification of drilling machines.
3. What is a sensitive drill press, and for what type of work is it used?
4. How does an upright drill differ from a vertical milling machine?
5. Describe the type of work done on a gang drill.
6. What is the difference between a plain and a universal radial drilling machine?
7. Describe the process of deep-hole drilling.
8. Sketch a taper-shank twist drill, and label all principal parts.
9. For what are way-type drilling machines used?
10. How are holes machined in thin metal?
11. How is the cutting speed of a drill determined?
12. State the procedure for producing an accurate hole in a disk mounted on a lathe chuck.
13. What are some of the important factors affecting drill performance?
14. How much material should be removed by a reamer?
15. What is a jig?
16. How are accurate measurements made on a jig borer?
17. For what type of work is a vertical boring mill used?
18. What type of tools are used on a vertical boring mill?
19. Describe how boring is done on a horizontal boring machine.
20. What is the difference between a lathe boring tool and one used on a jig borer?

References

BOLZ, R. W., *Production Processes,* Penton Publishing Company, Vol. 1, 1949.

COLVIN, F. H., and L. L. HAAS, *Jigs and Fixtures,* 4th edition, McGraw-Hill Book Company, 1943.

COLVIN, F. H., and F. A. STANLEY, *American Machinists' Handbook,* 8th edition, McGraw-Hill Book Company, 1945.

HINMAN, C. W., *Practical Design for Milling and Drilling Tools,* McGraw-Hill Book Company, 1938.

HOAGLAND, F. O., "Drill Points for Deep-Hole Drilling," *Machinery,* October 1940.

STEWART, G. D., "Precision Boring—Plus," *American Machinist,* June 11, 1941.

Tool Engineers Handbook, American Society of Tool Engineers, McGraw-Hill Book Company, 1949.

CHAPTER

19

MILLING MACHINES AND CUTTERS

A milling machine is a machine tool that removes metal as the work is fed against a rotating cutter. Except for rotation, the circular-shaped cutter has no other motion. It is called a *milling cutter* and has a series of cutting edges on its circumference, each of which acts as an individual cutter in the cycle of rotation. The work is held on a table which controls the feed against the cutter. In most machines there are three possible table movements, longitudinal, crosswise, and vertical, but in some the table may also possess a swivel or rotational movement.

The milling machine is the most versatile of all machine tools. Flat or formed surfaces may be machined with excellent finish and great accuracy. Angles, slots, gear teeth, and recess cuts can be made by using various cutters. Drills, reamers, and boring tools can be held in the arbor socket by removing the cutter and arbor. As all table movements have micrometer adjustments, holes and other cuts can be accurately spaced. Most operations performed on shapers, drill presses, gear-cutting machines, and broaching machines can likewise be done on the milling machine. It produces a better finish and holds to accurate limits with greater ease than a shaper. Heavy cuts can be taken with no appreciable sacrifice in finish or accuracy. Cutters are efficient in their action and can be used a long time before being resharpened. In most cases the work is completed in one pass of the table. These advantages plus the availability of a wide variety of cutters make the milling machine indispensable in the shop and toolroom.

Classification of Milling Machines

Milling machines are made in a great variety of types and sizes. The drive may be either a cone-pulley-belt drive or an individual motor. The feed of the work may be by hand, by mechanical means, or by a hydraulic system. There is also a variety of possible table movements. The usual classification is in accordance with the general

474

design, but even in this classification there is some overlapping. According to design, the distinctive types are:

1. Column and knee type
   - (a) Hand miller.
   - (b) Plain milling machine.
   - (c) Universal milling machine.
   - (d) Ram-type universal.
   - (e) Vertical milling machine.

2. Planer milling machine.

3. Fixed-bed type
   - (a) Simplex milling machine.
   - (b) Duplex milling machine.
   - (c) Triplex milling machine.

4. Special types
   - (a) Rotary table machine.
   - (b) Drum milling machine.
   - (c) Planetary milling machine.
   - (d) Stationary long table machine.
   - (e) Offset milling machine.
   - (f) Duplicator or profiling machine.
   - (g) Pantograph milling machine.

Types of Milling Machines

Hand milling machine. The simplest type of milling machine is hand-operated. It may have either the column and knee construction or the table mounted on a fixed bed. Machines operated by hand are used principally in production work for light and simple milling operations, such as cutting grooves, short keyways, and slotting. These machines have a horizontal arbor for holding the cutter and a work table which is usually provided with three movements. The work is fed to the rotating cutter either by the hand movement of a long lever or by a hand screw feed.

Plain milling machine. The plain milling machine is similar to the hand machine except that it is of sturdier construction and is provided with power-feeding mechanism to control the table movements. Plain milling machines of the column and knee type have three motions: longitudinal, transverse, and vertical. Those of the *fixed-bed type,* as shown in Figure 1, have only longitudinal table travel, but have provision for transverse and vertical adjustments on the spindle which holds the milling cutter arbor. The machine is a fast-cutting manu-facturing-type unit having complete electric control for all table and spindle movements. Twenty-eight feeds are provided, ranging from $\frac{1}{2}$ to 35 inches per minute, which may be operated in either direction. Fast table travel, up to 300 inches per minute, is provided for quick positioning of the table. Plain milling machines are especially adapted to form milling and other types of production work.

A hydraulically operated plain milling machine of the fixed-bed type is shown in Figure 2. This machine, which is designed for simple production jobs, is equipped with a fully automatic table cycle. The table can be rapidly traversed in either direction, automatically shifted from rapid traverse to feed, reversed, or stopped at any point. The table has only a longitudinal movement while vertical and transverse movements of the cutter are accomplished in the head assembly.

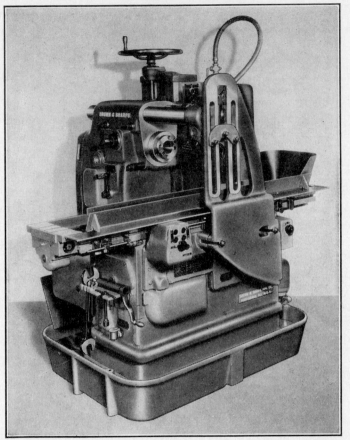

Courtesy Brown & Sharpe Manufacturing Company.

Fig. 1. Plain Milling Machine.

This machine can be used for many production jobs involving slotting, facing, plain and form cutting.

Universal milling machine. The universal machine is the most versatile of all the various types. It is essentially a toolroom machine, constructed for very accurate work. In appearance it is quite similar to the plain type of milling machine, but differs in that (1) the work table is provided with a fourth movement which permits the table to swivel horizontally, and (2) it is equipped with an index or dividing head. The machine was originally designed with the swiveling feature to permit the cutting of spirals, such as are found on drills, milling cutters, and cams. In Figure 3 is shown a universal machine of modern design. In addition to being equipped with the dividing-head equipment, universal millers may also be provided with vertical milling attachment, rotary-table attachment, vise, and other similar

Courtesy Kent-Owens Machine Company.

FIG. 2.   Plain Hydraulic Production Milling Machine.

accessories, all of which add to its utility as a toolroom machine. Aside from doing all types of milling operations, these machines will also do practically any type of operation that can be done on a shaper or a drill press.

Ram-type universal machine. Another universal machine, known as a ram-type, is shown in Figure 4. The cutter head is pivoted to the face of the ram and is capable of any angle adjustment between vertical and horizontal. The ram, which carries the cutter head, is provided with an in-and-out movement over the work table. With the combined adjusting features of the cutter head, ram, and work table, it is possible to do conventional horizontal, angular, or vertical milling. This range of adjustment often makes it possible to complete jobs with one setup without having to change to some other machine.

Vertical milling machine.   A typical vertical machine is shown in Figure 5.   It is so called because of the vertical position of the cutter spindle.   The table movements in this type of machine are the same as in plain machines.   Ordinarily no movement is given to the cutter other than usual rotational motion.   However, the spindle head may

Courtesy Kearney & Trecker Corporation.

Fig. 3.   Universal Milling Machine.

be swiveled, which permits setting the spindle in a vertical plane at any angle from vertical to horizontal.   This machine is also provided with a short axial spindle travel to facilitate step milling.   Some vertical milling machines are provided with rotary attachments or rotating work tables to permit the milling of circular grooves or continuous milling of small production parts.   Cutters used on vertical milling machines are all of the end-mill type.

Drilling, boring, and reaming can also be done on these machines.   Accurate spacing of holes is possible because of the micrometer adjustment of the table.   The machine is especially adapted to taking facing cuts and finishing in recesses.   Profiling and die-sinking machines are very similar to vertical milling machines in their operation.

Planer-type milling machine.   This type of milling machine receives its name from its resemblance to a planer.   The work is carried on a long table, having only a longitudinal movement, and is fed against

Courtesy Van Norman Company.

FIG. 4.   Ram-Type Universal Miller.

the rotating cutter at the proper speed.   The variable table-feeding movement and the rotating cutter are the principal features that distinguish this machine from a planer.   Transverse and vertical movements are provided on the cutter spindle carried.   These machines are designed for milling large work requiring heavy stock removal and for accurate duplication of contours and profiles.   A hydraulically operated unit of this type is shown in Figure 6.

Fixed-bed types of milling machines.   Machines of this type are essentially production machines and are of rugged construction.   The names *simplex, duplex,* and *triplex* indicate that the machine is provided, respectively, with single, double, and triple spindle heads. Figure 7 illustrates a duplex machine set up for rough-milling the master rod of an airplane engine.   This machine, known as a Duplex Hydromatic, is equipped with an automatic dog-controlled hydraulic

Courtesy Brown & Sharpe Manufacturing Company.

FIG. 5. Vertical Milling Machine.

table feed.   An infinite variety of feeds is available within the range of the machine, and it is also possible to change the feed automatically during the cut.   Any feed cycle needed can be obtained automatically. Since these are essentially manufacturing-type machines, many are equipped with a tracer control which guides the tool and permits the cutting of irregular contours.   A discussion of this type of tool control is given farther on in this chapter.

FIG. 6. Planer-Type Milling Machine.

FIG. 7. Hydromatic Duplex Milling Machine.

Special Milling Machines

Rotary table milling machine.   Rotary table machines, like the one shown in Figure 8, are adaptations of the vertical milling machine to a rather specialized use.   In this case there are two vertical spindles,

Courtesy The Ingersoll Mining Machine Company.

FIG. 8.   Rotary Table Milling Machine.

each equipped with a facing mill.   Cylinder heads are roughed at the first station and then finish-milled as they pass the second station. The operation is continuous and there is ample time for the operator to load and unload the machine during the milling. This machine is fast but is obviously limited to the milling of flat surfaces.

Drum-type milling machine. Drum-type millers are special machines designed for production work.   Machines of this type have a large drum fixture, similar to the turret on a turret lathe, upon which the work is mounted.   In operation, the drum fixture rotates slowly, carrying the work against the rotating cutters.   Usually there are four cutter spindles.   The operation is continuous, since the parts are removed and new ones are added after the work has completed its cycle.   Most of the work formerly done on drum millers is now done on broaching machines or process lines where the part is transferred from one station to another.

Offset milling machine. The offset miller is another production-type machine. In most of these millers the cutter is mounted on a vertical spindle which extends into a fixture. This fixture is offset, or mounted eccentrically with the cutter, so that, as it revolves, the work

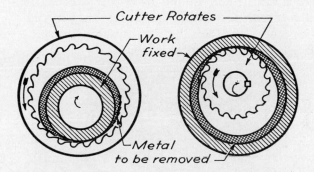

A. EXTERNAL MILLING   B. INTERNAL MILLING

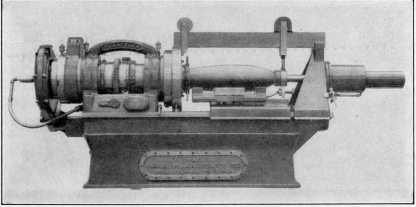

Courtesy The Hall Planetary Company.

Fig. 9. Planetary Milling Machine Setup for Milling Threads on Bomb End. *A* and *B* Show Cutter Action for Both External and Internal Milling.

is milled as it passes by. The operation is similar to internal grinding with the work being rotated. Only single milling operations are performed in this manner such as slotting or straddle cutting.

Planetary milling machine. Planetary milling machines are used for milling both internal and external short threads and surfaces. The work to be milled is held stationary, as shown on the machine in Figure 9, and all movements necessary for the cutting are made by the milling cutters. At the start of a job, the rotating cutter is in center or neutral position. It is first fed radially to the proper depth and then given a planetary motion either inside or around the work. The relation between the work and the cutters is illustrated by the line diagram above the machine in the figure. Both internal and external work can be done simultaneously. Typical applications of this machine include the milling of internal and external threads of all kinds of tapered surfaces, bearing surfaces, rear axle end holes, airplane crankcases, shell and bomb ends.

Courtesy Pratt & Whitney Division—
Niles-Bement-Pond Company.

FIG. 10.   Profiling with Former Pin.

Stationary long table milling machine.* This machine was developed to do contour milling on main spars, channel beams, and cap strips for modern airplanes. Because of the length of the parts to be machined the bed of the machine is stationary and is made up in sections to the desired length (bed lengths vary from 30 to 90 feet). All cutters are contained and operated within a carriage which is mounted on and travels the length of the bed. Work mounted on the bed is automatically milled to shape by vertical and horizontal cutters which, in turn, receive their direction from individual templates alongside of the work.

Duplicating and profiling machines. A large variety of machines have been developed for die and mold cutting, engraving, and profiling. Machines for these purposes are known as *duplicators, die sinkers, profiling machines, pantograph machines,* and so on. Most of them are a special adaptation of a vertical milling machine, although

* A machine of this type is manufactured by the Onsrud Machine Works.

Courtesy George Gorton Machine Company.

FIG. 11. Two-Dimensional Pantograph Machines Used for Engraving Work.

some few operate with the spindle in a horizontal position. The hand-profiling machine is perhaps the simplest, having a rotating cutter whose motion is controlled by hand movements of the work table. These movements are guided by moving the table so that the guide pin is in contact with some form or template as shown in Figure 10. This, in general, is the principle involved in all machines of this type, except that in many of them the movement is automatically controlled from a template by hydraulic or electrical means.

Pantograph engraving machines. These machines receive their name from the pantograph linkage used to reproduce from a template at either an enlarged or a reduced scale.

A two-dimensional pantograph used for engraving work is shown in Figure 11. The template is mounted at the upper rear of the machine and is engaged by a hand-guided pointer. This pointer controls the

Courtesy George Gorton Machine Company.

FIG. 12. Three-Dimensional Pantograph Machine Cutting Opening at End of Propeller Blade.

movement of the rotating cutter through the pantograph mechanism shown at the top of the machine. By changing the link arrangement of the pantograph, any figure or design can be enlarged or reduced in size according to desired proportions. The machine shown is for light work in one plane and is used for engraving and light-metal die work. For larger work and for jobs requiring three-dimensional machining, a machine such as is shown in Figure 12 can be used. This machine is capable of reproducing from a model of any shape or contour. Because it is equipped with a pantograph mechanism, an increase or reduction in size can be obtained.

The production of large forming dies for automobile fenders, tops,

Courtesy Ingersoll Milling Machine Company.

FIG. 13. Automatic Duplicator Machine for Die Work.

and panels is also an important use of duplicator machines. Such a machine, of large capacity, is illustrated in Figure 13. The machine itself rests on a track and is entirely automatic in its operation. Both the template and the die block are supported on the large angle bracket in front of the machine. A template of the part to be produced is first prepared and is mounted above as shown in the figure. These templates are made of hard wood, plaster of Paris, or other easily worked materials, as the only purpose they serve is to guide the pointer which controls the tool position. The method of cutting and general operation of the machine can be seen by reference to the figure.

Controls for Milling Cutters

The manual control of tools on profilers and pantograph machines, where the operator guides the tool from a template or model, is satisfactory for certain types of work, but is not economical in production jobs involving the removal of much metal.   Automatically controlled tracer methods have been developed which are operated by electrical or hydraulic means.   The movement of a roller or tracer on a template

Courtesy Cincinnati Milling Machine Company.

Fig. 14.   Milling Profile of a Locomotive Side Rod in One Setup, with a 360-Degree Tracer Unit Automatically Controlling Cycle of Operation.

is transferred through a properly arranged circuit to the cutting tool. During this movement forces are released which move the various machine slides in a manner to give the cutter identical movements with that of the tracer.   In Figure 14 two slides of the machine, at right angles to one another, are hydraulically controlled by the 360-degree tracer unit, and the complete profile of a locomotive side rod is milled in one setup.

For complete circumferential milling of an object vertical milling setups are necessary, the axis of the tracer unit being parallel to the milled surface.   When cutters are used on horizontal arbors, as in the milling of connecting rod sides in Figure 15, only 180-degree movement of the cutter is possible.   In this figure the tracer unit is at the left and the template which it rides is next to the machine column.   As the milling machine table is fed to the left, the cutters rise and fall as dictated by the tracer unit following the template.   Contour milling with the unit having 180-degree movement may also be done with vertical mills, the work and tracer being fed either in a straight line or rotated on duplex rotating tables.

Rise-and-fall movements on milling tables may also be accomplished by the use of heavy cams with roll followers in combination with trip dogs which start and stop various slide movements. This

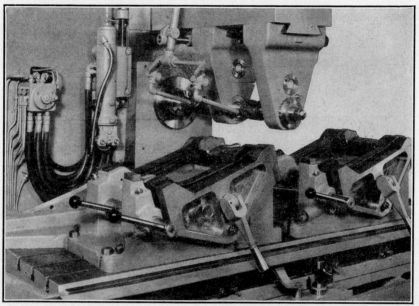

Courtesy Cincinnati Milling Machine Company.

FIG. 15. Plain Tracer Controlled Hydromatic Milling Machine Milling Sides of Connecting Rods.

direct control of the motion of one slide while the other is moving at a uniform feed rate imposes heavy loads on the driving mechanism and is not satisfactory for steep climbs. Hydraulically controlled tools require only light contact with form or template and have a much greater range of movement. Automatic-tracer-controlled tools make possible rapid and accurate machining of irregular surfaces otherwise difficult to machine with economy.

The Index Head and Its Operation

An *index* or *dividing head* is used to rotate the work through a certain number of degrees or through a fraction of a revolution, or while the table is feeding, as when cutting helical gears. It is a regular piece of equipment on a universal milling machine but may be used on some of the other types as well. In Figure 16 is shown an index head and its footstock mounted on the work table of a machine. Since much of the work to be machined has to be supported between centers, both units are necessary.

The index head is nothing more than a worm-gear reducer having a ratio of 40 to 1—that is, 40 turns of the crank will rotate the work

Courtesy Cincinnati Milling Machine Company.

Fig. 16. Index-Head Assembly Setup for Vertical-Milling a Ratchet Wheel.

one complete revolution. The work spindle which is attached to the worm gear has a tapered hole to receive the live center and is also threaded to hold a chuck. A U-shaped piece is ordinarily on the spindle to give positive motion to the work through a dog. Just back of this piece is a direct index plate having 24 equally spaced holes. The entire spindle assembly may be swiveled from horizontal to vertical position. The shaft which operates the worm gear extends to the side of the mechanism and through the index plate and sector. On its end is a crank, having an index pin, which fits into the holes on the index plate. Since the plate does not turn, the crank is locked when the index pin is engaged in one of the holes. The index plate is provided with several concentric circles of equally spaced holes to assist in determining the proper number of revolutions of the handle where a fraction of a revolution is involved. The sector arms on the plate are to eliminate the counting of spaces when the handle is being turned between cuts.

The three types of indexing used are *simple, direct,* and *differential.* Most indexing is of the first type and is accomplished by turning the crank a number of turns to rotate the work the desired amount, the index plate being held in a fixed position. With a ratio of 40 to 1, one revolution of the crank will rotate the work $\frac{1}{40}$ of a revolution. Hence, in cutting a gear with 40 teeth the crank would be locked to the plate by the index pin and a cut would be made. After the cut, the handle would be turned one revolution and another cut taken, and so on. To cut a gear with 20 teeth would require 2 turns of the handle, or to cut 8 flutes on a reamer 5 turns. As long as the number of cuts to be taken is a factor of 40, it is a simple matter to calculate the number of handle turns. By following these simple calculations it is quite obvious that an expression can be set up to compute the number of handle turns for a given condition. The rule to use is

$$\text{Turns of index handle} = \frac{\text{turns of handle to produce 1 turn of work (usually 40)}}{\text{cuts to be made in 1 revolution of work}}$$

When the number of cuts to be made is not evenly divisible into 40, it follows that fractional turns must be made, and for this it is necessary to use the sector device. Assume that it is desired to cut 32 teeth on a spur gear. If the afore-mentioned rule is used, the number of turns of the index handle would be $\frac{40}{32}$ or $1\frac{1}{4}$ turns. First select a circle on the index plate that is divisible by 4. If a 24-space circle is available, set the sector arms so that there are 6 spaces between them. Hence 1 revolution of the crank plus 6 spaces would give the work the required movement. The same results could be obtained by using a circle with 48 spaces and turning one turn plus 12 spaces. To cut a gear with 72 teeth, the number of turns would be in the ratio of $\frac{40}{72}$ or $\frac{5}{9}$. If a 54-space circle were available, the sector arms should be set for 30 spaces. In setting the arms, care must be exercised to count spaces and not holes.

Direct indexing is accomplished by using the index plate attached to the work spindle. This plate has 24 divisions and is engaged by a plunger pin on the head. The worm is disengaged from the worm gear, and the plate is turned the required amount by hand. This system of indexing is limited only to those divisions that are factors of 24. It is a quick method of indexing and is used when only a few cuts are required in a revolution.

When indexing is done by degrees with a 40-to-1 index head, each turn of the handle represents $\frac{360}{40}$ or 9 degrees. If a 27-space circle were selected, a movement of three spaces of the handle would move the work 1 degree.   Four spaces on a 36-hole circle would also represent 1 degree, whereas one space would move the work only ¼ degree. By similar calculations the work may be moved any number of degrees or through most common fractions of a degree.

Differential indexing is used when the work has to be turned an amount that cannot be obtained by simple indexing, owing to the lack of a circle on the index plate with the correct number of spaces. For such conditions the index plate is unlocked and geared to a train of gears which receive their motion from the worm-gear spindle. As the handle is turned, the index plate also turns, but at a different rate and perhaps in the opposite direction.   Its movement depends on the gears used to drive it.   Information for calculating the correct gears to use for a given condition may be found in machine instruction books.   After the gears are set up, the operation is similar to simple indexing.   Differential indexing makes it possible to rotate the work any fraction of a revolution with the usual index plates furnished with the equipment.

Spiral milling is accomplished by rotating the work as it moves against the rotating cutter.   This is done with the use of connecting gears from the lead screw of the work table to the handle spindle of the index head.   The lead of the spiral, the distance it advanced in one revolution, is controlled by these gears.   With a 40-to-1 reduction in the index head and a 4-pitch lead screw, the lead would be 10 inches, if no increase or reduction in the outside gears is assumed. The ratio for computing these gears is

$$\frac{\text{Product of the driving gears}}{\text{Product of the driven gears}} = \frac{10}{\text{desired lead}}$$

Spiral milling is used in cutting spiral gears, flutes on various tools, screws, worm gears, and some types of cams.

Types of Milling Cutters

The milling machine is most versatile because of the large variety of milling cutters available.   These cutters are usually classified according to their general shape, although in some cases they are classified by the way they are mounted, the material used in the teeth, or the method used in grinding the teeth.

There are three methods of mounting cutters on a milling machine, giving rise to three general types or designs of cutters, namely:

1. **Arbor cutters.**   These cutters have a hole in the center for mounting on an arbor.

2. Shank cutters. Cutters of this type have either a straight or tapered shank integral with the body of the cutter. When in use, these cutters are mounted in the spindle nose or in a spindle adapter.

3. Face cutters. These cutters are bolted or held on the end of short arbors and are generally used for milling plane surfaces.

Classification according to materials follows similar classifications of other types of cutting tools. Milling cutters are made of high-carbon steels or various high-speed steels, with sintered-carbide tips, or of certain cast nonferrous alloys. High-carbon steel cutters have a limited use, as they dull quickly if high cutting speeds and feeds are used. Most general-purpose cutters are made of high-speed steels, as such steels maintain a keen cutting edge at temperatures around 1000 to 1100 F. Consequently, they may be used at cutting speeds 2 to $2\frac{1}{2}$ times those recommended for carbon-steel cutters. Cast nonferrous metals such as Stellite, Crobalt, or Rexalloy, and carbide-tipped cutters, have even greater resistance to heat and are especially adapted to heavy cuts and high cutting speeds. These materials are either used as inserts held in the body of the cutter or brazed directly on the tips of the teeth.

Cutting speeds for these cutters range from two to five times those recommended for high-speed steel.

Teeth in milling cutters are made in two general styles according to the method used in sharpening them. *Profile cutters* are sharpened by grinding a small land back of the cutting edge of the tooth. This also provides the necessary relief at the back of the cutting edge. *Formed cutters* are made with the relief back of the cutting edge the same contour as the cutting edge. To sharpen these cutters the face of the cutter is ground so as not to destroy the tooth contour.

The types of cutters most generally used are shown in Figure 17. These cutters are classified principally according to their general shape or the type of work they will do.

1. Plain milling cutter. A plain cutter is a disk-shaped cutter having teeth only on the circumference. The teeth may be either straight or spiral, but they are usually spiral if the width exceeds $\frac{5}{8}$ inch. Wide spiral cutters of this type used for heavy slabbing work may have notches in the teeth to break up the chips and facilitate their removal.

2. Side milling cutter. This cutter is similar to a plain cutter except that it has teeth on the sides also. In some cases, where two cutters operate together, the cutter is plain on one side and has teeth on the other. Cutters of this type may have straight, spiral, or staggered teeth.

Courtesy Brown & Sharpe Manufacturing Company.

FIG. 17. Types of Milling Cutters.

(a) Spiral end mill cutter.
(b) T-slot milling cutter.
(c) Plain cutter with spiral teeth.
(d) Angle milling cutter.
(e) Woodruff keyseat cutter.
(f) Plain milling cutter.

(g) Inserted tooth cutter.
(h) Metal slitting saw cutter.
(i) Form cutter for gear teeth.
(j) Side milling cutter.
(k) Spiral double-end end mill.
(l) Extra-long spiral end mill.

3. Metal slitting saw cutter. This cutter resembles a plain or side cutter except that it is made very thin, usually $\frac{3}{16}$ inch or less. Plain cutters of this type are relieved by grinding the sides to afford clearance for the cutter.

4. Angle milling cutter. Any cutter, angle-shaped, comes under this classification. Cutters of this type are made into both single- and double-angle cutters. The single-angle cutters have one conical surface whereas the double-angle cutters have teeth on two conical surfaces. Angle cutters are used for such purposes as cutting ratchet wheels, dovetails, flutes on milling cutters, and reamers.

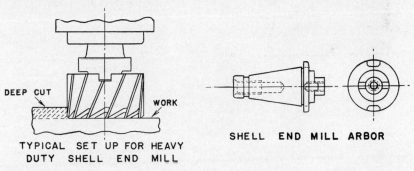

DEEP CUT   WORK

SHELL END MILL ARBOR

TYPICAL SET UP FOR HEAVY DUTY SHELL END MILL

Fig. 18. Shell End Mill and Arbor.

5. Form milling cutters. This name is applied to any cutter on which the teeth are given a special shape. This group includes convex and concave cutters, gear cutters, fluting cutters, corner-rounding cutters, and many others.

6. End-mill cutters. These cutters have an integral shaft for driving and have teeth on both periphery and ends. The flutes on these cutters may be either straight or helical. Large cutters of this type, called shell end mills, have the cutter part separate and are held to a stub arbor, as shown in Figure 18. Owing to the cost of high-speed steel, this construction results in a considerable saving in material cost. End mills are used for surfacing projections, squaring ends, cutting slots, and recess work such as in die making.

7. T-slot cutters. Cutters of this type resemble small plain or side milling cutters which have an integral straight or tapered shaft for driving. They are used for milling T slots. A special form of this cutter is the Woodruff keyseat cutter, which is made in standard sizes for cutting the round seats for Woodruff keys.

8. Inserted tooth cutter. As cutters increase in size, it is economical to insert the teeth made of expensive material into less expensive ordinary steel. Teeth in such cutters may be replaced when worn out or broken.

Milling-Cutter Teeth

A typical milling cutter, with various angles and cutter nomenclature, is shown in Figure 19. For most high-speed cutters positive *radial rake angles* of 10 to 15 degrees are used. These values are satisfactory for most materials and represent a compromise between

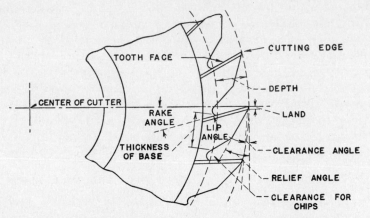

FIG. 19. Milling Cutter with Various Angles Indicated.

good shearing or cutting ability and strength. Milling cutters made for softer materials, such as aluminum, can be given much greater rake with improved cutting ability.

Usually only saw-type and narrow plain milling cutters have straight teeth with zero axial rake. As cutters increase in width, a positive-axial-rake angle is used to increase cutting efficiency.

For high-speed milling with carbide-tipped cutters, negative-rake angles (both radial and axial) are generally used. Improved tool life is obtained by the resultant increase in the *lip angle;* also, the tooth is better able to resist shock loads. Plain milling-type cutters with teeth on the periphery usually are given a negative rake of 5 to 10 degrees when steel is being cut. Alloys and medium-carbon steels require greater negative rake than soft steels. Exceptions to the use of negative-rake angles for carbide cutters are made when soft non-ferrous metals are milled.

The *clearance angle* is the included angle between the land and a tangent to the cutter from the tip of the tooth. It is always positive and should be small so as not to weaken the cutting edge of the tooth. For most commercial cutters over 3 inches in diameter the clearance angle is around 4 to 5 degrees. Smaller-diameter cutters have increased clearance angles to eliminate tendencies for the teeth to rub on the work. Clearance values also depend on the various work materials. Cast iron requires values of 4 to 7 degrees, whereas soft materials such as magnesium, aluminum, and brass are cut efficiently with clearance angles of 10 to 12 degrees. The width of the land should be kept small; its usual values are $\frac{1}{32}$ to $\frac{1}{16}$ inch. A *secondary clearance* is ground back of the land to keep the width of the land within proper limits.

Much research on cutter form and size has proved that coarse teeth are more efficient for removing metal than fine teeth. A coarse-tooth cutter takes thicker chips and has freer cutting action and more clearance space for the chips. As a consequence, these cutters result in increased production and decreased power consumption for a given amount of metal removed. Also, fine-tooth cutters have a greater tendency to chatter than those with coarse teeth. However, such cutters are recommended for saw cutters in the milling of thin materials.

Cutting Speed and Feed

The cutting speed of a milling cutter is determined by the peripheral or surface speed of the cutter. The movement of the work past the cutter is not considered in this calculation. The cutting speed may be expressed by the following equation:

$$CS = \frac{\pi D N}{12} = \text{feet per minute}$$

D is diameter of cutter in inches and N is revolutions per minute.

Since the cutting speed is seldom the unknown, the equation is generally expressed in terms of spindle revolution.

$$N = \frac{CS \times 12}{\pi D} = \text{rpm of spindle}$$

If the cutter diameter and cutting speed of the given material are known, this expression gives the proper rotational speed of the spindle. In the selection of the proper cutting speed the following factors should be considered:

1. Cutter material. Cutting speeds are usually given in values for high-speed steel cutters. These values are twice those for carbon-steel cutters and one-half to one-fifth those recommended for carbide-tipped cutters.

2. Kind of material being cut. Approximately, roughing cuts on cold rolled steel are 80–100 feet per minute, cast iron 50–60 feet per minute, brass 150–200 feet per minute, bronze 80–120 feet per minute, aluminum 400–500 feet per minute, and magnesium 600–800 feet per minute. Speeds about 20% higher can be used for finish cuts. Additional cutting speeds are given in Table 7.

3. Rigidity and size of machine. This factor is of particular importance when old or lightly constructed equipment is used.

4. Type of finish desired. Best finishes are obtained with light feeds and high cutting speeds.

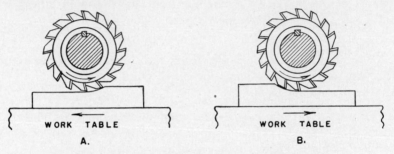

WORK TABLE

A.

WORK TABLE

B.

FIG. 20. Methods of Feeding Work on Milling Machine.

5. Size of cut. Heavy cuts which accumulate heat rapidly must be taken more slowly than shallow cuts.

6. Kind of coolant used. The heat generated in milling must be dissipated to protect the cutter and the work. To accomplish this, the tool and work are usually flooded with an appropriate coolant such as soluble, sulfurized, or mineral lard oil. An exception to this is cast iron, which is milled dry because of the abrasive action of the chips. Kerosene is frequently used as a coolant for aluminum. Since water mixtures present a fire hazard with magnesium, only straight cutting oils should be used in machining this metal.

There are two possible methods of feeding the work to the cutter, as shown in Figure 20. Feeding the work against the cutter, as in *A*, is usually recommended, as each tooth starts its cut in clean metal and does not have to break through possible surface scale. However, tests have proved that, when the work is fed in the same direction as cutter rotation (as shown at *B*), the cutting is more efficient. Larger chips are removed, and there is less tendency for chatter. This method is frequently used in production work, where large cuts are to be taken and the surface of the work is free from scale.

Feed on milling machines is expressed in either of two ways. On some machines it is expressed in thousandths of an inch per revolution of cutter. Such machines have feed changes ranging from 0.006 to as high as 0.300 inch. The other method is to express the feed of table in inches per minute, the usual range being from $\frac{1}{2}$ to 20 inches per minute.

Fixtures

All milling-machine work must be accurately located and rigidly held during the cutting operation. This is ordinarily done by using a *fixture* which holds the work securely but does not guide the tool. Fixtures should be designed with the following points in mind:

1. Work clamps should be quick-acting for loading and unloading the part.
2. The work piece must be accurately positioned within the fixture.
3. Provision should be made for the disposal of chips.
4. Fixture should be rigid.

Examples of various fixtures mounted on machines are shown in Figures 7, 8, and 15. These fixtures make possible the production of interchangeable parts at a reduced operation time.

Review Questions

1. Describe the process of milling, and state the type of work that can be done.
2. What is meant by a fixed-bed milling machine?
3. How does a universal milling machine differ from a plain milling machine?
4. How does a vertical milling machine differ from an upright drill press?
5. How do rotary- and drum-type milling machines differ?
6. Explain the operation of a planetary milling machine.
7. How does an engraving machine operate?
8. How does a planer milling machine differ from a planer?
9. Discuss the relative merits of a shaper and a milling machine for machining plane surfaces.
10. How are irregular surfaces machined on a milling machine?
11. Sketch and name eight types of milling cutters.
12. Describe an index head, and state its purpose.
13. If it is desired to cut 32 teeth on a spur gear, how many turns of the index crank should be made between each two cuts? Same for 66 teeth?
14. Explain how a spiral gear would be cut on a milling machine.
15. What factors determine the feed on a milling machine?
16. What is the purpose of notching the teeth on some cutters?
17. Why is a coarse-tooth cutter more efficient than a fine-tooth cutter?
18. How is the cutting speed of a milling cutter determined?

References

ARMITAGE, J. B., and A. O. SCHMIDT, "Rake Angles in Face Milling," *Mechanical Engineering*, June, July, August, 1945.

A Treatise on Milling and Milling Machines, 3d edition, Cincinnati Milling Machine Company, 1945.

HINMAN, C. W., *Practical Design for Drilling and Milling Tools,* McGraw-Hill Book Company, 1938.

LUCHT, FRED W., "Face-Milling with Carbide," *Mechanical Engineering,* March 1945.

Machinery's Handbook, 13th edition, Industrial Press, 1948.

MARTELLOTTI, M. (*a*) "Milling Cutters and How to Use Them," *American Machinist,* August 17, 1944. (*b*) "Special Rake Angles Used for Carbide Tools," *American Machinist,* February 15, 1945. (*c*) "Clearance and Relief Angles for Milling Cutters," *American Machinist,* March 15, 1945. (*d*) "Selection and Application of Milling Cutters," *American Machinist,* March 16, 1944.

MEYER, A. W., and F. R. ARCHIBALD, "Carbide Milling of Steel," *Mechanical Engineering,* October 1945.

Tool Engineers Handbook, American Society of Tool Engineers, McGraw-Hill Book Company, 1949.

CHAPTER
20

GEARS AND GEAR–CUTTING MACHINES

Gears are a common method of transmitting power or rotary motion from one shaft to another. They have the advantage over friction and belt drives in that they are positive in their action. Most machinery requires positive action, since exact speed ratios are essential; however, friction and surface-contact drives have some use in industry where high speeds and light loads are required and in a few cases where loads subjected to impact are transmitted. A gear differs from a friction disk in that it has projections or teeth built up on its circumference so that it may transmit motion through the meshing teeth without slippage.

If teeth were to be built up on the circumferences of two rolling disks in contact with each other, recesses would have to be provided between the teeth so as to eliminate interference. The original diameter of each disk would still figure in the gear calculations, however. This is known as the *pitch diameter*. It is only an imaginary circle and cannot be seen by inspecting a gear. A portion of a gear is shown in Figure 1 with the pitch circle indicated.

Kinds of Gears

The gears most commonly used are those that transmit power between two parallel shafts. Such gears having their tooth elements parallel to the rotating shafts are known as *spur gears*. If the elements of the teeth are twisted or helical, as shown in Figure 2, they are known as *helical gears*. These gears may also be made for connecting shafts that are at an angle in the same or different planes. The advantage of helical gears is that they are smooth acting, because there is always more than one tooth in contact. Some power is lost because of end thrust, and provision must be made to compensate for this thrust in the bearings. The *herringbone gear* is equivalent to two helical gears, one having a right-hand and the other a left-hand helix.

Usually when two shafts are in the same plane, but at an angle with one another, a *bevel gear* is used. Such a gear is similar in appear-

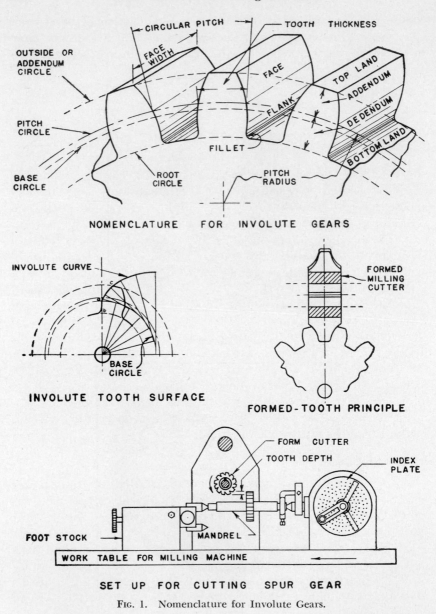

NOMENCLATURE FOR INVOLUTE GEARS

INVOLUTE TOOTH SURFACE

FORMED-TOOTH PRINCIPLE

SET UP FOR CUTTING SPUR GEAR

Fig. 1. Nomenclature for Involute Gears.

ance to the frustum of a cone having all the elements of the teeth intersecting at a point, as shown in Figure 7. Bevel gears are made with either straight or spiral teeth. When the shafts are at right angles and the two bevel gears are the same size, they are known as *miter gears* (see

Figure 3). *Hypoid gears,* an interesting modification of bevel gears (see Figure 4), have their shafts at right angles, but they do not intersect as do the shafts for bevel gears. Correct teeth for these gears are

Courtesy Foote Brothers Gear and Machine Corporation.

Fig. 2. Helical Gears.

Courtesy Foote Brothers Gear and Machine Corporation.

Fig. 3. Miter Bevel Gears.

difficult to construct, although a generating process has been developed that produces teeth with satisfactory action. *Zerol* gears have curved teeth but have a zero helical angle. They may be produced on machines that cut spiral bevels and hypoids. *Worm gearing* is used where a large speed reduction is desired. The small driving gear is called a *worm* and the driven gear a *wheel*. The worm in appearance

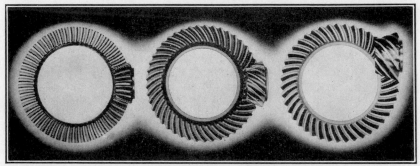

FIG. 4. Zerol, Spiral, and Hypoid Bevel Gears.

FIG. 5. Worm-Gear Sets.

resembles a large screw and is set in close to the wheel circumference, the teeth of the wheel being curved to conform to the diameter of the worm. The shafts for such gears are at right angles but not in the same plane. These gears are similar to helical gears in their application, but differ considerably in appearance and method of manufacture. Several worm-gear sets are shown in Figure 5.

In addition to the various kinds of gears just discussed, there are several special types that deserve mention. *Rack gears* are straight, having no curvature, and represent a gear of infinite radius. Such gears are used in feeding mechanisms and for reciprocating drives. They may have either straight or helical teeth. If the rack is bent in the form of a circle, it becomes a bevel gear having a cone apex angle of 180 degrees, which is known as a *crown gear*. The teeth all converge at the center of the disk and mesh properly with a bevel gear of the same pitch. A gear with internal teeth is known as an *annular gear*. It can be cut to mesh with either a spur or a bevel gear, depending on whether the shafts are parallel or intersecting.

Gear Nomenclature

The system of gearing used in the United States is known as the *involute system,* since the profile of a gear tooth is principally an involute curve. An *involute* is a curve generated on a circle, the normals of which are all tangent to this circle. The method of generating an involute is shown in Figure 1. Assume that a string, having a pencil on its end, is wrapped around a cylinder. The curve described by the pencil as the string is unwound is an involute, and the cylinder on which it is wound is known as the *base circle*. The portion of the gear tooth, from the base circle at A to the outside diameter at C, is an involute curve and is the portion of the tooth that contacts other teeth. From B to A the profile of the tooth is a radial line down to the small fillet at the root diameter. The location of the base circle on which the involute is described is inside the pitch circle and dependent on the angle of thrust of the gear teeth. The two systems most commonly used have their lines of action at $14\frac{1}{2}$ and 20 degrees, respectively. Other angles may be used, but the larger the angle is made the greater will be the radial force component tending to force the gears apart. If a common tangent is drawn to the pitch circles of two meshing gears, the line of action or angle of thrust is drawn at the proper angle ($14\frac{1}{2}$ degrees) to this line. The base circles, on which the involutes are drawn, are tangent to the line of action. Involute gears fulfill all the laws of gearing and have the advantage over some other curves that the contact action is not affected by slight variations of gear center distances.

Referring again to Figure 1, we see the nomenclature of a gear tooth clearly illustrated. The principal definitions and tooth parts for standard 14½-degree involute gears are:

The *addendum* of a tooth is the radial distance from the pitch circle to the outside diameter or addendum circle. Numerically, it is equal to one divided by the diametral pitch.

The *dedendum* is the radial distance from the pitch circle to the root or dedendum circle. It is equal to the addendum plus the tooth clearance.

Tooth thickness is the thickness of the tooth measured on the pitch circle. For cut gears the tooth thickness and tooth space are equal. Cast gears are provided with some *backlash*—the difference between the tooth thickness and tooth space, measured on the pitch circle.

The *face* of a gear tooth is that surface lying between the pitch circle and the addendum circle.

The *flank* of a gear tooth is that surface lying between the pitch circle and the dedendum circle.

Clearance is a small distance provided so that the top of a meshing tooth will not touch the bottom land of the other gear as it passes the lines of centers.

Table 9 gives the proportions of standard 14½-degree and 20-degree involute gears expressed in terms of diametral pitch and number of teeth.

TABLE 9.   AGMA STANDARD FOR INVOLUTE GEARING

	14½° Full Depth	*20° Stub Tooth*
Addendum	$\dfrac{1}{P}$	$\dfrac{0.8}{P}$
Clearance	$\dfrac{0.157}{P}$	$\dfrac{0.2}{P}$
Dedendum	$\dfrac{1.157}{P}$	$\dfrac{1}{P}$
Outside diameter	$\dfrac{N+2}{P}$	$\dfrac{N+1.6}{P}$
Pitch diameter	$\dfrac{N}{P}$	$\dfrac{N}{P}$

Pitch of Gears

The *circular pitch p* is the distance from a point on one tooth to the corresponding point on an adjacent tooth, and it is measured on the pitch circle. Expressed as an equation,

$$p = \frac{\pi D}{N}$$

where D is diameter of pitch circle and N is number of teeth.

The *diametral pitch P* is the ratio of the number of teeth to the pitch diameter. It may be expressed by the following equation:

$$P = \frac{N}{D}$$

Multiplying these two equations, we obtain the following relationship between circular and diametral pitch:

$$p \times P = \frac{\pi D}{N} \times \frac{N}{D} = \pi$$

Hence, knowing the value of either pitch, we may obtain the other by dividing it into π.

All gears and gear cutters are standardized according to diametral pitch, as this pitch can be expressed in even figures or fractions. Circular pitch, being an actual distance, is expressed in inches and fractions of an inch. A 6-pitch gear indicates one that has 6 teeth per inch of pitch diameter. If the pitch diameter is 3 inches, the number of teeth is 3×6 or 18. The outside diameter of the gear is equal to the pitch diameter plus twice the addendum distance, or 3 inches $+ 2 \times \frac{1}{6}$, which is 3.333 inches.

Any involute gear of a given pitch will mesh properly with a gear of any other size of the same pitch. However, in cutting gears of various diameters, a slight difference in the cutter is necessary, to allow for the change in curvature of the involute as the diameter increases. The extreme case would be a rack tooth, which would have a straight line as the theoretical tooth profile. For practical reasons, the number of teeth in an involute gear should be not less than 12.

Methods of Making Gears

Most gears are produced by some machining process. Accurate machine work is essential for high-speed long-wearing quiet-operating gears. Gears operating at slow speeds and under exposed conditions may be sand-cast, but such gears are not efficient in their power transmission. Die casting of small gears carrying light loads has proved very satisfactory. The materials for such gears are limited to low-temperature-melting metals and alloys; consequently, these gears do not have the wearing qualities of heat-treated steel gears. Stamping, although reasonably accurate, can be used only in making thin gears from sheet metal.

The various commercial methods employed in producing gears may be summarized as follows:

1. Casting
    (*a*) Sand and plaster casting.
    (*b*) Die casting.
2. Stamping.
3. Machining
    (*a*) Formed-tooth process
        (1) Form cutter in milling machine.
        (2) Form cutter in broaching machine.
        (3) Form cutter in shaper.
    (*b*) Templet process.
    (*c*) Cutter generating process
        (1) Cutter gear in shaper.
        (2) Hob cutter.
        (3) Rotary cutter.
        (4) Reciprocating cutters simulating a rack.
4. Powder metallurgy.
5. Extruding.

Formed-Tooth Process

A *formed* milling cutter, as shown in Figure 1, is commonly used for cutting a spur gear. Such a cutter is used on a milling machine, and the setup is shown in the lower part of the figure. The cutter is formed according to the shape of the tooth space to be removed. Theoretically, there should be a different-shaped cutter for each size of gear of a given pitch, as there is a slight change in the curvature of the involute. However, one cutter can be used for several gears having different numbers of teeth without much sacrifice in their operating action. Each pitch cutter is made in eight slightly varying shapes to compensate for this change. They vary from no. 1, which is used to cut gears from 135 teeth to a rack, to no. 8, which cuts gears having 12 or 13 teeth. Special cutters are available where greater accuracy is necessary.

The method of setting up a milling machine to cut gears is discussed in Chapter 19. The formed milling process may be used with accurate results for cutting spur, helical, worm, and worm gears. Although sometimes used for bevel gears, the process is not accurate because of the gradual change in the tooth thickness. When it is used for bevel gears, at least two cuts are necessary for each tooth space. The usual practice is to take one center cut of proper depth and about equal to the space at the small end of the tooth. Two shaving cuts are then taken on each side of the tooth space to give the tooth its proper shape.

The formed-tooth principle may also be utilized in a broaching machine by making the broaching tool conform to the tooth space. Small internal gears can be completely cut in one operation by having a round broaching tool made with the same number of cutters as the gear has teeth. Broaching is limited to large production because of the high cost of the cutters.

Courtesy Michigan Tool Company.

Fig. 6. Looking up Inside the Cutter Head of a "Shear-Speed" Gear Shaper. The Cutter Head Has Moved to Loading Position after Completing a Spur Shoulder Gear.

A recent development in the roughing and semifinishing of spur and spiral gears is a new machine known as a "shear speed" gear shaper. This machine is designed so that all teeth on a gear are cut simultaneously by a ring of form-cutting tools or blades surrounding the gear blank. In Figure 6 is shown a view looking up inside the cutter head of this machine after a spur shoulder gear has been cut.

The cutting action of the machine is as follows: The gear is clamped on an arbor and the cutting head lowered and locked into position. A ram holding the gear blank is reciprocated, and at each up stroke the radial blades are fed into the work an equal amount. At the upper end of the stroke the blades are retracted slightly to provide clearance as the work returns to starting position. As the blades approach the proper tooth depth, the feed is reduced by the controlling cam.

This method of gear cutting is very rapid; in many cases the actual cutting cycle is less than one minute. Accurate finishing of gears produced by this method is done on a gear-shaving machine.

Templet Gear-Cutting Process

In the *templet* process for cutting gear teeth, the form of the tooth is controlled by a templet instead of by a formed tool. The tool itself is similar to a side-cutting shaper tool and is given a reciprocating motion in the process of cutting. The·process is especially adapted to

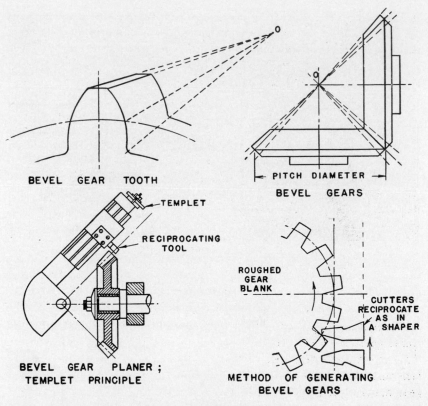

BEVEL   GEAR   TOOTH

PITCH   DIAMETER

BEVEL   GEARS

TEMPLET

RECIPROCATING TOOL

ROUGHED GEAR BLANK

CUTTERS RECIPROCATE AS IN A SHAPER

BEVEL   GEAR   PLANER ; TEMPLET   PRINCIPLE

METHOD   OF   GENERATING BEVEL   GEARS

FIG. 7.   Bevel-Gear Cutting.

cutting large teeth, which would be difficult with a formed cutter, and also to cutting bevel-gear teeth. The principle involved in a bevel-gear planer is shown in Figure 7. The frame carrying the reciprocating tool is guided at one end by a roller acting against a templet, while the other end is pivoted at a fixed point corresponding to the gear being cut. Three sets of templets are necessary, one for the center cut and one for each side of the tooth space. The gear blank is held stationary during the process and is moved only when indexed. This method of cutting produces an accurately formed tooth having the proper taper. Machines of this type are fully automatic in their operation.

For cutting gears with straight teeth, such as spur gears, the action is similar to that just described. In this case the cutter head is adjusted so that the tool travel is parallel to the elements of the teeth.

Cutter-Gear Generating Process

The *cutter-gear generating* process for cutting involute gears is based on the fact that any two involute gears of the same pitch will mesh together. Hence, if one gear is made to act as a cutter and is given

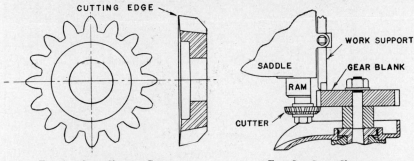

FIG. 8. Gear-Shaper Cutter.　　　FIG. 9. Gear Shaper.

a reciprocating motion, as in a shaper, it will be capable of cutting into a gear blank and generating conjugate tooth forms. A gear-shaper cutter of this description is shown in Figure 8, and the adjacent Figure 9 shows how it is mounted in a Fellows gear shaper. At the start of the operation the gear is held stationary, and the reciprocating cutter is fed into the blank to the correct tooth depth. The feed is then stopped, and both cutter and gear blank are given intermittent rotary motion of the same pitch-line velocity. The rotation, or cutter feed, takes place at the end of the stroke. The generating action of the cutter and gear blank is

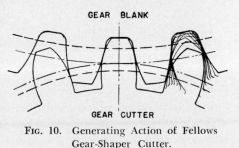

FIG. 10. Generating Action of Fellows Gear-Shaper Cutter.

shown in Figure 10, the fine lines indicating the amounts of metal removed by each cut in a given tooth space. The usual practice is to have the cut take place on the up stroke. However, in many cases, the cutting action is of necessity on the down stroke. A complete view of a Fellows gear shaper is shown in Figure 11.

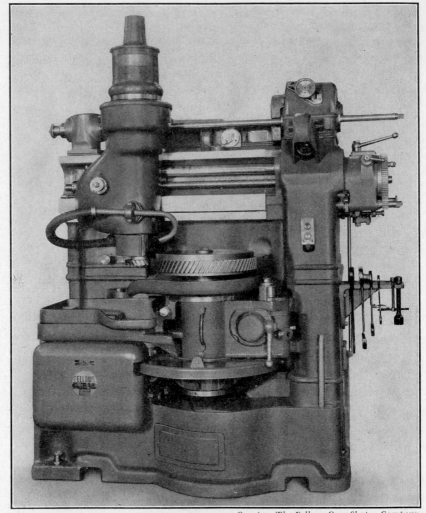

Courtesy The Fellows Gear Shaper Company.

Fig. 11.   Gear Shaper Setup for Cutting Helical Gear.

The cutter-gear method of generating gears is not limited to involute spur gears but has many other applications.   By using a spiral cutter and giving it a twisting motion on the cutting stroke, spiral or helical gears may be generated.   Worm threads may be cut in a similar fashion.   Figure 12 illustrates the application of this process in the cutting of internal gears.   In addition, this process may be used in cutting sprocket wheels, splines, gear-type clutches, cams, ratchet wheels, and many other straight and curved forms.

Two types of gear-shaper machines have been designed for high-production jobs: one a *rotary gear shaper,* having ten complete cutting units; and the other a multispindle planetary gear shaper. The rotary-type shaper with its ten gear-cutting units is mounted to rotate on a single base. Each unit operates independently of the others and is timed to complete a gear in one revolution of the machine. In other words, nine gears are being cut simultaneously while at one station

Courtesy The Fellows Gear Shaper Company.

FIG. 12. Shaping an Internal Gear.

unloading and loading is taking place. This machine has a production rate greater than ten single-spindle machines and requires much less floor space.

The cutter and gear arrangement for the *planetary gear shaper* is shown in Figure 13. This view shows the gap-type cutter in the position that it occupies on the machine with the work in various stages of completion located around the cutter. In operation the work rotates with a planetary motion about the reciprocating cutter—all six gears in various stages of completion are cut simultaneously. With this arrangement it is possible to rough- and finish-cut in one progressive operation.

Another interesting application of the cutter-gear generator principle is the Sykes gear-generating machine, well known for its ability to cut continuous herringbone teeth. One of these machines is illustrated in Figure 14. This machine employs two cutter gears mounted in a horizontal position, as shown in Figure 15. In the cutting of herringbone gears the cutters are given a reciprocating motion, one cutting in

Courtesy The Fellows Gear Shaper Company.

FIG. 13.   Cutter and Gear-Blank Arrangement on 6-Spindle Planetary Gear Shaper.

Courtesy Farrel-Birmingham Company.

FIG. 14.   Sykes Gear-Generating Machine for Continuous-Tooth Herringbone Gears.

one direction up to the center of the gear blank and the other cutting to the same point when the motion is reversed. The cutters not only reciprocate but also are given a twisting motion according to the helix angle. Both the gear blank and cutters slowly revolve, generating the teeth in the same fashion as the Fellows shaper does. Machines of this type are built in various sizes, up to those capable of cutting gears 22 feet in diameter.

FIG. 15. View of the Cutter Gears on Sykes Gear-Generating Machine.

An important feature of the cutter-gear process is its ability to cut double and single helical gears, internal gears, spur gears, worms, racks, pump rotors, and a large variety of special forms Two members of a cluster gear may be cut simultaneously, even though they are not the same type of gear nor of the same pitch. The machine generates tooth contours of true involute shape with teeth uniformly spaced and smoothly finished.

Bevel-Gear Generators

Correctly formed bevel gears can also be cut with reciprocating tools, utilizing the generating principle. The principle involved is based on the fact that any bevel gear will mesh with a crown gear of the same pitch having its center coinciding with the cone apex of the gear. In the lower right-hand corner of Figure 7 the two cutting tools used represent the sides of adjacent teeth of a crown gear. These cutting tools rotate about the point that would be the axis of the crown gear and at the same time are given a reciprocating motion. The gear blank is also rotated about its axis at the rate it would have were it

meshing with the crown gear.   As the tools are simulating the respective positions taken by the crown gear, the correct form of tooth is cut.
Both sides of a single tooth are cut on a single generating roll of the
tools and blank, and at the end of the cut the blank is withdrawn and
indexed, while the tools return to correct position for the next cut.

Courtesy Gleason Works.

FIG. 16.   Straight-Bevel-Gear Generator.

Before the generating process, the tooth spaces are roughed, as shown
in the figure, so that only a small amount of metal is removed by the
reciprocating tools when finishing.   Both operations can be done on
the straight-bevel-gear generator, although in some cases separate
roughing machines are used.   Frequently special form tools are used
to produce a closer shape in roughing.   A front view of a straight-bevel-
gear generator is shown in Figure 16.   This machine is fully automatic
and, when started, will complete a gear without further attention being
given it.   An important feature of this machine is its ability to obtain
localized tooth bearing in straight-bevel gears.   The slight crowning
on the tooth surface localizes the tooth bearing on the center three
quarters and eliminates load concentrations on the ends of the teeth.

The method of cutting spiral-bevel gears also uses the generating principle, but the cutter in this case is circular and rotates as a face milling cutter. The cutter is similar to the one in Figure 17, which is shown cutting a hypoid pinion. The spiral teeth on gears cut by this process are curved on the arc of a circle, the radius being equal

Courtesy Gleason Works.

FIG. 17. Close-Up of Work Head of a Hypoid Gear-Generating-Machine Cutting Pinion.

to the radius of the cutter. The blades of the cutter have straight cutting profiles to correspond with the tooth profile of a crown gear. The revolving cutters move through the same space as would be occupied by a crown gear tooth. As in the previous method, the teeth are first roughed out before the true shape is generated. The rotating cutters may be designed to cut only one or both sides of the tooth space, the latter-type cutter having the advantage of more rapid production. Spiral-bevel gears have an advantage over straight-bevel gears in that the teeth engage with one another gradually, eliminating any shock or noise in their operation.

A special type of gear, known as a hypoid gear, can be cut in the machine just described. The hypoid gear, widely used in drives for automobiles, streetcars, motorcycles, and similar applications, has the axis of the pinion offset and does not intersect the axis of the gear. Such a gear is shown in Figure 4. As the cutter rotates (see Figure 17) it is fed into the gear blank and then withdrawn. There is an accompanying rolling generating movement of the cutter cradle and gear blank to produce the correct tooth profile. The rolling motion corresponds to the meshing action between the gear and a crown gear of which the cutter represents a tooth. This operation is repeated until all teeth are cut. Heat-treated spiral-bevel, zerol, and hypoid gears may be ground by using a cup wheel and employing the principles just described.

Generating Gears with a Hob Cutter

Any involute gear of a given pitch will mesh with a rack of the same pitch. One form of cutting gears utilizes a rack as a cutter. If it is given a reciprocating motion, similar to cutting on a Fellows shaper, involute teeth will be generated on the gear as it rotates intermittently in mesh with the rack cutter. This method is shown diagrammatically in Figure 18. Such machines require a long rack cutter in order to

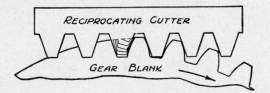

Fig. 18.   Rack-Type Cutter Generating Teeth of Spur Gear.

cut all the teeth on the circumference of a large gear, and for this reason they are little used in the United States.

The hobbing system of generating gears is somewhat similar to the principle just described. A rack is developed into a cylinder, the teeth forming threads and having a lead as in a large screw. Flutes are cut across the threads, forming rack-shaped cutting teeth. These cutting teeth are given relief, and, if the job is viewed from one end, it looks the same as the ordinary form gear cutter. This cutting tool, known as a *hob*, may be briefly described as a fluted steel worm. In Figure 19 is shown a hob in section and end view, as it appears when cutting a gear blank.

Hobbing, then, may be defined as a generating process consisting of rotating and advancing a fluted steel worm cutter past a revolving blank. This action is clearly illustrated in Figure 20, where the teeth on a spur gear are being cut to full depth by a rotating hob. In this

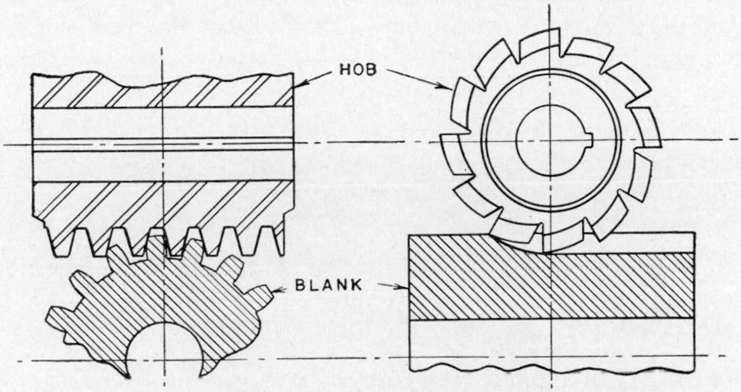

FIG. 19. Cutting Gear with Hob.

Courtesy The Cleveland Hobbing Machine Company.

FIG. 20. Hobbing a 1½ Diametral-Pitch Spur Gear to Full Depth in One Cut.

process all motions are rotary, there being no reciprocating or indexing movements. In the actual process of cutting, the gear and hob rotate together as in mesh. The speed ratio of the two depends upon the number of teeth on the gear and on whether the hob is single-threaded or multithreaded.

At the start of operations the gear blank is moved in toward the rotating hob until the proper depth is reached, the pitch-line velocity

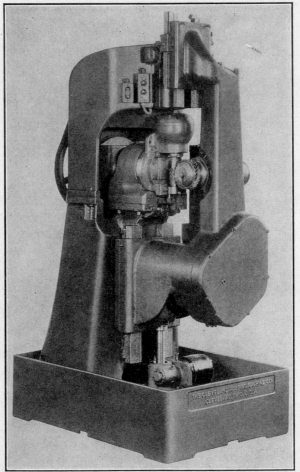

Courtesy The Cleveland Hobbing Machine Company.

FIG. 21. Cutting a Worm Gear in a Cleveland Single-Spindle Hobbing Machine.

of the gear being the same as the lead velocity of the hob.   The action is the same as if the gear were meshing with a rack.   As soon as the depth is reached, the hob cutter is fed across the face of the gear until the teeth are complete, both gear and cutter rotating during the entire process.

Inasmuch as the hob teeth have a certain amount of lead, the axis of the hob cannot be at right angles to the axis of the gear when cutting spur gears but must be moved an amount equal to the lead angle. For

Courtesy Gould and Eberhardt.

FIG. 22.   Hobbing Machine Setup for Cutting Three Helical Gears.

helical gears, the hob must be moved around an additional angle equal to the helix angle of the gears. Worm gears may be cut with the axis of the hob at right angles to the gear and the hob fed tangentially as the gear rotates. This operation is clearly shown in Figure 21.

In Figure 22 is shown a hobbing machine set up for cutting three helical gears. This is a universal machine and can be used for the production of spur gears, single- or double-helical gears, worm gears,

Courtesy Gould and Eberhardt.

Fig. 23. Hobbing Square Splines on a Stub Shaft Using a Hob.

worms, sprockets, or splines. A close-up view of this same machine, set up for cutting splines on a stub shaft, is shown in Figure 23.

It is interesting to note that gear hobs based on the rack principle will cut gears of any diameter. This eliminates the need for a variety of hobs for gears having the same pitch but varying in diameter. Special hobs, such as those used for cutting splines, will cut only the one part.

Finishing Operations Used on Gears

The object of any finishing operation on a gear is to eliminate slight inaccuracies in the tooth profile, spacing, and concentricity so that the gears will have conjugate tooth forms and give quiet operation at high speeds. These inaccuracies are very small dimensionally, frequently not exceeding 0.0005 inch, but even this amount is sufficient to increase wear and set up undesirable noises at high speeds. In spite of the accuracy of various gear-forming and gear-generating processes, slight errors enter into gears as a result of wear in machine bearings, lead screws, or gear trains; faulty mounting of cutter on work; use of improper material; heat treatment; and the like.

To remedy these errors in gears that are not heat-treated, such operations as *shaving* or *burnishing* are used. Burnishing is a cold-working operation accomplished by rolling the gear in contact and under pressure with three hardened burnishing gears. Although the gears may be made accurate in tooth form, the disadvantage of this process is that the surface of the tooth is covered with amorphous or "smear" metal rather than metal having true crystalline structure, which is desirable from a long-life standpoint. More accurate results may be obtained by a shaving process which removes only a few thousandths of an inch of metal. This process is strictly a cutting and not a cold-working process.

Two methods of shaving are in use: one rolling the gear in contact with a rack cutter and the other using a rotary cutter. Either method will produce accurately formed teeth. Both external and internal spur and helical gears can be finished by this process.

In Figure 24 is shown a *rack-type gear finisher*, the insert above showing a close-up view of the rack shaving cutter finishing a spur gear. The generating rack consists of straight replaceable blades, each tooth having a number of small vertical grooves separated by lands which form the parallel cutting edges. It is mounted on the table of the machine, which reciprocates similarly to a planer table. The gear to be finished is mounted above the rack on live centers and is driven by contact with the cutting rack. The gear shaving or finishing is accomplished by the gear rolling on the rack cutter and at the same time being reciprocated back and forth across the face of the cutter. At each stroke the gear is fed down into the rack cutter until the correct tooth depth is obtained. Spur gears are shaved with racks having blades at a slight angle, whereas straight-bladed racks are used for gears having helix angles up to 30 degrees. Only one rack is required for gears of the same pitch.

Finishing a Spur Gear with a Rack Shaving Cutter.

Both Photos Courtesy Michigan Tool Company.

Rack-Type Gear Finisher.

FIG. 24.

A close-up view of the *rotary crossed-axis gear finisher* in operation is shown in Figure 25.   The rotary cutter is a gearlike tool having a plurality of cutting edges on the teeth, which in turn are conjugate to the teeth to be produced on the gear in the machine.   On the surfaces of the rotary cutters are small cutting edges similar to those used on rack-type cutters.   Improved cutting action is obtained by having the axis of the gears and cutter at some angle ranging from 3 to 15 degrees.

Courtesy Michigan Tool Company.

Fig. 25.   Rotary Shaving Cutter Finishing Transmission Gears.

The cutter is the driver, and at the same time there is an axial movement of the cutter so as to finish the full width of the gear.   Both types of gear-finishing machines may be arranged for curve shaving, a process that produces teeth slightly thicker at the center to eliminate load concentrations on the ends of the teeth.   This operation is commonly known as *crowning*.

The time required for gear shaving is very short, and many thousand gears may be cut before the cutter must be resharpened.   Rack cutters are more expensive than rotary cutters, but the tool cost per gear is much lower by reason of the increased life of the cutter.   Rotary finishing machines, being less expensive, are economical for finishing varieties of gears in relatively smaller quantities.   Also, if the gears are extremely large, or if there is close interference (as in cluster gears), rotary shaving is economical.   The process of gear shaving is widely used in accurately finishing gears for transmissions, reduction units, machine tools, pumps, and numerous other high-speed applications.

Heat-treated gears can be finished either by *grinding* or by *lapping*. Grinding may be done by either the forming or the generating process. In the forming process the grinding wheel conforms to the tooth space to be ground. Three diamonds are mounted on the machine and controlled by templates through a pantograph mechanism to give the correct contour to the wheel. The generating process, as shown in Figure 26, uses a flat-faced grinding wheel which corresponds to the face of an imaginary rack meshing with the gear. One side of a tooth is ground at a time, the gear rolling on its pitch circle past the revolving wheel as if meshing with a rack. Another machine, operating on the same principle, will grind both surfaces of a tooth simultaneously. The disadvantage of gear grinding is that considerable time is consumed in the process. Also the surfaces of the teeth have small scratches or ridges which increase both wear and noise. To eliminate the latter defect, ground gears are frequently lapped a short time.

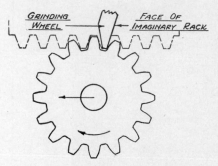

Fig. 26. Grinding Involute Gears.

Gear lapping is accomplished by having the gear in contact with one or more cast-iron lap gears of true shape. A two-lap gear finishing machine, operating on the crossed-axis principle similar to the rotary gear shaver, is shown in Figure 27. The work is mounted between centers and is slowly driven by the rear lap. It in turn drives the front lap, and at the same time both laps are rapidly reciprocated across the gear face. Each lap has individual adjustment and pressure control. A fine abrasive is used with kerosene of a light oil to assist in the cutting action.

The machines may be adjusted to provide an automatic lapping cycle of 4 seconds to 20 minutes, operating first in one direction, then reversing for the same length of time in the opposite direction. By adjusting the axis of the laps it is possible to crown the tooth slightly so that the major bearing is at the center.

The entire operation of lapping is essentially a corrective and finishing one, and very little material is removed in the process. The time consumed for average-sized gears is $\frac{1}{2}$ to 2 minutes per side of gear teeth. The results of lapping are demonstrated by longer-wearing and quieter-operating gears.

Courtesy Michigan Tool Company.

Fig. 27. Gear-Lapping Machine Using Two Laps.

Gear-Testing Equipment

Although modern gear-cutting and gear-generating machines are capable of producing correctly formed gears, it is advisable to subject gears required for high-speed and accurate machinery to some tests before their assembly. These tests vary, but include factors such as concentricity, size, noise, tooth bearing, and spacing. All tests should be made with accurate and rigid equipment and in the shortest possible time. The best method of testing and inspection is that which most nearly simulates the actual working conditions of the gears.

Numerous inspecting and testing devices have been developed for checking such factors as the pitch diameter, tooth form, eccentricity, tooth spacing, and helix angle. Minor defects, such as those caused by distortions during heat treatment, can be detected readily by these measuring devices. Similar equipment is available for checking gear hobs and cutters of other types. Although individual tests are necessary to locate some specific error, the final test of whether a gear is satisfactory or not is to run it under conditions as near the actual service operation as possible.

Review Questions

1. How does a spur gear differ from a helical gear?

2. What is a rack gear and for what purpose is it used?

3. Briefly describe the following types of gears: crown, annular, worm, zerol, and herringbone.

4. What is the difference between the pitch circle and the base circle of a spur gear?

5. What is the addendum of a gear tooth, and how does it differ from the dedendum?

6. Prove that the product of the diametral and circular pitches is equal to π.

7. Sketch an involute gear tooth, and indicate addendum, pitch circle, circular pitch, tooth face, and dedendum.

8. How is an involute curve drawn, and why is this curve desirable for a tooth profile?

9. A 14½-degree standard involute gear has a pitch diameter of 3 inches. If a 6-pitch cutter is used, how many teeth will the gear have? What should be the outside diameter of the gear?

10. A spur gear is cut with an 8-inch pitch cutter. Determine the circular pitch, addendum, and outside diameter if the gear has 40 teeth.

11. List the various processes used in making gears.

12. Describe three methods of making spur gears by the formed-tooth process.

13. Describe the method of generating a spur gear on a Fellows gear shaper.

14. How are gears cut on a shear-speed shaper?

15. What is the difference in the methods used for cutting spiral bevels or hypoids?

16. What is a hob, and why can it be used for cutting gears?

17. What is meant by "gear finishing," and why are such processes used?

18. How is gear shaving accomplished, and what two methods are used?

19. Briefly describe how heat-treated gears may be ground.

20. How are gears lapped?

21. What are important things to check in gear inspection?

References

BUCKINGHAM, EARLE, *Spur Gears,* McGraw-Hill Book Company, 1928.

COLVIN, F. H., and F. A. STANLEY, *Gear Cutting Practice,* McGraw-Hill Book Company, 1937.

Gears—Cutting, Finishing, Checking, Michigan Tool Company, 1945.

KENT's *Mechanical Engineers' Handbook,* 12th edition, John Wiley & Sons, 1950.

Machinery Handbook, 13th edition, Industrial Press, 1948.

STAUB, C. R., and M. R. ANDERSON, "Shaving and Lapping Gears," *Tool Engineer*, December 1940.

STRAUCHEN, D., "Producing Precision Gears in a Machine Tool Plant," *Machinery*, September 1939.

The Practical Art of Generating, Fellows Gear Shaper Company.

TRAUTSCHOLD, R., *Standard Gear Book*, McGraw-Hill Book Company, 1935.

WILDHABER, ERNEST, (a) "Precision Gears Cut Quickly," *American Machinist*, June 7, 1945. (b) "Basic Relationships of Bevel Gears," *American Machinist*, September 27, 1945. (c) "Special Analysis of Gear Mesh Clarifies Curvature Conditions," *American Machinist*, October 25, 1945.

YOUNG, GARDNER, "Modern Methods in Gear Manufacture," *Machinery*, October 1940.

CHAPTER
21

METAL SAWING

An important operation in any shop is the sawing of materials and bar stock for subsequent machining operations. Although most machine tools can do cutting-off operations to a limited extent, special machines are necessary for mass-production work and for miscellaneous work which requires a wide variety of shapes and sizes. Metal sawing is similar to wood sawing, except that the type of saw has teeth specially designed for metal work, with the proper spacing and angles for efficient cutting.

Hand sawing, used on many simple jobs and in situations where the work cannot be brought to a power saw, is done with a thin flexible blade, usually 8 to 12 inches in length, held in a hacksaw frame which is provided with a suitable hand grip. The tooth pitch of such saws will vary from 14 to 32 teeth per inch. Although coarse-tooth saws allow more chip space, the spacing will vary according to the thickness and kind of material being cut. An average pitch for handsaws is around 18 teeth per inch, but for thin materials and tubing a finer pitch is advisable.

Metal saws for power machines are made in *circular, straight,* or *continuous* shapes, depending on the type of machine with which they are to be used. The various types of power sawing machines are listed in the following classification:

METAL-SAWING MACHINES

1. Reciprocating saw
   (*a*) Horizontal hacksaw machine.
   (*b*) Vertical sawing and filing machine.

2. Circular saw
   (*a*) Metal saw.

   (*b*) Steel friction disk.
   (*c*) Abrasive disk.

3. Band saw
   (*a*) Saw blade.
   (*b*) Friction blade.

Reciprocating Sawing Machines

The reciprocating hacksaw, which may vary in design from light-duty crank-driven saws to large heavy-duty machines hydraulically driven, has long been a favorite because of its simplicity in design and low operating cost. It consists of a saw frame, a means for reciprocating the saw and frame, a work table and vise, a supporting base, and a source of power. Machines of this type vary in the manner in which the saw is fed into the work and the type of drive used.

The simplest type of feed is the *gravity feed,* in which the saw blade is forced into the work by the weight of the saw and frame. Uniform pressure is exerted in the work during the stroke, but some provision is usually made to control the depth of feed for a given stroke. Some machines of this type have weights clamped on the frame to give additional control to the cutting pressure. This may also be accomplished by means of springs with suitable adjustment. Positive-acting screw feeds, with some provision for overloads, provide a means of obtaining a definite depth of cut for each cutting stroke. Hydraulic feeds are now widely used, since they afford excellent control of the cutting pressures. Several machines with this type of feed are discussed in subsequent paragraphs of this chapter.

In general, methods of feeding can be classified as either *positive* or *definite pressure* feeds. A positive feed has an exact depth of cut for each stroke, and the pressure on the blade will vary directly with the number of teeth in contact with the work. Therefore, in cutting a round bar the pressure is light at the start and maximum at the center. A disadvantage of this method is that the saw is prevented from cutting fast at the start and the finish where the contact stroke is short. With definite pressure feeds, the pressure is uniform at all times, regardless of the number of teeth in contact. This condition prevails in gravity or friction feeds. Here the depth of cut varies inversely with the number of teeth in contact, so that the maximum pressure that can be used depends on the maximum load that a single tooth can stand. Many machines of recent design have incorporated both these systems into their design with automatic control. In all cases the pressure is released on the return stroke to eliminate wear on the saw blade.

The simplest drive for the saw frame is that with a crank rotating at a uniform speed. With this arrangement the cutting action is taking place only 50% of the time, since the time of the return stroke equals that of the cutting stroke. An improvement of this design provides a link mechanism which gives a quick-return action on the cutting stroke. Several such link mechanisms are used, including the Whitworth mechanism found on some shapers. These designs reduce the idle time to about one third of the total and result in faster cutting than the crank saws without increasing the cutting speed.

Figure 1 shows a hydraulic shear-cut production saw. The term "shear cut" describes a cutting action used in this machine, whereby the cutting edge of a metal saw is fed progressively and uniformly in a manner to give the most effective cutting. The feed is hydraulically operated and is equipped with valve control to give either a positive progressive feed or a flexible constant-pressure feed. The positive feed is recommended for production runs in the sawing of tough steels, such

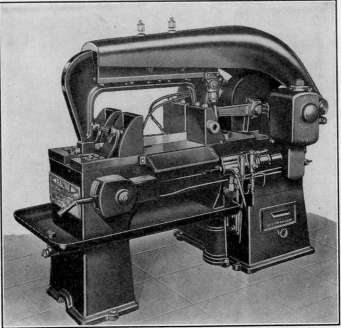

Courtesy Racine Tool & Machine Company.

Fig. 1. Hydraulic Heavy-Duty Metal-Cutting Machine.

as stainless steel, die blocks, and numerous other alloys. The flexible constant-pressure feed is used for automatically increasing or decreasing the feed in accordance with the area, shape, or density of the material being cut. In both cases the hydraulic-feed pressure is applied progressively during the cut, and each tooth produces a long curling chip. This machine can be provided with an automatic stock feed. With this device a single bar, or a bundle, can be cut to the desired lengths, leaving the operator free to do other work. The entire cycle is hydraulically controlled and positive in its action.

Another reciprocating saw, equipped with automatic bar feed and discharge tracks, is shown in Figure 2. Bars to be cut are loaded on a rolling dolly and vise, and are either manually or automatically moved forward by a chain arrangement. The usual cycle for automatic feed after the gage has been set is as follows: Bars move forward through open vise the desired distance, vise is clamped, pieces are cut off by saw, saw is raised to original position, vise is opened, and so on, until the desired length of bar has been cut up.

Courtesy Armstrong-Blum Manufacturing Company.

FIG. 2. Automatic Bar-Feed Hack-Saw Machine.

Hacksaw blades. Power-hacksaw blades are similar to those used for hand sawing. High-speed steel blades vary from 12 to 32 inches in length and are made in various thicknesses up to 0.100 inch. The pitch is coarser than for hand sawing, ranging from 2 to 18 teeth per inch, since the material being cut is usually much larger. For efficient cutting of ordinary steel and cast iron, as coarse a pitch as possible should be used to provide ample chip space between teeth. However, two or more teeth should always be in contact with the stock being cut.

High-carbon and alloy steels require a medium-pitch blade, whereas thin metal, tubing, and brass require a fine pitch. To provide ample clearance for the blade while cutting, the teeth are set to cut a slot or *kerf* slightly wider than the thickness of the blade. This is done by bending certain teeth slightly to the right or the left. A coolant is recommended for all power-hacksaw cutting to prevent overheating the blade and to wash away the small chips accumulating between the teeth. Cutting speeds range from 50 to 150 surface feet per minute, according to the machinability of the metal being cut.

Circular Sawing Machines

Machines using circular saws are commonly known as *cold sawing machines.* The saws are fairly large in diameter and operate at low

Courtesy The Motch & Merryweather Company.

FIG. 3.   Hydraulic-Feed Cold Sawing Machine.

rotational speeds. The cutting action is the same as that obtained with a milling cutter. The machine consists of a rotating saw, means for feeding the saw into the work, a vise for clamping the part to be cut, and a supporting frame.

In Figure 3 is shown a hydraulic-feed cold sawing machine capable of sawing round stock up to 10 inches in diameter. Nine changes of speed in geometric progression are provided for the saw blade. This

Fig. 4. Inserted-Tooth Disk-Saw in Use on Production Job.

affords a wide selection of cutting speeds, ranging from 18 feet per minute for hard materials to 134 feet per minute for softer materials. The feed for the saw carriage is hydraulically operated and provides a "stepless" variable feed as well as a quick return. The feed pressure may be set at a point that will protect the saw, regardless of the rate for which the feed is set. Hence, if the saw encounters a change in section or hardness of material which overloads the blade, the rate of feed is automatically decreased until the overload is eliminated. Another circular-sawing machine made by the Cochrane-Bly Company is illustrated in Figure 4. The inserted tooth saw and saw carriage are clearly shown in working position. A large bundle of rods is being cut to length on a typical production job.

Circular metal saws. Saws for rotating cutter machines are similar to the metal-slitting saws used with milling machines. However, metal-slitting saws are made only in diameters up to 8 inches, which is not sufficient for large-size work. Some solid blades, with diameters not exceeding 16 inches, are used in circular sawing machines. Their use is limited because of cost and the fact that broken or worn teeth cannot be replaced. Most large cutters have either replaceable inserted teeth or segmental-type blades. In the latter type the segments, each having about four teeth, are grooved to fit over a tongue on the disk and are riveted in place. Both inserted teeth and segmental-type blades are economical from the standpoint of cutter-material cost and have the additional advantage that worn teeth can be replaced.

Cutting speeds of circular blades range from 25 to 80 surface feet per minute for ferrous metals and have much higher speeds for the nonferrous metals. A clearance angle of 7 degrees is used for soft materials, and, if harder materials are to be cut, this figure should be increased slightly. Rake angles vary from 10 to 24 degrees, the smaller angles being for the harder materials. The use of cutting fluids is recommended both to lubricate the cutter and to remove chips from the teeth.

Steel friction disks. Steel disks operating at high peripheral speeds provide a rapid means of cutting through structural-steel members and other steel sections. When the disk is rotating at rim speeds from 18,000 to 25,000 feet per minute, the heat of friction quickly melts a path through the part being cut. About one-half minute is required to cut through a 24-inch I beam. Large-diameter disks are used in this work, ranging in diameter from 24 to 60 inches. They are usually furnished with small indentions on the circumference about $\frac{3}{32}$ inch deep. The disks are slightly hollow ground to provide side clearance in cutting through a large member. Water cooling is recommended in this type of cutting. Large machines have the disk wheel mounted on a carriage which is controlled by power feed, whereas light machines ordinarily use a hand- or foot-pedal feed. Friction sawing of nonferrous metal is unsatisfactory.

Abrasive disks. A small dry-cutting machine equipped with a thin abrasive wheel is illustrated in Figure 5. This machine will cut solid stock up to ¾ inch in diameter as well as tool bits, drills, and other hardened materials. Abrasive-disk machines operate either wet or dry,

Courtesy A. P. De Sanno and Son.

Fig. 5. Radiac Cutoff Machine Equipped with Abrasive-Disk Wheels.

but, when heavy cutting is involved, a coolant should be used. The disks are either rubber- or resinoid-bonded, since, being thin, they must have some flexibility. The resinoid-bonded wheels are operated at higher speeds (16,000 sfpm) and are generally used dry, whereas rubber-bonded wheels, operating at lower speeds (9000 sfpm), are used for wet cutting. Although most work done on abrasive-disk machines is less than 2 inches in diameter, sizes up to 6 inches can be cut on automatic machines with the wheel reciprocating across the work. Abrasive cutting can be used for almost all materials. The finish and accuracy is much better than that obtained from using steel friction blades.

Band-Sawing Machines

Band sawing. The sawing machines described thus far are designed for taking straight cuts and are used primarily for cutting-off purposes.

Cutting saws of the *band type* can also be used for this work but, in addition, can cut irregular curves in metal. This widens the field of usefulness for the band saw, since it enables the machine to do a great

Courtesy The DoALL Company.

FIG. 6. Machine for Contour Sawing, Band Filing, and Polishing.

variety of work that formerly had to be done with other machine tools. Contour sawing of dies, jigs, cams, templates, and numerous other parts that formerly had to be made entirely on other machine tools or by hand at much greater expense is now done with band saws. Recent developments of these machines include suitable and accurate arrangements for continuous filing and polishing, both necessary operations in contour finishing.

Band-sawing machines for metals are very similar in appearance to those used for wood but differ in the saw-cutting speed and type of saw. Most machines are designed with the saw running in a vertical position, the work being supported on a horizontal table having a tilting adjustment for cutting angles. Another type is quite similar in design to the ordinary hacksaw machine. The work is held in a vise while a small band saw operates above the work in nearly a horizontal position. Both types are widely used for cutting off stock in the same way that such work is done on circular and reciprocating sawing machines.

A contour machine for *band sawing, filing,* and *polishing* is shown in Figure 6. This machine employs saw blades $\frac{1}{16}$ to $\frac{1}{2}$ inch in width, file bands in three different sizes, and emery bands for polishing work. It has an infinitely variable-cutting-speed range of 50 to 375 feet per minute. An indicating dial showing the exact operating speed of the saw in feet per minute is mounted on the face of the column. Just below this dial, in a convenient position, is a resistance-type butt welder which automatically provides the proper welding current for any saw $\frac{1}{16}$ to $\frac{5}{8}$ inch wide. This procedure is followed in doing internal cutting: The saw blade is first cut, then inserted through a hole drilled in the work, and finally butt-welded together. A small built-in grinder is provided for dressing the ends of saws and grinding the welds.

Band-saw blades. An important step in precision sawing is the selection of the proper saw for each job. The width is determined by the feed that is to be used and by the curvature to be cut. It is a good rule always to use the widest blade possible.

The temper or hardness of the saw varies with the type of material to be cut. A hard temper should be used for cutting alloy steels; a softer temper is recommended for nonferrous materials.

The number of teeth per inch is also a function of the material being worked on. This factor does not vary directly with the hardness of the material but is determined from actual cutting experience; manufacturers' recommendations should be followed in this respect.

The *set* refers to the type of tooth construction on a saw. A *straight-tooth saw* has one tooth set to the right and the next tooth to the left. This type of saw is used for brass, copper, and plastics. On the *raker-tooth saw* one straight tooth alternates with two teeth set in opposite directions. This tooth construction is used for most steel and iron cutting. A *wave set* consists of an alternate arrangement of several teeth set to the right and several teeth set to the left. This design is used in cutting tubes and light sheets of metal.

Band-friction cutting. High-speed band-sawing machines, designed for friction cutting, have a surface speed range of 3000 to 15,000 surface feet per minute. Saws for these machines must be selected with care as the teeth should be properly spaced according to the material thickness. The pitch varies from 10 for thick materials to 18 for thin materials. This type of cutting is limited to relatively thin ferrous

Courtesy The DoAll Company.

Fig. 7.   Friction-Sawing Hardened Steel.

metals and some thermoplastic materials. Figure 7 shows the operation of band-saw friction cutting and illustrates the fact that material hardness is not a limiting factor in this process.

Band filing. When the machine is to be used for filing work, the saw band is removed and a file band is put in its place. The file band is made up of 26 files mounted on a flexible Swedish steel band. A snap joint, shown in Figure 8, is provided for quick fastening and unfastening for internal filing. A light-to-medium pressure is used on contour filing, and the filing speeds range from 50 to 200 feet per minute. An advantage of this type of filing is that it is accomplished with a continuous downward stroke. The absence of a back stroke greatly lengthens the life of the file and helps in holding the work on to the table.

Files used on this machine have the same shapes and styles found on standard commercial files. *Single cut, double cut,* and *rasp cut* are the terms used in describing the cut of the file. Rasp cut differs from the other two in that the teeth are disconnected from each other, each tooth being made by a single punch. The coarseness of the teeth is described by the terms *rough, coarse, bastard, double cut,* and *smooth.* File cross sections are indicated by such terms as *flat, oval, half round,* and *mill.*

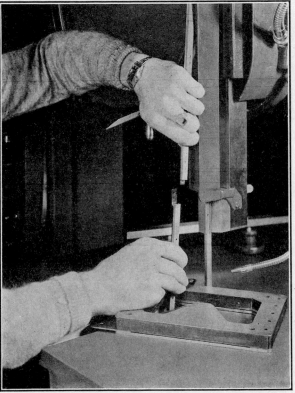

Courtesy The DoAll Company.

FIG. 8. Setting Up File Band for Internal Filing.

Band polishing. A third function of band machines is polishing. This work calls for an endless band of emery cloth which is mounted in the same way as the band saws. At the point of work the cloth band is backed up by a rigid plate. The band is made of the same kind of emery cloth and in the same grits that are conventionally used in hand-polishing work.

Review Questions

1. Prepare a list of the various kinds of power saw machines.

2. What factors should be considered in the selection of the pitch for a hacksaw blade?

3. What methods of feeding the saw into the metal are used on reciprocating saws?

4. Describe the operation of a bar-feed carrier on a power hacksaw.

5. What are the advantages and disadvantages of positive feed on a hacksaw?

6. Explain the meaning of the term *kerf*.

7. What three types of saws are used on a cold sawing machine?

8. What kinds of disks are used in abrasive cut-off machines? At what surface speeds are they operated?

9. Discuss the various types of work that can be done on a metal band saw.

10. In band-saw work what determines the width of the saw, the number of teeth per inch, and the set?

11. How are files used on a band-sawing machine?

12. Why is a coolant used in most sawing work?

13. Discuss the subject of cutting speeds as applied to sawing machines.

14. Distinguish between straight set, raker set, and wave set as applied to hacksaw and band-saw blades.

References

Handbook on Contour Sawing, Continental Machine Specialties Company.

HOLLOWAY, R. C., "Friction Sawing," *American Machinist*, June 7, 1945.

Tool Engineers Handbook, American Society of Tool Engineers, McGraw-Hill Book Company, 1949.

WIESE, R. R., "Cutting with Abrasives," *American Machinist*, February 19, 1941.

BROACHING MACHINES AND TOOLS

Broaching is the operation of removing metal by means of an elongated tool having a number of successive teeth of increasing size which cut in a fixed path. A part is completed in one stroke of the machine, the last teeth on the cutting tool conforming to the desired shape of the finished surface. In most machines the broach is moved past the work, but equally effective results are obtained if the tool is stationary and the work is moved. Although the process of broaching has been known for many years, it has not been used extensively in production work until recently. The first developments of broaching were confined principally to internal operations, such as the broaching of holes and keyways. Many cuts, both external and internal, can be made on recently designed machines at a high rate of production and with satisfactory accuracy and finish.

Types of Broaching Machines

A broaching machine consists of a work-holding fixture, a broaching tool, a drive mechanism, and a suitable supporting frame. Although the component parts are few, several variations in design are possible. A brief classification of broaching according to method of operation is as follows:

1. **Pull broaching.** The broaching tool moves, and the work is stationary.
2. **Push broaching.** The broaching tool moves, and the work is stationary.
3. **Surface broaching.** Either the work or the broaching tool moves across the other.
4. **Continuous broaching.** The work is moved continuously against stationary broaches. The path of movement may be either straight or circular.

According to actual construction, most broaching machines are of horizontal- or vertical-type design. The decision of which design to use is dependent on such factors as size of part, size of broach, quantity, and type of broaching to be done. In general, vertical machines are well adapted for surface broaching, with the tool supported on a

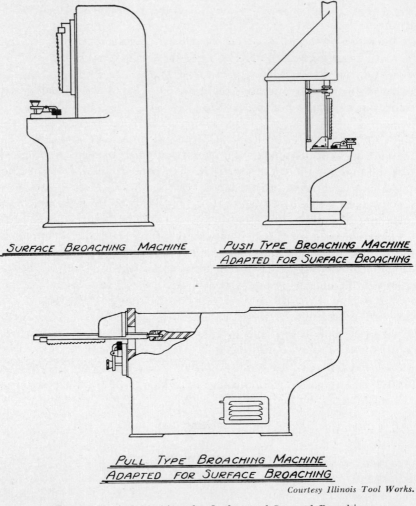

SURFACE BROACHING MACHINE

PUSH TYPE BROACHING MACHINE
ADAPTED FOR SURFACE BROACHING

PULL TYPE BROACHING MACHINE
ADAPTED FOR SURFACE BROACHING

Courtesy Illinois Tool Works.

FIG. 1. Typical Machines for Surface and Internal Broaching.

suitable slide, although both pull- and push-type internal broaching machines are made in this design. Horizontal machines pull the broach and are often used on internal broaching of small and medium-sized work. However, they too have many surface broaching applications. Figure 1 illustrates the versatility of broaching machines and shows how surface broaching can be done by each of the three methods of operation listed above.

Another variation in broaching machines is the method of drive. Because a large force is required, most modern machines are hydraulically driven. Such a drive is smooth-acting, economical, and readily adjustable for both speed and length of stroke. Other drive systems are operated by means of gears, power screw, chain, or a link mechanism. The chain type of drive is especially adapted to the continuous broaching machine. On all intermittent-type machines, a quick-return feature is incorporated in the drive. The return stroke is two to five times the speed of the cutting stroke.

Advantages and Limitations of Broaching

Broaching machines have been rapidly adopted for mass-production work because of their exceptionally high rate of production. The actual cutting time is only a matter of seconds, since the operation is completed in one stroke of the machine. Rapid loading and unloading of fixtures keep the total production time to a minimum.

These machines can also be used for either internal or external surface finishing. Operations formerly performed on milling machines, planers, and the like can frequently be done with broaches equally well and in a much shorter time. Any form that can be reproduced on a broaching tool can be machined. This includes a wide variety of irregular shapes as well as plane surfaces. Tolerances can be maintained which are suitable to interchangeable manufacture. Finishes comparable to milling work are obtained, and in some cases burnishing teeth are incorporated on the broach to improve the surface finish.

A limiting factor in broaching is the cost of the broaching tools, many of which are extremely expensive because of their large size and irregular shape. High tooling cost eliminates broaching for short-run jobs, but it is not an important factor in mass production. Parts being broached must be capable of being rigidly supported and must be able to withstand the broaching forces set up. This is particularly true of surface-broaching work, where the force of the cut is not central. The surface of the work to be broached cannot have any obstruction. Likewise, on internal work, the broaching tool must have free passage through the opening.

Broaching Machines

Vertical single-slide surface machine. The operation being performed on the vertical machine shown in Figure 2 is the broaching of the gasket surface on water-pump bodies. In this case 0.070 inch of metal is removed from the surface at a production rate of 110 pieces

Fɪɢ. 2. Broaching Surface on Water-Pump Body on Single-Slide Vertical-Surface Broaching Machine.

per hour. Parts are held on a two-station rotary fixture to permit loading and unloading during the broaching operation and the return stroke.

Vertical double-slide surface machine. A broaching machine of this type (Figure 3) is shown finishing the sides and ends of connecting-rod bolt bosses at the rate of 600 per hour. This machine differs from the single-slide machine in that it has two slides which operate opposite one another. The work is held on shuttle tables which move out during the unloading and loading operations while the ram returns to its starting position. While this is going on, the other ram is at work. Single-slide machines are usually equipped with a quick return,

Courtesy The Oilgear Company.

FIG. 3. Finish Sides and Ends of Connecting-Rod Bolt Bosses on Double-Slide Vertical Broaching Machine.

but the return and cutting strokes on these machines are the same. This machine is well suited for subsequent operations on connecting rods such as cutting the cap from the rod, and finishing bearing and joint faces. It is adapted to quantity production of flat and contour surfaces, slots, and cutting-off operations.

Vertical push broaching. The operation of push-broaching the internal diameter of gears at the rate of 450 per hour is shown in Figure 4. This production speed is facilitated by the use of an indexing-type fixture which makes possible rapid loading of the gears away

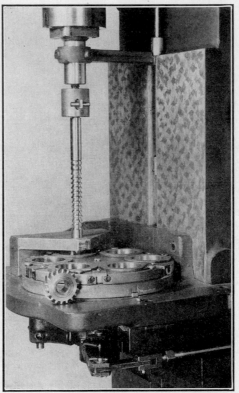

Courtesy Colonial Broach Company.

FIG. 4. Illustrating Use of Indexing Fixture in Push-Broaching Internal Diameter of Gears.

from the operation. As soon as the broach returns to starting position, the fixture is indexed, and the previously broached piece drops below to a tote box. Push broaching requires comparatively short broaches of sufficient cross section so that there is no column action due to the load imposed on it during the operation. Push broaching can be done on simple utility presses.

Vertical pull-down broaching machines. Vertical pull-down machines are adapted to internal broaching, as shown in Figure 5. Parts to be broached in this manner are placed in a fixture on the work table, the pulling mechanism being in the base of the machine. Broaching tools are suspended above by an upper carriage. As the operation starts, the broaches are lowered through the holes to be broached and

FIG. 5. Broach Bolt Holes in Two Caps on Vertical Pull-Down Broaching Machine.

are automatically engaged by the mechanism which pulls them through the part. Upon removal of the work, the tools rise, are engaged by the upper holders, and return to their starting position. Machines of this type have the advantage over pull-up machines in that the positioning of the part is easier and large parts are handled without difficulty.

Vertical pull-up broaching machines. These machines are also adapted to internal broaching and are frequently preferred for small parts. In many machines there are four or more broaching tools involved. Although the general cycle of operation is similar to the pull-down machine, it is reversed. At the starting position the parts to be broached are placed over the shanks of the broaches then being held by the lower mechanism. As the broaches rise, they engage the upper pulling mechanism, and the parts are then held against the lower side of the work table. At the completion of the operation the parts fall and are deflected into a container. In this and most other broaching machines the operator has only to load and unload the work.

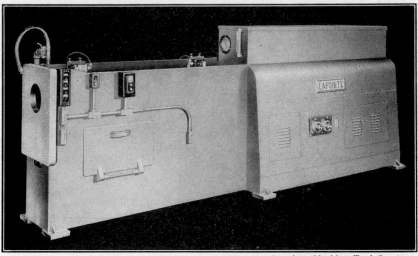

Courtesy Lapointe Machine Tool Company.

Fig. 6.   Horizontal Hydraulic Broaching Machine.

Horizontal broaching machine. Although horizontal broaching machines have many surface-broaching applications, they are generally used for internal broaching of medium and large-size parts. A single-slide machine of 15 tons capacity and 52 inches maximum stroke is illustrated in Figure 6. The work is held in a fixture mounted on a face plate at the end of the machine. In operation the broach is threaded through the work and fastened to the slide just back of the face plate. The hydraulic cylinder which pulls the slide and the broach is housed in the end of the machine at the right. Variable cutting speeds of 10 to 30 feet per minute are provided, with return speeds up to 100 feet per minute. In most machines the shank of the broach is manually threaded through the work, but, where large heavy broaches are used, the machines are frequently equipped with semi-automatic broach-handling means.

An example of surface broaching on a horizontal machine is shown in Figure 7. In this case a number of teeth having a depth of $\frac{3}{16}$ inch are cut on a segment gear at a production rate of 180 pieces per hour. In order to eliminate manual handling of the heavy broaching tool, the tool slide extends past the face plate that holds the work fixture.

Courtesy Colonial Broach Company.

Fig. 7. Broaching Teeth of Gear Segment on a Horizontal Broaching Machine.

For the broaching of parts too bulky or large for convenient handling on vertical equipment, large hydraulically operated horizontal machines have been developed. These machines do not require high ceilings and are at a convenient height for loading and unloading parts that are to be broached. The machine illustrated in Figure 8 is a 15-ton, 84-inch-stroke unit and is set up for broaching large connecting rods. In operation, the fixture platen swings to cutting position, the ram traverses its full cutting stroke, the fixture swings back to loading position, the ram returns and stops. The holding fixture used in this case is a two-station unit, and the work progresses from upper to lower station. At station 1, the operation consists of broaching the bolt bosses to width, parting faces, half bore, and bolt seats. In station 2 the half-bore and parting faces are finished. The production rate on this job is 109 per hour. Other jobs, typical of work done on machines of this type, include the broaching of joint faces on automotive manifolds, surfaces of oil-well drilling-bit segments, tractor-track links, cylinder heads, and crank cases.

An interesting development in horizontal broaching* is the cutting of helical grooves or splines by pulling a broach through the part and, at the same time, either rotating the part or broaching tool according to the helix desired. This procedure has been adopted by many gun manufacturers in rifling small-caliber and light-cannon-gun barrels. Horizontal machines are used, equipped with either single or six-station-type fixtures. Both arrangements pull the broaches through

Courtesy Cincinnati Milling Machine Company.

Fig. 8.   Horizontal Hydro-Broach Machine.

the barrels, and a positive lead is usually provided which will turn either the barrel or the broach. Two passes are used in the single-fixture machines, one for roughing and one for finishing. In the multiple-type fixture having six stations, one is used for loading and five for reaming, broaching, and finishing the bore. Rifling produced by broaching is more economical and more rapid than by the old hook-cutter method, and the rejections are much fewer.

Rotary-broaching machines. Rotary broaching consists in mounting the work in fixtures supported on a revolving table which moves past stationary broaches. These broaches are made in short sections so that they can be easily adjusted and sharpened. A rotary-broaching machine, known as a "mill broach," is illustrated in Figure 9. In this particular case the operation was so short that one piece could be completed in one half of a revolution. By duplicating the tooling and using automatic clamping and ejection fixtures, two operators

* Swindle, T. A., "Rifling Gun Barrels by Broaching," *American Machinist,* October 14, 1943.

stationed opposite each other attained a production rate of 4800 pieces per hour. The loading and unloading position is shown at the right of the machine. After the work is ejected, it falls into a chute and is carried away by a conveyor. An automatic control is provided to stop the machine instantly if a part is not properly located in the fix-

Courtesy Cincinnati Milling & Grinding Machines.

FIG. 9. Rotary-Broach Setup for Brake Spreader Cams.

ture. Rotary-broaching machines are used for squaring distributor shafts, slotting, straddle milling, form milling, and the facing of small parts.

Continuous broaching machine. Continuous broaching machines are adapted only for surface broaching. This type of broaching machine consists of a frame and driving unit with several work-holding fixtures, mounted on an endless chain which carries the work in a straight line past the stationary broaches. A view of a continuous machine equipped with a motor-driven conveyor for removing work from the machine is shown in Figure 10. Loading is done by an operator who drops the parts in the fixtures as they pass the loading station. The work is automatically clamped before it passes into the fixture tunnel in which the broaches are held. After the fixtures pass through the broach cut, they are automatically released by a cam, and at the unloading position the work falls out of the fixtures into the work chute. Production is high, as the operator handles only the work in the loading position; the output of the machine varies with the ability of the operator to keep the machine loaded.

The design of this machine permits the use of long broaches, and each tooth has only a small amount of metal to remove. The first teeth are roughers and remove the major portion of the metal; the last teeth do the final finishing and sizing. Broaches are made up in short sections to facilitate replacement. A variable cutting speed of 20 to 40 feet per minute is provided by a gear drive.

Examples of surface-broaching operations are shown in Figure 11. Where there are several surfaces to be broached, such as on a hexagonal

Courtesy The Foote-Burt Company.

FIG. 10.   Continuous-Surface-Broaching Machine Equipped with Motor-Drive Conveyor Used in Removing Work from Machine.

section, an indexing fixture can be used, with three pairs of broaches mounted in the broach holder and spaced so that the fixture can be indexed between each pair of broaches.

In addition to the above applications, some large tunnel broaches are designed for finish-broaching the tops of engine cylinders and cylinder heads. The part to be broached is held in a fixture which is pushed under the stationary broaches by a hydraulic ram. A wire cable then pulls the finished part onto an exit conveyor while the fixture returns to starting position. Six-cylinder blocks can be surfaced in this manner at the rate of 120 per hour.

Broaching Tools

Broaching tools differ from most other production tools in that they are usually adapted to a single operation. The feed of the tool must be predetermined, and, once a broach is made, the feed remains a constant. These facts necessitate having complete information concerning the job, the material, and the machine to be used before a broach can be made. A few types of flat or regular section broaches

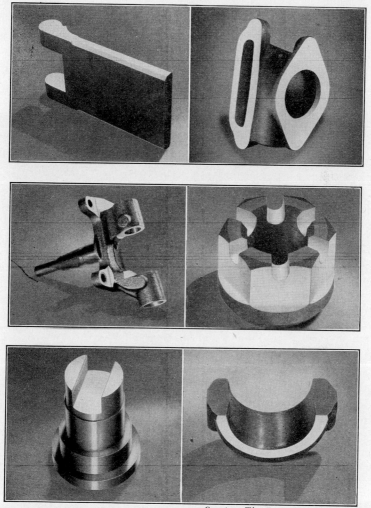

Courtesy The Foote-Burt Company.

FIG. 11. Examples of Surface Broaching.

can be made up in advance, but those that finish unusual surfaces and shapes are specially designed. In designing and constructing a broach, the following information must be known:

1. Kind of material to be broached.
2. Size and shape of cut.
3. Quality of finish required.
4. Hardness of material.
5. Tolerance to be maintained.

6. Number of parts to be made.
7. Type of machine to be used.
8. Method of holding broach.
9. Pressure that the part will stand without breakage.

Fixtures are frequently designed simultaneously with the broaching tools in order to work out the best arrangement. A fixture for broaching serves the same purpose as for milling operations; that is, it merely holds the work piece in proper relation to the cutter and does not in any way guide the cutting tool. All broaching fixtures should be as quick acting as possible and must support the work rigidly against the heavy forces imposed on it during the operation. Reference to most of the previous figures will show various fixtures in use.

A common example of broaching is the finishing of round holes. This method of finishing is more rapid than reaming or boring and at the same time can be held to accurate limits. The life of the tool is long, since the broach has a great number of cutting teeth with each taking only a very small cut. Two round broaches, one *push-type* and one *pull-type,* are shown in Figure 12. Finished holes can be made from holes previously drilled, reamed, bored, punched, or cored. At least $\frac{1}{64}$ inch of stock should be allowed for the finish when one is broaching holes that have been previously machined. Either an ordinary *burnishing broach* or a broach that has several burnishing teeth on its end can be used if an extremely fine finish is desired. This is a cold-working action which produces a hard smooth surface.

Square, hexagonal, and other uniformly shaped holes usually start from round holes. The first teeth of such broaches conform to the original hole, but gradually the broach changes in section according to the final shape of hole desired. If the starting-hole diameter for a square hole can be slightly larger than the finished side, a more economical broach can be made.

The broaching of internal keyways is one of the oldest uses of this process. A keyway broach and its adapter are shown in Figure 13. The adapter guides the broach and also assists in holding and locating the work. Broaching tools for this purpose are extremely simple and can be obtained for general-purpose use. If multiple keyways of splines are to be cut, a single broach can be used with the work, the proper amount being indexed after each cut. This procedure is used only for large splines or in jobs where the production is small, since spline broaches can be obtained for any number of keys desired.

Internal-gear broaches are similar to spline broaches except for the involute contours on the sides of the teeth. Broaches for internal gears can be made to cut any number of teeth and are used for broaching as small as 48-diametral pitch. This method of gear cutting is known as the form-tooth process, and the accuracy of the

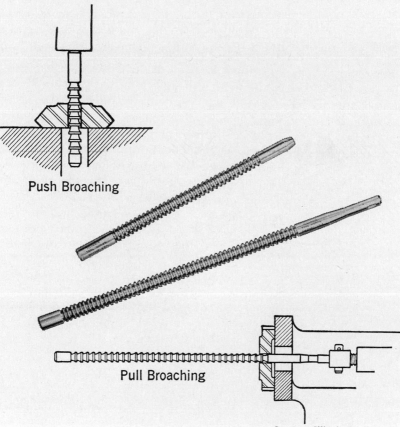

Push Broaching

Pull Broaching

Fig. 12. Round Broaches for Push-and-Pull-Type Machines.

teeth is entirely dependent on the accuracy of the form cutter. External-gear teeth may also be broached, but external-gear cutting is usually limited to cutting teeth on sector gears where only a few teeth are involved.

Surface broaching has grown rapidly to be a very important means of surface finishing. The simplest broaches are designed for flat sur-faces. These can be made up with either straight or angular teeth, but the latter produce a smoother cutting action. Since the entire

length of such broaches is supported on a slide, it is possible to make
them up in short sections. Heavy-duty broaches frequently have
inserted teeth to reduce the initial cost and facilitate replacements.
Many irregular or intricate shapes can be broached, but the tools must
be specially designed for each job.

A group of miscellaneous pull, push, and surface broaches of various
shapes and sizes is shown in Figure 14. The method of holding these
broaches in the machine depends on the type of broach as well as on

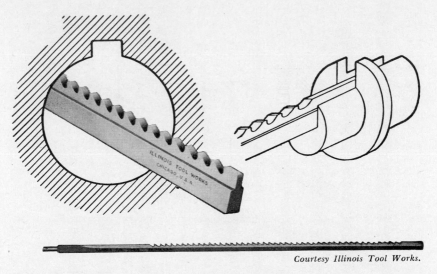

Courtesy Illinois Tool Works.

Fɪɢ. 13.   Keyway Broaching.

its size and shape. One requirement of all types of puller ends is that
they must permit rapid insertion and removal of the broach. The
attachment of surface-type broaches presents no difficult problem, as
their entire length is supported on the slides of the machines.

Broaching terms and angles. Reference to Figure 15, showing a
pull-type broach, will illustrate some of the terms usually applied to
broaches. Starting at the puller end, that portion of the tool up to
the first teeth is known as the *shank*. It is made up of the *keyed* or
pull end and the *front pilot,* which is a short section next to the teeth.
The first teeth of the broach are the *cutting teeth;* the last few are
called the *finishing teeth*. The distance from a point on one tooth to
the corresponding point on an adjacent tooth is the *pitch*. This
depends on the length of broach, chip thickness, and the kind of
material being broached. The short end next to the finish teeth is
the *rear pilot*.

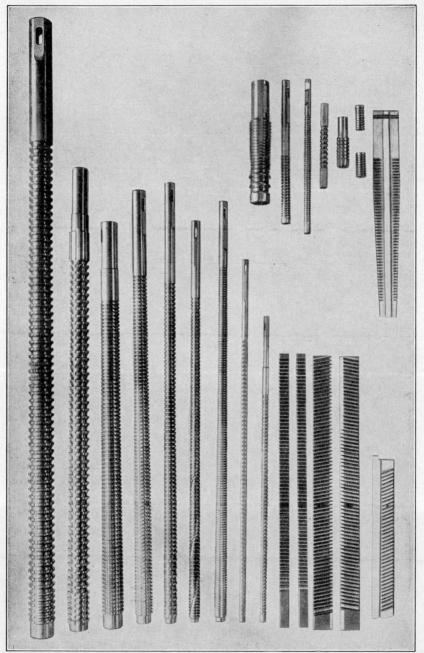

FIG. 14. Pull, Push, and Surface Broaches of Various Shapes.

The shapes or angles used on broaching tools are not necessarily the same throughout the length of the broaching tools. Figure 16 shows an enlarged tooth form with terms and angles indicated. The top portion of a tooth is called the *land* and in most cases is ground to give a slight clearance. This angle, called *backoff* or *clearance angle,* is usually 1½ to 4 degrees on the cutting teeth. Finish teeth have a smaller angle, ranging from 0 to 1½ degrees. There should

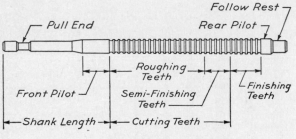

FIG. 15.   Internal Pull-Type Broach.

be no regrinding on the lands of most broaching tools, because this changes the size of the broach. Sharpening is done by grinding the face or front edge of the teeth. The angle to which this surface is ground corresponds to the rake angle on a lathe tool and is called the *face angle, hook angle, undercut angle,* or *rake angle.* The last term is probably the best, as it is the term used for this angle on other cutting tools. The rake angle varies according to the material being

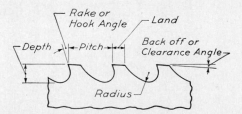

FIG. 16.   Tooth Form on Broach with Principal Terms and Angles Indicated.

cut and, in general, increases as the ductility increases. Values of this angle range from 0 to 20 degrees, but for most steels a value of 12 to 15 degrees is recommended. This angle has considerable effect on the force required to make the cut and the finish. A large angle might give excellent results, but from the standpoint of lengthening tool life a smaller angle would be used. Frequently the first cutting teeth are rugged in shape and have a small rake angle, while the finish teeth are given a larger rake angle to improve the finish. Side-rake angles of 10 to 30 degrees are widely used on surface broaching to improve the finish of the cut.

Review Questions

1. Define broaching, and state how it is done.
2. What are the advantages and limitations of the broaching process?
3. Classify broaching machines according to method of operation.
4. What is meant by surface broaching?
5. What types of broaches and presses are used in push broaching?
6. Describe the operation of a pull-down broaching machine.
7. What type of work is done on a horizontal broaching machine?
8. How is rifling put in gun barrels?
9. What type of work is done on a rotary-broaching machine?
10. What type of broaching machine do you recommend for broaching the following parts: keyway in gear, involute teeth on gear segment, top of engine cylinder, splines in gears, and cutting cap from connecting rod?
11. What is meant by burnishing, and how is it done on a broaching machine?
12. Describe the operation of a continuous broaching machine.
13. What is a broaching fixture?
14. What information must be known in order to purchase or design a broach?
15. Sketch a tooth on a broach, and indicate rake angle, clearance angle, pitch, and land.

References

BAUMBECK, W., "Development of Broach Rifling at Rock Island Arsenal," *Mechanical Engineering*, June 1943.

BOLZ, R. W., *Production Processes*, Vol. 1, Penton Publishing Company, 1949.

Broaches and Broaching, Broaching Tool Institute, 1944.

CADY, E. L., "Broaching of Machine Gun Barrels," *Metals & Alloys*, February 1943.

EINSTEIN, S., and M. ROMAINE, (*a*) "Surface Broaching in High Production Industries," *Mechanical Engineering*, May 1937. (*b*) "Recent Developments in Broaching Automatic Parts," *Machinery*, February 1940. (*c*) "Rifle Parts Broached," *American Machinist*, November 1940.

GOTBERG, H. H., "Simplified Tools Designed for Broaching Spline Forms," *American Machinist*, October 25, 1945.

LIEBERT, HUGO W., "Broached Blades for Navy Turbines," *American Machinist*, August 5, 1943.

Metal Cutting Tool Handbook, Metal Cutting Tool Institute, 1949.

ROMAINE, M., "Broaching Cylinder Blocks and Heads in the Latest Engine Plant," *Machinery*, April 1938.

Tool Engineers Handbook, American Society of Tool Engineers, McGraw-Hill Book Company, 1949.

CHAPTER
23

ABRASIVES, GRINDING WHEELS, AND GRINDING MACHINES

Grinding

To grind means "to abrade, to wear away by friction or to sharpen." As applied to machine-shop practice, it refers to the removal of metal by means of a rotating abrasive wheel. The action of a grinding wheel is very similar to that of a milling cutter. It is made up of many small abrasive grains bonded together, each one acting as a small cutting tool. Definite elongated metal chips may be seen clearly by examining the material removed under a microscope.

The grinding process is one of extreme importance in production work. It possesses certain advantages that are not found in other cutting processes:

1. It is the only method of cutting such materials as hardened steel. Parts requiring hard surfaces are first machined to shape while the metal is in an annealed state, only a small amount of excess material being necessary for the grinding operation. The amount of this allowance depends on the size, shape, and tendency of the part to warp during the heat-treating operation. The sharpening of hand cutting tools is an important use of this process.

2. It produces finishes that are extremely smooth and, hence, very desirable at contact and bearing surfaces. This is due to the many small cutting edges on the wheel. As the wheel has considerable width, there are no marks as a result of feeding it across the work.

3. This process can finish work to very accurate dimensions in a short time. Since only a small amount of material is removed, the grinding machines require a close regulation of the wheel, and it is possible to hold work to a fraction of a thousandth of an inch with considerable ease.

4. Very little pressure is required in this process, thus permitting its use on very light work that would otherwise tend to spring away

from the tool. This characteristic permits the use of magnetic chucks for holding the work in many applications of grinding.

Abrasives

An *abrasive* is a hard material which can be used to cut or wear away other materials. Theoretically, any material can act as an abrasive to other materials that are softer. However, certain few materials are known that have suitable characteristics for grinding work, and it is these materials that we have in mind when we speak of abrasives. A brief classification of the common abrasive materials used for grinding wheels is given here:

ABRASIVES FOR GRINDING WHEELS

1. Natural
   (*a*) Sandstone or solid quartz.
   (*b*) Emery, 50–60% crystalline Al_2O_3 plus iron oxide.
   (*c*) Corundum, 75–90% crystalline Al_2O_3 plus iron oxide.
   (*d*) Diamonds.
2. Manufactured
   (*a*) Silicon carbide, SiC.
   (*b*) Aluminum oxide, Al_2O_3.
   (*c*) Boron carbide.

For many years it was necessary to rely on natural abrasives in the manufacture of grinding wheels. *Sandstone* wheels are still used to some extent for hand-operated grindstones. Although they are cut from high-grade quartz or sandstone, they have the disadvantage that they frequently do not wear evenly in use because of the variations in the natural bond. Most wheels of this type are made in Ohio, where suitable deposits of sandstone are found.

Corundum and *emery* have long been used for grinding purposes. Both are made up of crystalline aluminum oxide in combination with iron oxide and other impurities. In the United States corundum is found in Tennessee, Georgia, and South Carolina. Emery first came from Greece and Asia Minor but is now mined in New York and Massachusetts. Like sandstone these minerals lack a uniform bond and, consequently, are not suitable for high-speed grinding work. Before the discovery of artificial abrasives, these abrasives were crushed and bonded with various materials in the manufacture of grinding wheels. The best results were obtained by using the vitrified process. Although they were a great improvement over natural stones, these wheels still lacked uniform structure because of the impurities associated with the emery and corundum.

Diamond wheels, made with a resinoid bond, are especially useful in sharpening cemented-carbide tools.   In spite of high initial cost, they have proved economical because of their rapid cutting ability, slow wear, and free cutting action.   Very little heat is generated with their use, which is an added advantage in tool grinding.

Manufactured or electric-furnace abrasives were not known until the latter part of the 19th century.   *Silicon carbide* was first discovered

"Lecture Course on Coated Abrasives," Behr-Manning.

FIG. 1. Silicon Carbide Furnace Charged with Coke, Sand, and Sawdust under Operating Conditions.   Note inflammable gases escaping at the sides.

by E. G. Acheson of Monongahela City, Pa., in 1891, while he was attempting to manufacture precious gems in an electric furnace. The hardness of this material, according to Mohs's scale,* is slightly over 9.5, which approaches the hardness of a diamond.   Realizing the possibilities of this hard crystalline material as an abrasive, the Carborundum Company developed the process for its manufacture on a commercial scale.   The raw materials now used are silica sand, petroleum coke, sawdust, and salt.   The furnace employed (see Figure 1) is quite long and of the resistance type.   The raw materials are piled

* Mohs's scale of hardness: (1) Talc, (2) gypsum, (3) calc spar, (4) fluorspar, (5) apatite, (6) feldspar, (7) quartz, (8) topaz, (9) sapphire, (10) diamond.

around the carbon electrode and walled up on each side with loose brick. The purpose of the sawdust is to give porosity to the mixture and to permit the escape of the carbon monoxide gas. The furnace is heated to around 4200 F and held there for a considerable period of time. The product consists of a mass of crystals surrounded by partially unconverted raw material. After cooling, the material is broken up, graded, and then crushed to the desired grain size. Silicon carbide crystals are very sharp and extremely hard, but their use as an abrasive is limited because of brittleness.

The development of *aluminum oxide* occurred a few years after the discovery of silicon carbide through experiments made by C. B. Jacobs of the Ampere Electro-Chemical Company of Ampere, N. J. The raw material for this process is the claylike mineral *bauxite* (mined in Arkansas), which is the principal source of the metal aluminum. Bauxite consists principally of aluminum oxide in combination with water and various impurities. In brief, the process consists in first driving off the excess moisture by heating the ore, adding small amounts of coke and iron filings to the ore to act as reducing and purifying agents, and then putting it into the electric furnace of the arc type. The furnace consists of an unlined conical shell which is placed on a carbon base. Two carbon electrodes hang down inside the shell, and the bauxite is charged from above, filling the space around the electrodes. The current arcs from one electrode to the mass and then into the other electrode, producing intense heat which melts the mass and eliminates the impurities. The finished product is a large pig, weighing several tons, which is broken up and graded. The purest material is at the center of the mass. Aluminum oxide is slightly softer than silicon carbide, but it is much tougher. Most manufactured wheels are made of aluminum oxide for this reason.

Manufacture of Grinding Wheels

The process of making a grinding wheel is the same for both the aluminum oxide and silicon carbide materials. In brief, the procedure is:

1. The material is first reduced to small sizes by being run through roll and jaw crushers. Between crushing operations the fines are removed by passing the material over screens.

2. All material is passed through magnetic separators to remove iron compounds.

3. A washing process removes all dust and foreign material.

4. The grains are graded by being passed over vibrating standard screens. (A standard 30-mesh screen has 30 meshes per inch or 900 openings per square inch. No. 30-size material is that which passes through a no. 30 screen and is retained on the next finer size, which in this case is no. 36.)

5. Grains are mixed with bonding material, molded or cut to proper shape, and heated. The heating or burning procedure varies considerably, according to the type of bond used.

6. The wheels are bushed, trued, tested, and given a final inspection.

Bonding Processes

1. Vitrified process. The abrasive grains are mixed with claylike ingredients which are changed to glass upon being burned at a high temperature. In the puddling process sufficient water is added to form a thick smooth mixture. It is then poured into a steel mold and allowed to dry for several days in a room with controlled temperature. The dry-press process requires the addition of little water. In this case the wheels are shaped in metal molds under a hydraulic press. Wheels made this way are dense and are accurately shaped. The time for burning varies with the wheel size, being anywhere from 2 to 14 days. The process is similar to burning tile or pottery.

The advantages of vitrified wheels are that they are porous, strong, and unaffected by water, acids, oils, and climatic or temperature conditions. About 75% of all wheels are made by this process. The recommended speed for these wheels is 5500 feet per minute with a maximum speed of 6500 feet per minute.

2. Silicate process. In this process silicate of soda is mixed with the abrasive grains, and the mixture is tamped in metal molds. After drying several hours, the wheels are baked at 500 F 1 to 3 days.

Silicate wheels are milder acting than those made by other processes and wear away more rapidly. This type of wheel is suitable for grinding edge tools where the heat must be kept to a minimum. This process is also to be recommended for very large wheels, as they have little tendency to crack or warp in the baking process. The hardness of the wheel is controlled by the amount of silicate of soda used and the amount of tamping given the material in the mold.

3. Shellac process. The abrasive grains are first coated with shellac by being mixed in a steam-heated mixer. The material is then placed in heated steel molds and rolled or pressed. Finally, the wheels are baked a few hours at a temperature around 300 F.

This type of bond is adapted to thin wheels, as it is very strong and has some elasticity. Shellac-bonded wheels are also used for grinding camshafts and other parts where a high polish is desired. Other applications are sharpening large saws, cutting-off operations, and finishing large rolls.

4. Rubber process. Pure rubber with sulfur as a vulcanizing agent is mixed with the abrasive by running the material between heated mixing rolls. After it is finally rolled to desired thickness, the wheels are cut out with proper-shaped dies and then vulcanized under pressure. Very thin wheels can be made by this process because of the elasticity of the material. Wheels having this bond are used for high-speed grinding (9000–16,000 feet per minute), since they afford rapid removal of the stock. They are used a great deal as snagging wheels in a foundry and also for cutting-off wheels.

5. Bakelite or resinoid process. The abrasive grains in this process are mixed with a synthetic-resin powder and a liquid solvent. This plastic mixture is then molded to proper shape and baked in an electric oven at 312 F $\frac{1}{2}$ to 3 days. This bond is very hard and strong, and wheels made by this process can be operated at speeds around 9500 to 16,000 feet per minute. These wheels are used for general-purpose grinding and are widely used in foundries and billet shops for snagging purposes because of their ability to remove metal rapidly.

Grinding-Wheel Selection

The proper selection of a grinding wheel for a definite purpose is important. There is a great variation in the wheels from which one may choose, and the selection is somewhat difficult because of the many factors involved. The factors to be considered in ordering a wheel are:

1. Size and shape of wheel. The principal grinding wheel shapes have been standardized by the United States Department of Commerce and the Grinding Wheel Manufacturers Association. *Standard shapes* which are available are shown in Figure 2, each having its own type number. These types may be obtained from any wheel manufacturer. In addition, all principal dimensions must be given. Grinding wheels of the straight wheel type have also been standardized according to *wheel face* as shown in Figure 3. These wheels are used for grinding special contours, sharpening saws, and other special applications, and are designated by letters.

2. Kind of abrasive. A decision as to whether to use silicon carbide or aluminum oxide is largely dependent on the physical properties of the material to be ground. Silicon carbide wheels are recommended for materials of low tensile strength, such as cast iron, brass, stone, rubber, leather, and cemented carbides. The aluminum oxide wheels are best used on materials of high tensile strength, as hardened steel, high-speed steel, alloy steel, and malleable iron.

3. Grain size of abrasive particles. In general, coarse wheels are used for fast removal of materials. Fine-grained wheels are used where finish is an important consideration. Coarse wheels may be used for soft materials, but generally a fine grain should be used for hard and

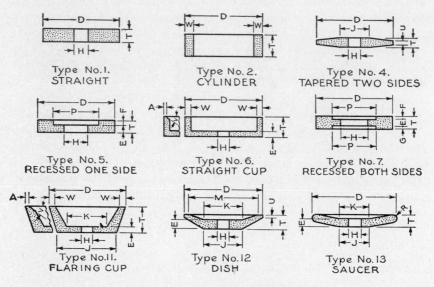

FIG. 2. Standard Grinding-Wheel Shapes.

brittle materials. Grain size is specified according to standard screen sizes. The Norton Company classes abrasives from no. 6 to no. 24 coarse, no. 30 to no. 60 medium, no. 70 to no. 120 fine, and no. 150 to no. 240 very fine. Flour sizes run as high as no. 600 mesh.

4. Grade or strength of bond. The grade depends on the kind and hardness of the bonding material used. If the bond is very strong and capable of holding the abrasive grains against the force tending to pry them loose, it is said to be hard. If only a small force is needed to release the grains, the wheel is said to be soft. Most companies indicate the grade of the wheel by a letter. Although company standards differ, in general, the grade letters increase in hardness from D to Z. Hard wheels are recommended for soft materials, and soft wheels for hard materials.

5. Structure or grain spacing. The structure refers to the number of cutting edges per unit area of wheel face as well as to the number and size of void spaces between grains. The structure to use depends principally on the physical properties of the material to be ground and the type of finish desired. Soft, ductile materials require a wide spacing. A fine finish requires a wheel with a close spacing of the abrasive particles.

6. Kind of bond material. The vitrified bond is most commonly used, but, where thin wheels are required or high operating speed or high finish is necessary, the selection of other types is advantageous.

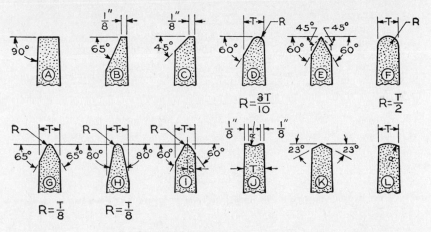

FIG. 3.   Standard Grinding-Wheel Faces.

7. Function of grinding wheel.* The use or purpose for which a grinding wheel is to be employed is a definite factor in wheel selection. Following are listed the basic functions of grinding wheels:

   (*a*) Generation of size or grinding to close tolerance.
   (*b*) Generation of surface finishes or effects which may or may not involve close tolerances.
   (*c*) Removal of a large amount of stock, as in snagging.
   (*d*) Cutting-off operations.
   (*e*) Production of sharp edges or points as in knife grinding.
   (*f*) Reduction of material to particle form.

8. Other factors that must be given some consideration are the wheel speed, speed of work, materials to be ground, and general condition of the machine. Table 10 lists recommended grinding-wheel speeds.

* *Grinding Facts,* Carborundum Company, 1944.

TABLE 10. RECOMMENDED GRINDING-WHEEL SPEEDS

Type of Grinding	Wheel Speed, Surface Ft per min
Internal	2000–6000
Hemming cylinders	2100–5000[1]
Machine knives	3500–4500
Surface	4000–5000
Cutlery—large wheels offhand	4000–5000
Wet tool	5000–6000
Cylindrical	5500–6500
Snagging—vitrified bond	5000–6000
Snagging—resinoid and rubber bond	7000–9500
Cut-off—rubber, resinoid, and shellac bond	9000–16,000[1]

[1] Recommended only where bearings, protection devices, and machine rigidity are adequate (Abrasive Company).

A standard system* of marking grinding wheels, recently adopted by the American Standards Association, is shown in the accompanying chart. Although the standard greatly facilitates ordering, from the standpoint of uniform marking of all wheels, there is no assurance that

STANDARD MARKING SYSTEM CHART

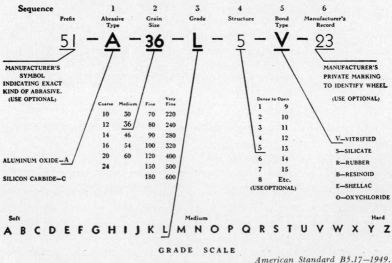

American Standard B5.17—1949.

competitors' wheels marked alike will cut the same. Provision for each manufacturer to incorporate into the system such symbols as

* American Standard B5.17—1949.

further describe the wheel and qualify the standard markings are stated in the first and last symbols of the identification marking.

Grinding Machines

Grinding machines are designed principally to finish parts having cylindrical, flat, or internal surfaces. The type of surface machined largely determines the type of grinding machine used; thus, a machine grinding cylindrical surfaces is called a cylindrical grinder. Machines designed for some special function such as tool grinding or cutting off, are designated according to the type of operation they perform.

A classification of grinding machines according to type of surface generated or work done is as follows:

CLASSIFICATION OF GRINDING MACHINES

1. Cylindrical grinder
   (a) Work between centers.
   (b) Centerless.
   (c) Tool post.
   (d) Crankshaft and other special applications.
2. Internal grinder
   (a) Work rotated in chuck.
   (b) Work rotated and held by rolls.
   (c) Work stationary.
3. Surface grinder
   (a) Planer type (reciprocating table)
       (1) Horizontal spindle.
       (2) Vertical spindle.
   (b) Rotating table
       (1) Horizontal spindle.
       (2) Vertical spindle.
4. Tool grinder
   (a) Universal.
   (b) Special
       (1) Drill.
       (2) Tool bit.
       (3) Cutter.
       (4) Pedestal, etc.
5. Special grinding machines
   (a) Swinging frame—snagging.
   (b) Cutting off—sawing.
   (c) Portable—offhand grinding.
   (d) Honing and lapping—accurate finishing.
   (e) Superfinishing.
   (f) Flexible shaft—general purpose.
6. Surface finishing
   (a) Disk.
   (b) Flexible band.
   (c) Two-wheel polishing or buffing machine.

Cylindrical Grinders

As the name implies, this type of machine is used primarily for grinding cylindrical surfaces, although tapered and simple formed surfaces may also be ground on most cylindrical grinders. This type of

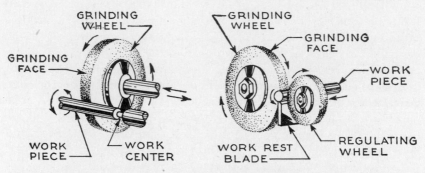

FIG. 4.   Illustrating the Methods of Supporting Work in the Center and the Centerless Types of Cylindrical Grinding.

machine may be further classified according to the method of supporting the work.   Schematic diagrams illustrating the essential difference in supporting the work between the center and the centerless grinders are shown in Figure 4.   In the centerless type, the work is supported

Courtesy Landis Tool Company.

FIG. 5.   14 × 96 Hydraulic Cylindrical Grinding Machine.

by the arrangement of the work rest, a regulating wheel, and the grinding wheel itself.   Both types use plain grinding wheels with the grinding face as the outside diameter.

An illustration of a hydraulic center-type cylindrical grinding machine is shown in Figure 5.   In the design of machines of this type three movements are incorporated that are necessary in the operation of cylindrical grinding:

1. Rapid rotation of the grinding wheel at the proper grinding speed, usually 5500 to 6500 surface feet per minute.

2. Slow rotation of the work against the grinding wheel at a speed to give best performance (this varies from 60 to 100 surface feet per minute in the grinding of steel cylinders).

3. Horizontal traverse of the work back and forth along the grinding wheel so as to grind the entire surface of a long piece.

In some machines the work remains stationary except for its rotation, and the wheel is slowly fed back and forth across the work. The narrower the face of the wheel, the slower must be the traverse and the faster should be the work revolution. For most cases the work should be traversed nearly the entire width of the wheel during each revolution of the work. In finishing, the traverse may be reduced to one-half the width of the wheel.

The depth of the cut is controlled by feeding the wheel into the work. Roughing cuts around 0.002 inch may be made, but for finishing the feed should be reduced to about 0.00025 inch. In selecting the amount of infeed, consideration must be given to the size and rigidity of the work and the finish desired and to whether or not a coolant is used.

Where the face of the wheel is wider than the part to be ground, it is not necessary to traverse the work. This is known as "plunge-cut" grinding and is common practice in the grinding of crankshafts. Cuts up to 9 inches wide may be made in this manner if the work is properly supported. Grinders for crankshaft work are usually built especially for that purpose, owing to the special features necessary for supporting and driving the crankshaft. Another special machine of this general type is the camshaft grinder. In order for the cams to be ground to proper shape, the movement of the work to and away from the wheel is controlled by master cams at the end of the shaft.

The *tool-post grinder* is used for miscellaneous and small grinding work on a lathe. It is held on the tool post and fed across the work, the regular longitudinal or compound rest feed being used. A common application of this grinder is the truing up of lathe centers.

Centerless grinders are designed so that they support and feed the work by using two wheels and a work rest, as illustrated diagrammatically in Figure 6. The large wheel is the grinding wheel and the smaller one the pressure or regulating wheel. The regulating wheel is a rubber-bonded abrasive wheel having the proper frictional characteristics to rotate the work at its own rotational speed. The speed of this wheel may be controlled and varies from 50 to 200 surface feet per minute. Both wheels are rotated in the same direction. The slide assists in supporting the work while it is being ground and is extended on both sides to direct the work travel to and from the wheels.

The axial movement of the work past the grinding wheel is obtained by tilting the wheel at a slight angle from horizontal. An angular

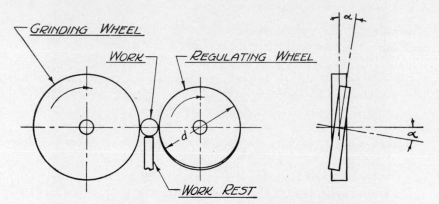

FIG. 6. Sketch Illustrating the Principle of Centerless Grinding.

adjustment of zero to 8 or 10 degrees is provided in the machine for this purpose. The actual feed can be calculated by this formula:

$$F = \pi \, d \, N \, \sin \alpha$$

where

$F =$ feed in inches per minute
$N =$ revolutions per minute
$d =$ diameter of regulating wheel in **inches**
$\alpha =$ angle of inclination of wheel

The formula assumes no slippage, and, in actual practice, the error is slight. This type of grinding may be applied to any cylindrical parts of one diameter, as shown in Figure 7. In production work on such parts as piston pins, a magazine feed is arranged, and the parts may go through several machines before completion, each grinder removing from 0.0005- to 0.002-inch stock.

Where parts are not uniformly of the same diameter, or where they require form grinding as a ball bearing (see Figure 8), the *infeed* type of centerless grinding must be used. The method of operation corresponds to the plunge-cut form of grinding, and the length of the section to be ground is limited to the width of the grinding wheel. The part is placed on the work rest and is moved against the grinding wheel with the regulating wheel. Upon completion, the gap between

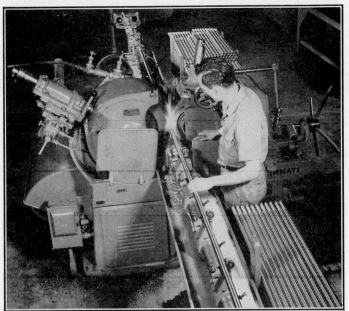

Courtesy Cincinnati Milling & Grinding Machines.

FIG. 7. Tube Grinding in Centerless Grinder.

the wheels is increased either manually or automatically and the work is ejected from between the wheels. This type of grinding is also illustrated in Figure 9, in the grinding of a textile spindle of several

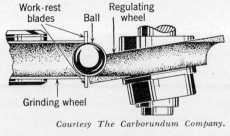

Courtesy The Carborundum Company.

FIG. 8. Centerless Grinding of Ball Bearings.

diameters. In this case the loading and unloading of the spindle is done by a holding cradle and elevator mechanism which is operated by and synchronized with the infeed mechanism.

A third type of centerless grinding called *end feed* has been devised for use only on short taper work. Both wheels are dressed to the

Courtesy Cincinnati Grinders.

Fig. 9. Centerless Grinding of Long Shaft Using Work Handling Device.

correct taper, and the work is automatically fed in from one side to a fixed stop.

The advantages of centerless grinding are:

1. Less skill is required in the operation of the machine.
2. No chucking or mounting of the work on mandrels or other holding devices is required.
3. The work is rigidly supported, and there is no tendency for chatter or deflection of the work.
4. The process is rapid and especially adapted for production work. Idle machine time is negligible.
5. The size of the work is easily controlled.
6. As a true floating condition exists during the grinding process, less grinding stock is required.

Some disadvantages are:

1. Work with flats and keyways cannot be ground.
2. In hollow work there is no assurance that the outside diameter will be concentric with the inside diameter.
3. Work having several diameters is not easily handled in this type of machine.

Internal Grinders

The work done on an internal grinder is diagrammatically shown in Figure 10. Tapered holes, or those having more than one diameter, may also be accurately finished in this manner. Although especially

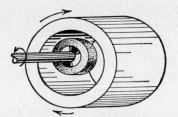

FIG. 10. Sizing to Close Tolerance by Internal Grinding.

adapted for heat-treated parts, internal grinding is frequently used on production parts that have not been heat-treated to save on reamer cost and maintenance.

According to general construction there are several types of internal grinders.

1. The wheel is rotated in a fixed position while the work is slowly rotated and traversed back and forth.
2. The wheel is rotated and at the same time reciprocated back and forth through the length of the hole. The work is rotated slowly but otherwise has no movement. The usual setup for this type of work is shown in Figure 11. The bearing is fastened to the slowly rotating chuck while the grinder wheel is rotated at high speed against one side of the hole.
3. The work remains stationary, and the rotating wheel spindle is given an eccentric motion, according to the diameter of hole to be ground. This type of grinder is frequently called the planetary type, and it is used for work that is difficult to rotate. In actual construction the wheel spindle is adjusted eccentrically in a larger one that rotates about a fixed axis. The wheel spindle is driven at high speed and at the same time rotates about the axis of the large spindle.

Courtesy Landis Tool Company.

FIG. 11.   Internal Grinder.

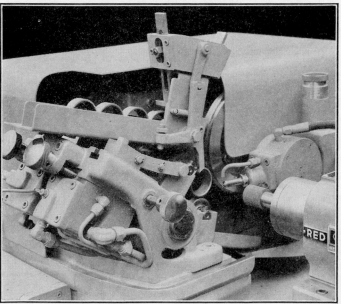

Courtesy The Heald Machine Company.

FIG. 12.   Centerless Internal Grinding with Automatic Loading and Unloading
Device.

4. In another type of grinder which embodies the principle of centerless grinding, the work is rotated on the outside diameter by driven rolls, thus making it possible to grind the bore absolutely concentric with the outside diameter. This arrangement lends itself to production work, as loading is simplified and magazine feed may be used if desired.

A centerless internal grinder, with an automatic loading and unloading device, is shown in Figure 12. Three rolls are used to support and drive the work: a regulating roll, a supporting roll, and a pressure roll. Since the entire cycle is automatic, one operator can handle several machines. Other advantages of centerless grinding include the elimination of work-holding fixtures and the ability of the machine to grind both straight and tapered holes.

Since internal-grinding wheels are small in diameter, the spindle speed is much higher than for cylindrical grinding in order to attain surface speeds up to 6000 feet per minute. Most toolroom grinding is done dry, but common practice on production work is to grind steel wet and to grind bronze, brass, and cast iron dry. The amount of metal to be allowed for internal grinding depends on the size of the hole to be ground; in most cases this allowance is around 0.010 inch.

Surface Grinding

The grinding of flat or plane surfaces is known as *surface grinding*. Two general types of machines have been developed for this purpose: those of the planer type with a reciprocating table and those having a rotating work table. Each type of machine has the possible variation of having the grinding-wheel spindle in either a horizontal or a vertical position. The four possibilities of construction are diagrammatically illustrated in Figure 13.

A large surface grinder with a horizontal spindle and reciprocating table is shown in Figure 14. Straight or recessed wheels (types 1, 5, and 7) grinding on the outside face or circumference are used on machines of this type. This grinder has hydraulic control of the table movement with possible speeds up to 100 feet per minute. Likewise a hydraulic cross-feed is used which may be varied up to width of wheel face if desired. This type of grinder is well adapted for reconditioning dies, as the large-diameter wheels permit this operation without the guide pins being removed. Other applications include the grinding of grooves, ways on machine tools, and other long surfaces.

Another type of construction for planer-table grinders is the vertical spindle design, the grinding being done by a large-diameter ring-shaped wheel. A machine of this design, hydraulically operated and rigidly constructed for production work, is shown in Figure 15. This machine has a fixed column for holding the grinding head; however, other similar machines are constructed to permit the head to be moved in and out over the work table to grind wide or irregularly shaped surfaces.

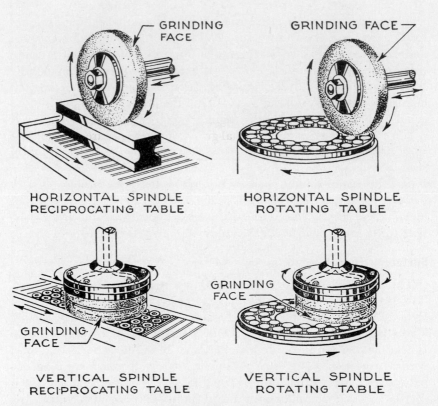

FIG. 13. Types of Surface-Grinding Machines.

Several types of wheels used on these machines are shown in Figure 16. The wheel is a hollow cylinder which cuts on its end and may be made up as a *plain cylindrical* wheel, a *sectored* wheel, or a *segment* wheel. All three of these wheels are illustrated in this figure. The cylinder and sectored wheels are set with sulfur into a cast-iron ring which fastens to the face plate of the spindle. The segment wheel uses a chuck secured to the face plate in which the segment blocks are clamped. Because of the large area of work in contact with these wheels, they are especially adapted to grinding large surfaces. It is

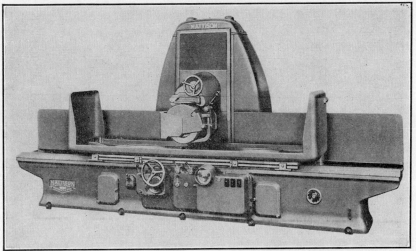

Courtesy Mattison Machine Works.

FIG. 14. Precision Surface Grinder with Horizontal Spindle.

Courtesy The Thompson Grinder Company.

FIG. 15. Vertical Spindle Surface Grinder.

Courtesy The Blanchard Machine Company.

FIG. 16.   A Sectored Wheel, a Plain Cylindrical Wheel, and a Segment Wheel, Used in Vertical-Spindle Surface Grinding.

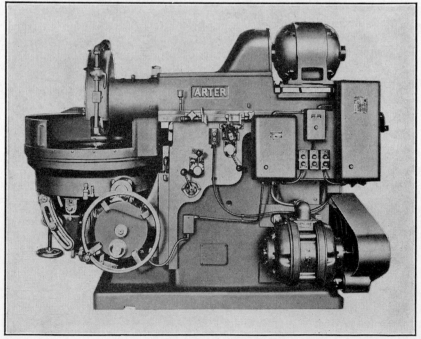

Courtesy Arter Grinding Machine Company.

FIG. 17.   Rotary Surface Grinder.

also possible to place many small parts on a magnetic chuck and grind them with equal effectiveness.

Two other surface grinders with rotating tables, but with horizontal and vertical wheel spindles, are shown in Figures 17 and 18 respectively. In the Arter machine, shown in the first figure, the work is held on a magnetic chuck and slowly rotated under the grinding wheel. The

Courtesy The Blanchard Machine Company.

FIG. 18.   Surface Grinder with Vertical Spindle and Adjustable Work Table.

wheel and spindle assembly is given a reciprocating movement during the grinding operation.   This type of surface grinder is adapted to circular work, such as milling cutters, piston rings, saws, and valves. By tilting the work-table bevels, concave surfaces or short tapers may be ground.   The Blanchard grinder, shown in the other figure, uses a cylindrical-type wheel in connection with the vertical spindle.   The work to be ground is placed on a rotary magnetic chuck which rests on a table body that may be moved out from under the wheel.   After the table is loaded, body and chuck are moved along the base to bring the center of the chuck just under the near edge of the wheel.   In that position the work is rotated continuously in one direction, and the

165 pounds per square inch. The equipment for furnishing the direct current consists of a motor-generator set and demagnetizing switch.

All parts held on a magnetic chuck should be demagnetized after the work is finished. Several types of demagnetizers are available, operating on either alternating or direct current, which successfully remove the residual magnetism from knives, bearing races, blades, and many other parts.

Permanent-magnet chucks do not require any electric equipment, and work can be held on these chucks as long as desired without

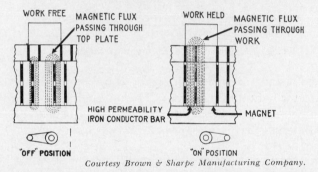

Courtesy Brown & Sharpe Manufacturing Company.

FIG. 22. Diagrammatic Sketch Showing How Work Is Held on Permanent-Magnet Chuck.

damage to work or chuck. The operation of this chuck is by means of a lever on one side. Figure 22 shows what takes place when the operating lever is shifted. In the "off" position the conductor bars and separator are shifted in such a way that the magnetic flux passes through the top plate and is short-circuited from the work. When the handle is turned to the "on" position, the conductor bars and non-magnetic separators line up so that magnetic flux, in following the line of least resistance, goes through the work in completing the circuit. The holding power, obtained by the magnetic flux passing through, is sufficient to withstand the action of grinding wheels and other light machining operations. Both this type of chuck and the d-c chucks may be used for either wet or dry operations.

Tool and Cutter Grinders

In grinding tools by hand (known as offhand grinding) a bench- or pedestal-type grinder is used. The tool is held by hand and moved across the face of the wheel continually to avoid excessive grinding in one spot. This type of grinding is used to a large extent on single-point tools and is dependent on the skill of the operator for good results.

In large production plants much of this type of grinding is done on special single-purpose grinders. Special drill or tool-bit grinders are justified by the large amount of grinding work necessary to keep production tools in proper cutting condition. In addition, tools can be ground uniformly and with accurate cutting angles.

Courtesy Cincinnati Grinders.

FIG. 23. Universal Tool and Cutter Grinder.

For the sharpening of miscellaneous cutters a universal-type grinder as shown in Figure 23 is used. It is equipped with a universal head, vise, headstock and tailstock, and numerous other attachments for holding tools and cutters. Although essentially designed for cutter sharpening, it can also be used for cylindrical, taper, internal, and surface grinding.

Honing

Honing is a grinding or abrading process in which very little material is removed and is used primarily to remove the grinding or tool marks left on the surface by previous operations. The cutting action is obtained from abrasive sticks (aluminum oxide and silicon carbide) mounted in a mandrel or fixture. A floating action between the work and tool prevails so that any pressure exerted in the tool is transmitted equally to all sides. The honing tool is given a slow reciprocating motion as it rotates, having resultant honing speeds ranging from 50 to 200 surface feet per minute. This action results in rapid removal of stock and at the same time the generation of a straight and round surface. Defects such as a slight eccentricity, a wavy surface, or a slight taper, caused by previous operations, can be corrected by this process. Parts honed for finish remove only 0.001 inch or less; however, where certain inaccuracies must be corrected, amounts up to 0.020 inch represent usual practice. Coolants are essential to the operation of this process to flush away small chips and to keep temperatures uniform. Sulfurized mineral-base or lard oil mixed with kerosene is generally used.

Courtesy Sunnen Products Company.

Fig. 24. Portable Hone.

A portable-type hone, used in connection with electric or pneumatic hand tools, is shown in Figure 24. Such hones are used in repair and salvage work, as well as on small-lot production jobs. External honing may also be done by rotating the work and moving the honing stones back and forth as they are held in a suitable fixture.

Semiautomatic honing machines used in the finishing of automobile cylinder bores are vertical-type machines and of the general design shown in Figure 25. Both single- and multiple-spindle machines are used for this operation. Horizontal machines are used only for honing long gun barrels and similar work. Manually operated machines hold the work in a horizontal position, and the rotational movement only is supplied by the machine.

All honing gives a smooth finish with a characteristic cross-hatch appearance. The depth of these hone marks can be controlled by variations in pressure, speed, and type of abrasive used. Very accurate dimensions can be maintained by this process by the use of automatic size-control devices in connection with the hone.

Lapping

The purpose of lapping is to produce geometrically true surfaces, correct minor surface imperfections, improve dimensional accuracy, or provide a very close fit between two contact surfaces. Although it is a material-removing operation, it is not an economical one. The amount of material removed is usually less than 0.001 inch. Lapping is used on flat, cylindrical, spherical, or specially formed surfaces.

The actual operation consists of having the work surfaces in contact with a *lap*, the two having motion with one another in such a way that

Courtesy Barnes Drill Company.

Fig. 25. Single-Spindle Hydraulic Honing Machine with Indexing Fixture for Honing 8-Cylinder V-Type Motor Block.

fresh contacts are constantly being made. Loose abrasive, carried in some vehicle such as oil, grease, or water, is used between the lap and work to do the necessary abrading. In some cases the abrasive is in the form of a bonded wheel, and the lapping operation is similar to that of centerless and vertical spindle surface grinding. Metal laps used must be softer than the work and for machine lapping are usually made of close-grained gray iron. Other materials as steel, copper, lead, and wood are used in special cases where cast iron is not suitable. By having the lap softer than the work, the abrasive particles (usually boron carbide, silicon carbide, or aluminum oxide in fine-screened sizes or flour) become embedded in the lap and cause the greatest wear to occur on the hard surface being worked on.   In the lapping of carbide tools and jewels, diamond particles permanently embedded in copper laps are most successful.

Vertical lapping machines, similar to the one shown in Figure 26, are used for both flat and cylindrical lapping.   These machines have two laps: a lower one which supports the work and rotates at relatively

Courtesy Hauser Machine Tool Corporation.

FIG. 26. Vertical Lapping Machine for Cylindrical and Flat Lapping Operations.

slow speeds, and a stationary upper lap.   The upper lap floats on the work and supplies pressure for the abrading action.   Cylindrical work is loosely held and guided in a plate-type holder so that it travels on an off-radial axis; however, the work propels the holder from motion received from the lower lap.   A similar holder is used in the lapping of flat surfaces, but, in this case, the holder propels the work.   Either it is provided with drive pins which impart to it a rotary and gyratory motion, or it is given a planetary motion.   In either case the work is brought in contact with the entire surface of the lap in an ever-changing path.   Commercial accuracy can be held to 0.000024 inch readily and to even closer limits if desired.   Products commonly finished by this process include gages, piston pins, valves, gears, roller bearings, thrust washers, and optical parts.

Superfinishing

All machining operations as well as the usual grinding processes leave a surface coated with fragmented, noncrystalline, or smear metal which though easily removed by sliding contact results in excessive wear, increased clearances, noisy operation, and lubrication difficulties. Superfinishing is a surface-improving process which removes this undesirable fragmentation metal, leaving a base of solid crystalline metal. It is somewhat similar to honing, as both processes use an abrasive

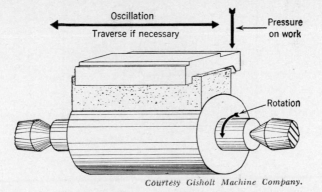

Courtesy Gisholt Machine Company.

Fig. 27. Motions Employed between Abrasive Stone and Work in Cylindrical Superfinishing.

stone, but differs in the type of motions given to the stone. Furthermore, superfinishing is largely confined to exterior regular surfaces, both flat and curved. This process, which is essentially a finishing process and not a dimensional one, can be superimposed on other commercial finishing operations.

In cylindrical superfinishing (see Figure 27), a bonded-form abrasive stone, having a width about two-thirds the diameter of the part to be finished and the same length, is operated at low speed and pressure. The motion given to the stone is an oscillating one (1/16 to 1/4 inch amplitude) of about 450 cycles per minute. If the part is of greater length than the stone, an additional longitudinal movement of either stone or work is necessary. The work is rotated at a speed of around 50 surface feet per minute and during the operation is flooded with a light oil which carries away the minute particles abraded from the surface by the short oscillating stone strokes. The stone action is similar to a scrubbing movement and removes all excess and defective metal on the surface. This is accomplished with low abrasive stone pressures of 3 to 40 pounds per square inch.

The superfinishing of flat surfaces is illustrated in Figure 28. In this case a rotating cup-shaped abrasive stone is used with the work resting on a circular table carried by a rotating spindle. An additional oscillating movement can be given to the stone, but, since both it and the work are rotating, this action is not so important in developing

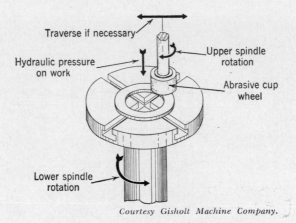

Traverse if necessary

Hydraulic pressure on work

Upper spindle rotation

Abrasive cup wheel

Lower spindle rotation

Courtesy Gisholt Machine Company.

FIG. 28.   Basic Features of Flat Superfinishing.

a continually changing path of the abrasive particles. The superfinishing of spherical surfaces is similar to that used for flat surfaces except that the formed cup spindle is at an angle to the work spindle and no oscillating motion can be used.

It is interesting to note that, when a surface has been made smooth by this process, any further stone action has little or no effect, owing to the supporting oil film between the stone and the work. With proper equipment it takes only 5 to 30 seconds to finish a single bearing area. Surfaces may be processed to a mirror finish or may be given a slight cross-hatch pattern, desirable in certain bearing surfaces. A special superfinishing machine, designed for finishing the bearings of a crankshaft, is shown in Figure 29. The time for completing the operation varies from 15 to 50 seconds, depending on the initial condition of the surface. Numerous other variations of the superfinishing process have been worked out for the many other bearing surfaces found in high-speed machinery.

Coated Abrasives

When abrasive particles are glued to paper or other flexible backings, as illustrated in Figure 30, they are known as coated abrasives. Any of the abrasives used in wheel manufacture may be applied in this way. The most common type is the ordinary "sandpaper," which name is frequently applied to this entire group. The abrasive in this case is a flint quartz, which is mined in large lumps and then crushed to size and graded. Another important natural abrasive is the red mineral garnet. Of the several kinds of garnet known, the one called

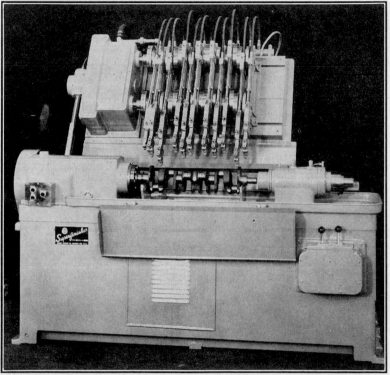

Courtesy Gisholt Machine Company.

FIG. 29.   Crankshaft Superfinisher.

almandite is the best for abrasive coatings. It is much harder and sharper than flint and, when broken down, breaks into crystals with many cutting edges. The best garnet comes from the Adirondack Mountains in New York State. Other natural abrasives used are emery and corundum. The two manufactured abrasives that have wide application in this work are silicon carbide and aluminum oxide. Figure 31 is a photomicrograph of three natural abrasive grains compared with common sea sand, showing outstanding differences in shape and structure.

The three types of backing used are paper, cloth, and a combination of the two.   Paper-coated abrasives are cheapest but lack flexibility. For applications requiring both strength and flexibility, a cloth backing is used.   Combination backings are used where a backing stronger than paper but not with the extreme flexibility of cloth is needed.

Courtesy The Carborundum Company.

Fig. 30.   Various Types of Metal-Working Coated Abrasives.

An important phase in the manufacture of coated abrasives is the application of the abrasive particles on the backing material.   The abrasive grains must be securely held in a manner to give the best cutting action for the type of work to be done.   For severe service, closed coating is recommended, the grains completely covering the surface of the backing.   Where increased flexibility is desired, with no tendency for the particles to become loaded or clogged, an open coating is used. Particles are separated at predetermined distances, leaving the base surface of the backing exposed.

Machines for using coated abrasives are usually of the disk- or belt-type. On the disk machines parts to be finished are supported on a work table and manually moved back and forth while being pressed against the disk. Belt machines have backing rollers or plates against which pressure is exerted. Both types of machines can be used for

"Lecture Course on Coated Abrasives," Behr-Manning.

FIG. 31. Photomicrographs of Three Natural Abrasive Grains.

either wet or dry grinding. Dimensional accuracy of this form of grinding is not very close, and the process is used primarily as one to prepare surfaces for further treatment. The quality of surface finish is governed by the fineness of the abrasive grains on the cloth.

All forms of woodwork, such as mill work, patterns, floors, and furniture, are finished in this manner. Leather goods, felt hats, metallurgical specimens, and many metal parts also rely on coated abrasives in manufacturing operations. The selection of the proper coated abrasive for a given job depends on the finish desired, amount of stock to be removed, speed and pressure used by the sanding equipment, and the kind of surface to be sanded. These factors should be considered for each application, as they influence the selection of the grit number, type of abrasive, the abrasive spacing, and the backing material.

TABLE 11.   GRADING CHART FOR COATED ABRASIVES

Garnet Silicon Carbide Aluminum Oxide	Flint Paper	Emery Cloth	Description
500			
400 or 10/0			
360			
320 or 9/0			
280 or 8/0			Very fine
240 or 7/0	5/0		
220 or 6/0	4/0		
	3/0		
180 or 5/0		3/0	
150 or 4/0		2/0	Fine
	2/0		
120 or 3/0			
	0	0	
100 or 2/0			
	½	½	
80 or 0		1	
	1	1½	Medium
60 or ½			
		2	
50 or 1	1½		
40 or 1½	2	2½	
	2½		Coarse
36 or 2			
30 or 2½	3	3	
24 or 3	3½		
20 or 3½			
16 or 4			Very coarse
12 or 4½			

Table prepared by Behr-Manning Company.

Unfortunately, all coated abrasives are not graded in the same manner. Flint paper and emery cloth each have their own system while garnet and manufactured abrasives are graded by another system.   Table 11 will be of assistance in the selection of the proper grades to use.

Review Questions

1. What advantage does the grinding process have over other cutting processes?
2. List the abrasives used for grinding wheels.
3. Why are natural abrasives inferior to manufactured abrasives?
4. How is silicon carbide made?
5. State briefly how vitrified wheels are made.

6. What bonding materials are used in wheel manufacture?

7. In purchasing a wheel for a specific purpose, what factors must be considered?

8. What are the basic functions of a grinding wheel?

9. What type of wheel is best adapted for grinding hardened steel?

10. What three movements are necessary in the operation of cylindrical grinding?

11. Describe the operation of a centerless grinder.

12. What are the advantages and limitations of centerless grinding?

13. What is meant by "plunge-cut" grinding?

14. List and describe the several types of surface grinders.

15. What are the four types of design used in internal grinders?

16. Describe the type of wheel used on a vertical spindle surface grinder.

17. For what type of work is honing used, and how much metal is usually removed in this operation?

18. What is the purpose of lapping?

19. What abrasives are used in lapping, and how are they applied?

20. Briefly describe the superfinishing process.

21. How does superfinishing differ from honing?

22. What type of work is done with coated abrasives?

References

Bolz, R. W., *Production Processes*, Vol. 1, Penton Publishing Company, 1949.

Boston, O. W., *Metal Processing*, Chapter XV, John Wiley & Sons, 1951.

Burghardt, H. D., *Machine Tool Operation*, Part II, McGraw-Hill Book Company, 1922.

Colvin, F. H., and F. A. Stanley, *Grinding Practice*, 1st edition, McGraw-Hill Book Company, 1937.

Heywood, J., *Grinding Wheels and Their Uses*, Penton Publishing Company, 1938.

Hine, C. R., *Machine Tools for Engineers*, McGraw-Hill Book Company, 1950.

Kline, J. E., "Desired Characteristics of Surface Finishes," *Mechanical Engineering*, Vol. 57, no. 12, 1935.

Principles of Tool Room Grinding, Carborundum Company, 1944.

Rose, Kenneth, "Ultra-Fine Surfaces on Metals," *Metals & Alloys,* July 1945.

Shoemaker, S. S., "Selecting the Correct Speeds and Feeds for Cylindrical Grinding," *Machinery*, February 1945.

Swigert, A. M., *The Story of Superfinish*, Lynn Publishing Company, 1940.

Tool Engineers Handbook, American Society of Tool Engineers, McGraw-Hill Book Company, 1949.

Trowbridge, T., "Use of Coated Abrasives in Woodworking Industries," *Mechanical Engineering*, June 1945.

Textbooks on Machine-Shop Practice

Barritt, J. W., *Machine Shop Operations*, American Technical Society, 1937.

Bolz, R. W., *Production Processes*, Vol. 1, The Penton Publishing Company, 1949.

Boston, O. W., *Metal Processes*, 2d edition, John Wiley & Sons, 1951.

Burghardt, H. D., *Machine Tool Operation*, Parts I and II, 1st edition, McGraw-Hill Book Company, 1919 and 1922.

Clapp and Clark, *Engineering Materials and Processes*, 2d edition, International Textbook Company, 1949.

Cole, C. B., *Tool Making*, American Technical Society, 1939.

COLVIN, F. H., and F. A. STANLEY, *Running a Machine Shop*, McGraw-Hill Book Company, 1941.

COLVIN, F. H., and F. A. STANLEY, *Drilling and Surfacing Practice*, 3d edition, McGraw-Hill Book Company, 1948.

COLVIN, F. H., and F. A. STANLEY, *American Machinist Handbook*, 8th edition, McGraw-Hill Book Company, 1945.

FREY, C. J., and S. S. KOGUT, *Metal Forming by Flexible Tools*, Pitman Publishing Corporation, 1943.

Henry Ford Trade School Shop Theory, Henry Ford Trade School, Dearborn, Michigan, 1934.

HESSE, H. C., *Engineering Tools and Processes*, D. Van Nostrand Company, 1941.

HEYWOOD, J., *Grinding Wheels and Their Uses*, Penton Publishing Company, 1938.

HINE, C. R., *Machine Tools for Engineers*, McGraw-Hill Book Company, 1950.

JONES, E. J. H., *Production Engineering*, Chemical Publishing Company, 1941.

JONES, F. D., *Machine Shop Training Course*, Vols. 1 and 2, Industrial Press, 1940.

JONES, M. M., and A. AXELROD, *Introductory Shopwork*, McGraw-Hill Book Company, 1943.

KENT's *Mechanical Engineers' Handbook*, 12th edition, John Wiley & Sons, 1950.

KIPERS, R. F., *Manufacturing Analysis*, McGraw-Hill Book Company, 1949.

LYTLE, C. W., and A. F. GOULD, *Manufacturing Equipment and Processes*, International Textbook Company, 1951.

Machining—Theory and Practice, American Society for Metals, 1950.

Manual on Cutting Metals, ASME Committee on Cutting Metals, American Society of Mechanical Engineers, 1939.

Precision Measurement in the Metalworking Industry, educational department, International Business Machines Corporation, 1941.

SMITH, R. E., *Machining of Metal*, McKnight & McKnight, 1949.

SMITH, R. H., *Advanced Machine Work*, 7th edition, Industrial Education Book Company, 1940.

Tool Engineers Handbook, American Society of Tool Engineers, McGraw-Hill Book Company, 1949.

TURNER, F. W., and O. E. PERRIGO, *Machine Shop Work*, American Technical Society, 1941.

TURNER, W. P., and H. F. OWEN, *Machine Tool Work*, McGraw-Hill Book Company, 1945.

YOUNG, J. F., *Materials and Processes*, John Wiley & Sons, 1944.

INDEX

Abrasive disks, 537
Abrasives, 563
  classification, 563
  coated, 592
A-c arc welding, 170
Acetylene gas, 160
Acme thread, 406
Acrylic resins, 278
Addendum, 506
Adjustable bevel, 310
Air-acetylene welding, 162
Air furnace, 77
Air gage, 331
Alcoa direct-chill process, 122
Allotropic changes, 127
Allowance, definition, 301
Allowances, pattern, 43
Alloys, aluminum, 105
  copper, 107
  die casting, 103
  lead, 108
  magnesium, 107
  tin, 108
  zinc, 104
Aluminum-base alloys, 105
Aluminum oxide, 565
Angle blocks, 312
Angle milling cutter, 495
Angular measurements, 310
Annealing, 134
  processes, 135
Annular gears, 505
Apron, lathe, 342
Arbor, 372
Arch press, 234
Arc welding, 168
Asarco process, 120
Atomic-hydrogen arc welding, 174
Austempering, 133
Austenite, 128
Automatic die heads, 418
Automatic lathe, 386
Automatic screw machine, 393
Automatic-transfer processing machine, 453

Automatic turret lathe, 379
Automatic vertical multistation lathe, 382

Bainite, 137
Band filing, 540
Band-friction cutting, 540
Band polishing, 541
Band saw, 51, 537
Band-saw blades, 539
Band-sawing machine, 537
Bellows, 7
Bench lathe, 336
Bench molding, 7
Bevel-gear generator, **515**
Bevel gears, 501
Bevel protractor, 310
Billet, 196
Blast furnace, 63
Blind riser, 15
Bloom, 195
Blowing plastics, 291
Board hammer, 198
Bonding processes, 566
Boring, 445
Boring machine, 465
  horizontal, 469
Boring tools, 471
Bot, 75
Bottom board, 5
Box tool, 378
Brake press, 238
Brass, 83
  die casting, 107
Brazing, 183
  definition, 145
Broaching, advantages and limitations, 545
  definition, 543
Broaching machine, continuous, 553
  horizontal, 550
  push type, 548
  rotary, 552
  types of, 543
  vertical double slide, 546